TABLES OF POWERS AND ROOTS

No.	Squares	Cubes	Square Roots	Cube Roots	No.	Squares	Cubes	Square Roots	Cube Roots
1	1	1	1.000	1.000	**51**	2 601	132,651	7.141	3.708
2	4	8	1.414	1.259	**52**	2 704	140,608	7.211	3.732
3	9	27	1.732	1.442	**53**	2 809	148,877	7.280	3.756
4	16	64	2.000	1.587	**54**	2 916	157,464	7.348	3.779
5	25	125	2.236	1.709	**55**	3 025	166,375	7.416	3.802
6	36	216	2.449	1.817	**56**	3 136	175,616	7.483	3.825
7	49	343	2.645	1.912	**57**	3 249	185,193	7.549	3.848
8	64	512	2.828	2.000	**58**	3 364	195,112	7.615	3.870
9	81	729	3.000	2.080	**59**	3 481	205,379	7.681	3.892
10	100	1 000	3.162	2.154	**60**	3 600	216,000	7.745	3.914
11	121	1 331	3.316	2.223	**61**	3 721	226,981	7.810	3.936
12	144	1 728	3.464	2.289	**62**	3 844	238,328	7.874	3.957
13	169	2 197	3.605	2.351	**63**	3 969	250,047	7.937	3.979
14	196	2 744	3.741	2.410	**64**	4 096	262,144	8.000	4.000
15	225	3 375	3.872	2.466	**65**	4 225	274,625	8.062	4.020
16	256	4 096	4.000	2.519	**66**	4 356	287,496	8.124	4.041
17	289	4 913	4.123	2.571	**67**	4 489	300,763	8.185	4.061
18	324	5 832	4.242	2.620	**68**	4 624	314,432	8.246	4.081
19	361	6 859	4.358	2.668	**69**	4 761	328,509	8.306	4.101
20	400	8 000	4.472	2.714	**70**	4 900	343,000	8.366	4.121
21	441	9 261	4.582	2.758	**71**	5 041	357,911	8.426	4.140
22	484	10,648	4.690	2.802	**72**	5 184	373,248	8.485	4.160
23	529	12,167	4.795	2.843	**73**	5 329	389,017	8.544	4.179
24	576	13,824	4.898	2.884	**74**	5 476	405,224	8.602	4.198
25	625	15,625	5.000	2.924	**75**	5 625	421,875	8.660	4.217
26	676	17,576	5.099	2.962	**76**	5 776	438,976	8.717	4.235
27	729	19,683	5.196	3.000	**77**	5 929	456,533	8.774	4.254
28	784	21,952	5.291	3.036	**78**	6 084	474,552	8.831	4.272
29	841	24,389	5.385	3.072	**79**	6 241	493,039	8.888	4.290
30	900	27,000	5.477	3.107	**80**	6 400	512,000	8.944	4.308
31	961	29,791	5.567	3.141	**81**	6 561	531,441	9.000	4.326
32	1 024	32,768	5.656	3.174	**82**	6 724	551,368	9.055	4.344
33	1 089	35,937	5.744	3.207	**83**	6 889	571,787	9.110	4.362
34	1 156	39,304	5.830	3.239	**84**	7 056	592,704	9.165	4.379
35	1 225	42,875	5.916	3.271	**85**	7 225	614,125	9.219	4.396
36	1 296	46,656	6.000	3.301	**86**	7 396	636,056	9.273	4.414
37	1 369	50,653	6.082	3.332	**87**	7 569	658,503	9.327	4.431
38	1 444	54,872	6.164	3.361	**88**	7 744	681,472	9.380	4.447
39	1 521	59,319	6.244	3.391	**89**	7 921	704,969	9.433	4.464
40	1 600	64,000	6.324	3.419	**90**	8 100	729,000	9.486	4.481
41	1 681	68,921	6.403	3.448	**91**	8 281	753,571	9.539	4.497
42	1 764	74,088	6.480	3.476	**92**	8 464	778,688	9.591	4.514
43	1 849	79,507	6.557	3.503	**93**	8 649	804,357	9.643	4.530
44	1 936	85,184	6.633	3.530	**94**	8 836	830,584	9.695	4.546
45	2 025	91,125	6.708	3.556	**95**	9 025	857,375	9.746	4.562
46	2 116	97,336	6.782	3.583	**96**	9 216	884,736	9.797	4.578
47	2 209	103,823	6.855	3.608	**97**	9 409	912,673	9.848	4.594
48	2 304	110,592	6.928	3.634	**98**	9 604	941,192	9.899	4.610
49	2 401	117,649	7.000	3.659	**99**	9 801	970,299	9.949	4.626
50	2 500	125,000	7.071	3.684	**100**	10,000	1,000,000	10.000	4.641

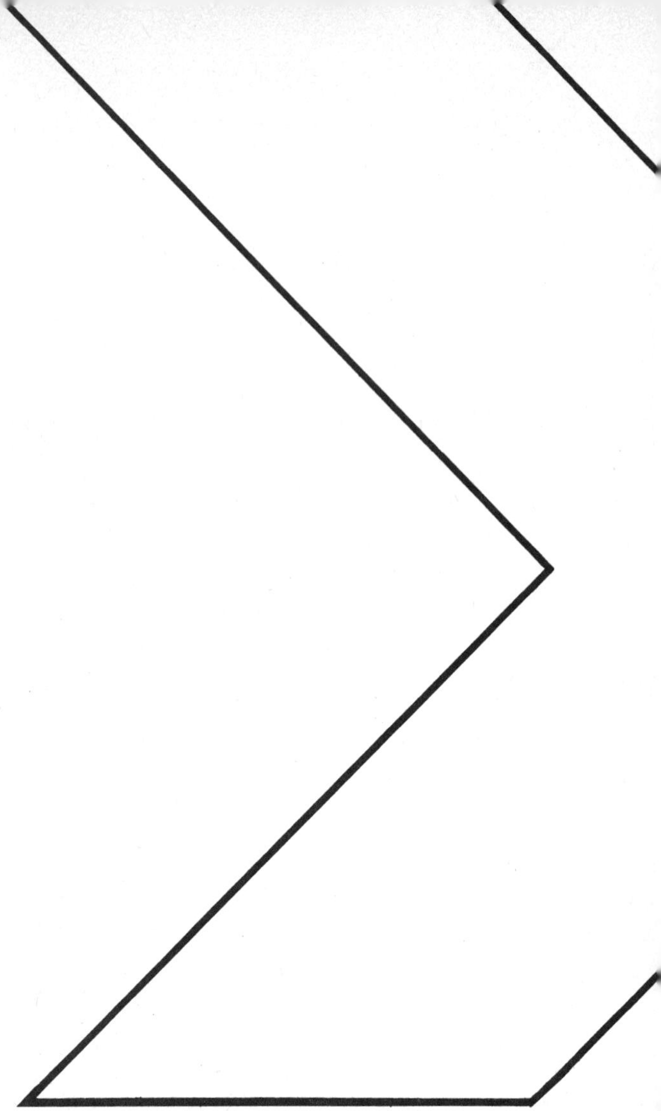

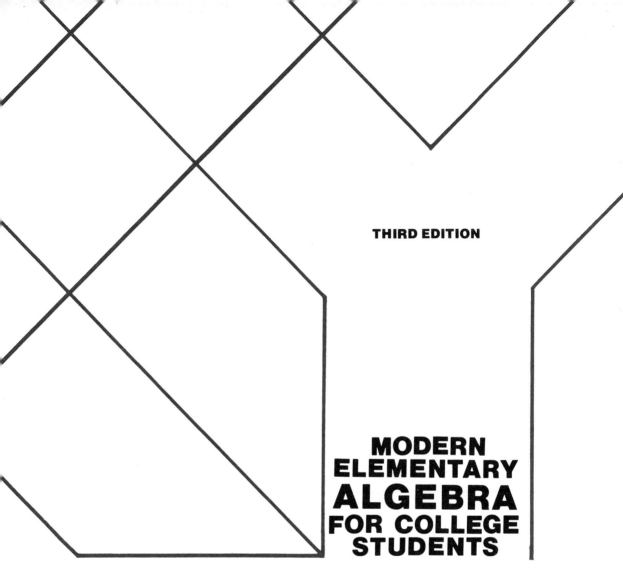

THIRD EDITION

MODERN ELEMENTARY ALGEBRA FOR COLLEGE STUDENTS

Vivian Shaw Groza

Susanne M. Shelley

HOLT, RINEHART AND WINSTON

New York Chicago San Francisco Atlanta Dallas Montreal Toronto London Sydney

PREFACE

Library of Congress Cataloging in Publication Data

Groza, Vivian Shaw.
Modern elementary algebra for college students.
Includes index.
1. Algebra. I. Shelley, Susanne, joint author.
II. Title.
QA152.2.G76 1977 512.9′042 76-30368
ISBN 0-03-018846-6

Printed in the United States of America
9 0 032 9 8 7 6 5 4

Acknowledgments:

Cameo of François Viète on page 20 courtesy of Brown Brothers.

Cameo of Girolamo Cardano on page 43 courtesy of The New York Public Library, Astor, Lenox, and Tilden Foundations.

Cameo of René Descartes on page 221 and cameo of Pythagoras on page 247 courtesy of David Eugene Smith Collection, Columbia University Libraries.

Cover and text design: Joan Stoliar

Our students and colleagues continue to instruct us. This third edition of *Modern Elementary Algebra for College Students* incorporates many changes suggested by users of the previous editions.

Units on linear inequalities in one and two variables have been added.

The two chapters in the previous edition that dealt with exponents, radicals, complex numbers, and quadratic equations have been replaced by one chapter on quadratic equations. This new chapter includes those operations on square root radicals that the student needs to solve quadratic equations having real solutions.

Greater flexibility of presentation is also provided. Chapter 5 on graphing and linear systems is essentially independent of Chapter 4 on fractions and may precede it if desirable. Similarly, Chapter 6 on quadratic equations may precede Chapter 5.

The exposition is less formal, in keeping with the trend toward the intuitive manner of presentation which seems more appropriate for an introductory course in algebra. Concepts of set theory are only introduced when they are thought to be an aid to comprehension.

Historical notes have been revised in the hope of increasing their appeal and supplying additional motivation to the student.

The basic approach is still a problem-solving one with applications providing a unifying thread throughout the text. Every chapter contains a generous variety of applied problems, and many of these use metric measures and conversions. (We use the -re spellings of metre, centimetre, and kilometre in accordance with the recommendations made in 1975 by the Interstate Consortium on Metric Education.)

The format of the exercises has been changed so that the odd-numbered problems in a set are similar in content and level to the even-numbered problems in that set.

Each chapter now contains review exercises.

The answers to all review exercises and to all odd-numbered problems are in the back of the book. There is still an abundance of exercises, each exercise set beginning with basic problems and leading to successively more challenging ones.

We would like to thank the following people for their many helpful and constructive suggestions: Mike Sullivan, Chicago State University, Chicago, Illinois; Michael J. MacCallum, Long Beach, California; Arthur P. Dull, Los Medanos College, Pittsburg, California; Sherry Masters, Madison Area Technical College, Madison, Wisconsin; Louis S. Perone, State University of New York at Farmingdale, Farmingdale, New York; Al Sawyer, Orange Coast Community College, Costa Mesa, California; Arlene F. Sego, Cuyahoga Community College, Parma, Ohio; Mary Carter Smith, Laney College, Oakland, California; and Duane E. Veroda, El Camino College, Torrance, California.

V. S. G. and S. M. S.

CONTENTS

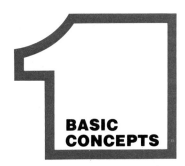

1 BASIC CONCEPTS

2 LINEAR EQUATIONS

3 OPERATIONS ON POLYNOMIALS

4 FRACTIONS

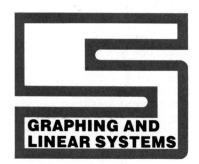

5 GRAPHING AND LINEAR SYSTEMS

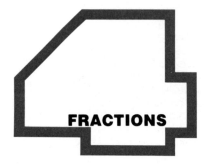

6 QUADRATIC EQUATIONS

BASIC CONCEPTS

THE WORD ALGEBRA

The word *algebra* first appeared around 825 A.D. in the work *Hisâb al-jabr w'al-muqâbalah* by the Arabic scholar al-Khowârizmi. Literally this title means "science of restoration and opposition." A more common meaning of *al-jabr* was introduced into Spain by the Moors: An algebrista was a person who reset or "restored" broken bones.

The red-and-white striped pole in front of barber shops goes back to the days when barbers also practiced medicine; in Spain barbers also had these words above the door: *Algebrista y Sangrador* ("bonesetter and bloodletter").

Elementary algebra is a study of **numbers** and their properties.

Number problems have played an important role in people's existence for thousands of years. At first these problems were written in words. Gradually the words were replaced by abbreviations of the words, and finally the words and abbreviations were replaced by **symbols.** The use of symbols reduced the amount of writing that was necessary and enabled the problem to be seen and understood more rapidly.

For example, contrast the verbal account of the financial transaction stated below with its symbolic representation, which follows.

Verbal Account

A dealer sold a car for two thousand three hundred ninety-five dollars. The car cost him one thousand nine hundred eighty dollars. His profit was four hundred fifteen dollars.

Symbolic Account

$2395.00 *S*
$1980.00 *C*

$ 415.00 *P*

The letter *S*, written at the right of $2395.00, indicates that this amount is the selling price of the car. Similarly, the letter *C* is used to indicate the cost, and the letter *P* is used to indicate the profit.

It is easy to see that, in general, the profit is found by subtracting the cost from the selling price. In symbols, one writes

$P = S - C$

In summary, symbols are used in algebra for the following reasons:

1. To economize the amount of writing that is necessary.
2. To promote clarity and understanding of the problem.
3. To facilitate the discovery and generalization of number properties.

In this chapter you will be introduced to the symbols used for numbers, for the operations of addition, subtraction, multiplication, division, squaring, cubing, finding square roots

EARLY NAMES FOR ALGEBRA

Algebra was not always called algebra. Since the unknown quantity was referred to as the *thing,* which in Italian is *cosa,* we find algebra called the *Regola de la Cosa* by some Italian writers, *Die Coss* by German writers, and *Cossike Arte* by the English.

In the fifteenth and sixteenth centuries Italians referred to algebra as the *greater* art, and to arithmetic as the *lesser* art. Cardano (1501–1576) called his book on algebra *Ars magna;* other Italians used *l'arte maggiore.* The Spaniard Juan Diez used *l'arte mayor* in his book *Sumario compendioso,* published in 1556, the first mathematical work published in the New World.

The name *algebra* was established through the success of a book by the Swiss mathematician Leonhard Euler. His *Vollstaendige Anleitung zur Algebra* ("Complete Introduction to Algebra"), published in 1770, was so popular that it served as the model of algebra texts for many years.

and cube roots, and for the equal, less than, and greater than relations.

Then you will learn the meaning of signed numbers and how to find sums, products, differences, and quotients of signed numbers.

Finally, the concept of substitution and how to use this concept in the evaluation of algebraic expressions and formulas will be presented.

By the end of the chapter you should be able to read, understand, and use the basic language of algebra.

1.1 NUMBERS, NUMERALS, OPERATIONS

NUMBERS AND NUMERALS

The abstract concept of number was developed to answer the question "How many?" The first numbers to be invented were the **counting numbers:** one, two, three, four, five, and so on.

zero is NOT a natural (counting) number.

whole numbers consist of zero and natural numbers

To keep records of numbers, people invented symbols or numerals to serve as the names of numbers.

Numerals are symbols that name numbers according to a specified system, such as the Hindu-Arabic system of numeration. The Hindu-Arabic system of numeration is the modern decimal system in use today. The symbols 1, 2, 3, 4, 5, 6, 7, 8, and 9, which name the first nine counting numbers, and the zero symbol, 0, are called the **digits.** The numerals that name the other counting numbers are formed from these ten digits by using the principles of a positional numeral system with base ten.

For example, 346 is the *numeral name* of a number whose *word name* is three hundred forty-six.

Letters of the alphabet are also used as the names of numbers. A letter is used to designate a number whose numeral name is unspecified.

For example, in the formula $P = S - C$, the letters P, S, and C are used to designate numbers that represent the profit, the selling price, and the cost, respectively.

As another example, $y = x + 5$ means that y represents a number that is five more than the number represented by x.

A **set** is a well-defined collection of objects called *elements* or *members* of the set.

Particular sets may be defined by two general methods, the *listing* method and the *description* method.

In the **listing method,** the set is defined by listing or stating the names of its members enclosed by braces and separated by commas.

For example, the set of **digits** may be defined by the listing method as follows:

$\{0, 1, 2, 3, 4, 5, 6, 7, 8, 9\}$

As another example, the set of **natural numbers** (another name for the set of counting numbers) may be defined as follows:

$\{1, 2, 3, 4, 5, 6, 7, 8, 9, 10, \ldots\}$

where the 3 dots indicate that this list continues in this manner without ending.

Note that zero is *not* a natural number.

The set of **whole numbers** is the set consisting of the number zero and the natural numbers.

The set of natural numbers and the set of whole numbers are infinite sets, whereas the set of digits is a finite set.

In the **description method,** the set is defined by "describing" the set or stating a property possessed by each member of the set. For example,

S is the set of digits exactly divisible by 3

Using the listing method,

$S = \{0, 3, 6, 9\}$

A **constant** is a letter that names exactly one number. Letters at the beginning of the alphabet, such as a, b, or c, are usually used to name a constant. The Greek letter π (read "pi") is used to designate the constant ratio of the circumference C of any circle to its diameter d; that is, $\pi = \dfrac{C}{d}$.

A **variable** (also called an unknown) is a letter that names a number belonging to a set consisting of more than one member.

Any letter can be used to name a variable, but usually the letters at the end of the alphabet, such as x, y, and z, are used, following the example of the French mathematician René Descartes, who perfected much of the symbolism of algebra.

OPERATIONS

Elementary algebra is concerned with six operations that are performed on numbers:

1. Addition
2. Subtraction
3. Multiplication
4. Division
5. Raising to a power
6. Root extraction

All these operations are indicated by symbols. The set of numbers on which the operations are performed is always designated. In this section, all numbers will be restricted to belong to the set of **whole numbers**—that is, the number zero and the natural numbers (counting numbers).

Furthermore, the operations discussed in this section will be restricted to addition; subtraction; multiplication; division; two special cases of raising to a power, namely, squaring and cubing; and two special cases of root extraction, namely, extracting square roots and cube roots.

Addition: $x + y$

The result of adding two numbers is called the **sum** of the two numbers. The numbers that are added are called **terms.**

In symbols, $x + y$ indicates the sum of the terms x and y and is read "x plus y" or "the sum of x and y."

For example, the sum of x and 5 is $x + 5$.

Subtraction: $x - y$

The result of subtracting one number from another is called the **difference** or **remainder.**

In arithmetic, the name **subtrahend** is given to the number that is subtracted from the other number, called the **minuend.**

In algebra, both the subtrahend and the minuend are called **terms.**

In symbols, $x - y$ indicates the difference between the terms x and y, when y is subtracted from x. Thus $x - y$ is read "x minus y" or "y subtracted from x."

For example, the difference when 5 is subtracted from x is $x - 5$.

Multiplication: xy, $3x$, $3 \cdot 4$, $3(4)$, $(3)(4)$

The result of multiplying two numbers is called the **product.** The numbers that are being multiplied are called **factors.**

In arithmetic, multiplication is indicated by the "cross" symbol, $\times$, such as 3×4. However, because this symbol can be confused with the letter x used to name an unspecified number, the $\times$ symbol is not used in algebra to indicate multiplication.

In algebra, multiplication is indicated in three different ways. If two numerals are used to name the factors, then the dot symbol, $\cdot$, is used, as in $3 \cdot 4$, which means the product of 3 and 4, or 12. The dot is written at half the vertical height of the numerals so that it will not be confused with the decimal point.

If two letters or a numeral and a letter are used to name the factors, then multiplication is indicated by juxtaposition—that is, the symbols for the numbers are written side by side. For example, $3x$ means the product of 3 and x, and xy means the product of x and y. Twice x is written $2x$.

Multiplication is also indicated by writing one factor next to the other factor with either factor or both enclosed in parentheses. For example, 3(4) and (3)(4) mean the product of 3 and 4.

Division: $\frac{x}{y}$

The result of dividing one number by another is called the **quotient.** The name **dividend** is given to the number that is being divided by the other number, called the **divisor.**

In arithmetic, division is indicated by the symbol ÷. In algebra, division is indicated by using the fractional notation, $\frac{x}{y}$. The expression $\frac{x}{y}$ is read "x divided by y" or, more informally, "x over y."

For example, the quotient when x is divided by 5 is written $\frac{x}{5}$. This can also be read "x over five."

Squaring: x^2

Multiplying a number by itself is called **squaring.** The result of squaring is called the **square** of the number. The numeral 2, called an **exponent,** is written to the upper right of another number symbol, x, called the **base.** The exponent 2 indicates that the base x is to be used twice as a factor.

For example, 3^2 (read "three square") means $3 \cdot 3$, or 9. Similarly, 5^2 means $5 \cdot 5$, or 25. In general, x^2 means xx.

Cubing: x^3

The product obtained by using a number as a factor three times is called the **cube** of the number. The numeral 3, the exponent, is written to the upper right of another number symbol, x, the base. The exponent 3 indicates that the base x is to be used three times as a factor.

For example, 5^3 (read "five cube") means $5 \cdot 5 \cdot 5$, or 125. In general, x^3 means xxx.

Squaring and cubing are special cases of the more general operation, called **raising to a power,** written as x^n where n is a counting number. The exponent n indicates that the base x is to be used n times as a factor.

Root Extraction: Square Root and Cube Root

To extract the square root of a number means to find a number whose square is the given number. The operation of square-root extraction is indicated by the symbol $\sqrt{\ }$, which has evolved from the letter "r," the first letter of the word "root." For example, $\sqrt{9}$, which is read "the square root of nine," designates the number 3, since 3^2 is 9.

Similarly, $\sqrt[3]{x}$, read "the cube root of x," designates the number whose cube is x. For example, $\sqrt[3]{125}$ names the number 5, since 5^3 is 125.

Table 1.1 summarizes the operation symbols. Numerical tables are also useful for finding squares, cubes, square roots, and cube roots of some natural numbers. An extensive table is found on the inside cover of this book.

TABLE 1.1 SUMMARY OF THE OPERATION SYMBOLS

OPERATION	*NUMERALS*	*NUMERAL AND LETTER*	*TWO LETTERS*
Addition	$3+4$	$x+4$	$x+y$
Subtraction	$7-3$	$x-4$	$x-y$
Multiplication	$3 \cdot 4$ or $3(4)$	$3x$	xy
Division	$\frac{12}{3}$	$\frac{x}{3}$	$\frac{x}{y}$
Squaring	3^2	x^2	(Not applicable)
Cubing	5^3	x^3	
Square root	$\sqrt{9}$	$\sqrt{x}$	(Not applicable)
Cube root	$\sqrt[3]{27}$	$\sqrt[3]{x}$	

EXAMPLE 1 Perform each of the following operations:

$$6 \cdot 4,\ 20-8,\ \frac{15}{3},\ 9+7,\ 6^2,\ 2^3,\ \sqrt{81},\ \sqrt[3]{64}$$

Solution

$6 \cdot 4 = 24$	(Multiplication)
$20 - 8 = 12$	(Subtraction)
$\frac{15}{3} = 5$	(Division)
$9 + 7 = 16$	(Addition)
$6^2 = 6 \cdot 6 = 36$	(Squaring)
$2^3 = 2 \cdot 2 \cdot 2 = 8$	(Cubing)
$\sqrt{81} = 9$	(Square root)
$\sqrt[3]{64} = 4$	(Cube root)

EXAMPLE 2 Translate each of the following into algebraic expressions:

	Solution
The product of 3 and y	$3y$
The quotient when t is divided by 3	$\frac{t}{3}$
The cube of a	a^3
The sum of 4 and z	$4 + z$
The square of b	b^2
The difference when c is subtracted from 8	$8 - c$
The square root of the sum of x and 3	$\sqrt{x + 3}$
The cube root of the product of m and 2	$\sqrt[3]{2m}$
The product of 3 and the square root of x	$3\sqrt{x}$

EXERCISES

Perform the indicated operations in Exercises 1–40.

1. $4 \cdot 6$

2. $(8)(9)$

3. $\frac{12}{6}$

4. $\frac{25}{5}$

5. $7 + 8$

6. $6 + 7$

7. $12 - 4$

8. $14 - 3$

9. 5^2

10. 3^2

11. 4^3

12. 2^3

13. $9 + 0$

14. $0 + 4$

15. 7^2

16. $\frac{24}{1}$

17. 9^3

18. $\sqrt[3]{27}$

19. $23 - 0$

20. $\sqrt[3]{64}$

21. $\frac{6}{1}$

22. $\sqrt{64}$

23. $(10)(20)$

24. $35 + 65$

25. $\sqrt{121}$

26. $\sqrt{1}$

27. $0 \cdot 9$

28. $\frac{5}{5}$

29. $\frac{200}{10}$

30. $\sqrt[3]{0}$

31. $\sqrt[3]{125}$

32. $\frac{200}{200}$

33. $100 - 0$

34. $\sqrt{(4)(9)}$

35. $\sqrt{16+9}$

36. 3^3

37. 6^3

38. $\sqrt[3]{(9)(3)}$

39. $\sqrt{16}+9$

40. $(\sqrt{4})(\sqrt{9})$

Translate Exercises 41–80 into algebraic (symbolic) expressions.

41. The sum of x and 8
42. The product of 8 and x
43. The square of n
44. The cube of t
45. The difference when 4 is subtracted from y
46. The quotient when x is divided by 6
47. n minus m
48. The product of s and t
49. c square
50. z cube
51. x plus y
52. x times y
53. The difference when x is subtracted from y
54. The quotient when x is divided by y
55. The product of 25 and 45
56. The square root of the sum of 15 and y
57. The cube root of the difference when p is subtracted from 7
58. The product of m and the square root of t
59. The product of the cube of t and the cube root of s
60. The quotient of x over the square of y
61. The sum of r and s
62. The product of r and s
63. The square root of m
64. The square of m
65. The difference when x is subtracted from 7
66. The quotient when 5 is divided by y
67. The product of a and the square of b
68. The sum of the square of x and the cube of x
69. p square times q
70. 5 minus p
71. The product of 15 and 5
72. The difference when x is subtracted from 10
73. The difference when 10 is subtracted from x
74. The cube of x
75. The cube root of x
76. 8 more than x
77. 8 less than x
78. 8 times x
79. The quotient when 8 is divided by x
80. The sum of the square root of y and the cube root of y

1.2 SPECIAL SETS OF NUMBERS

The **empty set,** also called the **null set,** is the set that has no members. It is denoted symbolically by $\varnothing$ or by $\{\ \}$.

For example, the set of digits that are greater than 17 is the empty set.

The empty set is considered a finite set.

A **universal set,** U, is a set to which the elements of all other sets in a particular discussion must belong.

For example, let $U = \{1, 2, 3, 4, 5, 6, 7, 8, 9\}$. Now if A is the set of numbers that are exactly divisible by 3, then $A = \{3, 6, 9\}$. The number 12 cannot be a member of A because 12 does not belong to the universal set, U, that was selected.

THE "ABSURD" AND "FICTITIOUS": NEGATIVE NUMBERS

The Chinese were familiar with negative numbers as early as 200 B.C. They were known to write positive numbers in red and negative numbers in black.

The Greek Diophantus (ca. 275), in his *Arithmetica,* calls the equation $4x + 20 = 4$ "absurd," since its solution would be -4. Diophantus did not seem to comprehend the abstract concept of a negative number.

The negative number is first mentioned as such in the works of the Hindu Brahmagupta (ca. 628). The Hindus indicated a negative number by placing a dot above a numeral or placing a circle above or around the numeral, such as $\dot{5}$, $\mathring{5}$, or ⑤.

Around 1225 the Italian Leonardo Fibonacci interpreted the negative solution of a financial problem to mean a loss.

In his *Ars magna* (1545), Cardano presented the elementary properties of negative numbers, although he was unable to give a clear interpretation of these numbers. He referred to the positive numbers as "true" numbers and to the negative numbers as "fictitious" numbers.

In 1544 Stifel stated that numbers such as $0 - 3$ were "absurd."

The concept of the negative number became thoroughly understood in the Western world through the works of Viète, Fermat, Descartes, and other mathematicians.

1.2 SPECIAL SETS OF NUMBERS

In a particular discussion, the universal set that is selected is always stated or understood.

In this section our universal set will be the set of natural counting numbers. In other words, the word *number* shall mean *natural number*.

DEFINITION

We say that the number r is a **multiple** of the number s, or that r is **divisible** by s, if r can be obtained by multiplying s by some natural number.

EXAMPLE 1 List the set of multiples of 6 that are less than 50.

Solution The multiples of 6 are obtained by multiplying 6 by each of the natural numbers. Since $6(1) = 6$, $6(2) = 12$, $6(3) = 18$, $6(4) = 24$, $6(5) = 30$, $6(6) = 36$, $6(7) = 42$, and $6(8) = 48$, the set of multiples of 6 less than 50 is

$$\{6, 12, 18, 24, 30, 36, 42, 48\}$$

DEFINITION

We say that the number r is a **factor** of s, or that r is a **divisor** of s, if r can be obtained by dividing s by some natural number.

EXAMPLE 2 List the factors of 15.

Solution The factors of 15 are obtained by dividing 15 by natural numbers. When the quotient and the divisor are natural numbers, both these numbers are factors. Since

$$\frac{15}{1} = 15$$

1 and 15 are factors, and since

$$\frac{15}{3} = 5,$$

3 and 5 are factors. These are the only possibilities. Thus the factors of 15 are the set

$$\{1, 3, 5, 15\}$$

DEFINITION

A natural number n is **even** if and only if 2 is a factor of n.

EXAMPLE 3 List the set of even numbers less than 25.

Solution $\{2, 4, 6, 8, 10, 12, 14, 16, 18, 20, 22, 24\}$

DEFINITION

A natural number n is **odd** if and only if it is not even.

EXAMPLE 4 List the set of odd numbers less than 20.

Solution $\{1, 3, 5, 7, 9, 11, 13, 15, 17, 19\}$

DEFINITION

A natural number p is a **prime** if and only if $p \neq 1$ and p has no divisors different from 1 and itself.

The set of the first 10 primes is $\{2, 3, 5, 7, 11, 13, 17, 19, 23, 29\}$.

DEFINITION

A natural number n is a **composite** if and only if $n \neq 1$ and n is not a prime.

The set of the first 10 composite numbers is $\{4, 6, 8, 9, 10, 12, 14, 15, 16, 18\}$.

EXAMPLE 5 List the factors of 70 that are prime numbers.

Solution First find the factors of 70:

$1 \cdot 70 = 70,\ 2 \cdot 35 = 70,$
$5 \cdot 14 = 70,\ 7 \cdot 10 = 70$

The factors of 70 are $\{1, 2, 5, 7, 10, 14, 35, 70\}$. Select from these the numbers that are prime. The prime factors of 70 are the set

$\{2, 5, 7\}$

EXAMPLE 6 List the factors of 70 that are composite.

Solution We first find the factors of 70 (see Example 5). We reject 1, because 1 is not composite, and we reject all prime factors. Those remaining are the composites. Therefore the set of composite factors of 70 is

$\{10, 14, 35, 70\}$

EXAMPLE 7 Write 70 as the product of prime numbers.

Solution $70 = (2)(5)(7)$

EXAMPLE 8 Write 2200 as the product of prime factors.

Solution Divide 2200 by prime numbers beginning with 2, then trying 3, then 5, then 7, then 11, and so forth.

$$
\begin{array}{r|l}
2 & 2200 \\
2 & 1100 \\
2 & 550 \\
5 & 275 \\
5 & 55 \\
11 & 11 \\
 & 1
\end{array}
$$

Thus, $2200 = 2^3 \cdot 5^2 \cdot 11$

EXERCISES

In Exercises 1–38, list each of the following sets.

1. The even numbers between 17 and 25
2. The even numbers between 35 and 45
3. The odd numbers between 56 and 63
4. The odd numbers between 70 and 80
5. The multiples of 3 between 29 and 50
6. The multiples of 4 between 29 and 50
7. The multiples of 10 that are less than 100
8. The multiples of 12 that are less than 100
9. The factors of 28
10. The factors of 24
11. The factors of 30
12. The factors of 26
13. The divisors of 50
14. The divisors of 18
15. The prime numbers that are less than 20
16. The prime numbers between 30 and 50
17. The prime numbers between 50 and 80
18. The prime numbers between 80 and 100
19. The composite numbers between 19 and 27
20. The composite numbers between 71 and 83
21. The factors of 28. Which are prime numbers?
22. The factors of 24. Which are prime numbers?
23. The prime factors of 30
24. The prime factors of 26
25. The prime factors of 50
26. The prime factors of 18
27. The even factors of 36
28. The odd factors of 42
29. The odd factors of 16
30. The even factors of 35
31. The composite factors of 19
32. The composite factors of 48
33. The common multiples of 3 and 5 that are less than 50 (A common multiple is a multiple of *both* 3 and 5.)
34. The common multiples of 4 and 6 that are less than 50
35. The common multiples of 18 and 12 that are less than 200
36. The common multiples of 52 and 65 that are less than 300
37. The common divisors of 12 and 18. (A common divisor is a divisor of *both* 12 and 18.)
38. The common divisors of 30 and 45

Write the numbers in Exercises 39–48 as the products of prime numbers.

39. 15 **40.** 14 **41.** 18 **42.** 40 **43.** 66
44. 52 **45.** 78 **46.** 60 **47.** 98 **48.** 75

In Exercises 49–56, determine whether each statement is true or false. If false, say why.

49. All prime numbers are natural numbers.
50. All natural numbers are prime numbers.
51. 39 is a prime number.
52. 63 is a composite number.
53. The only even prime number is 2.
54. All even numbers except 2 are composite.
55. All natural numbers are either even or odd.
56. All natural numbers are either prime or composite.

1.3 GROUPING SYMBOLS

After an operation has been performed on two numbers, an operation can be performed again on the resulting number and a third number. This process can be continued as often as desired.

In order to indicate which operation was performed first, which second, which third, and so on, grouping symbols are used. The grouping symbols that are most frequently used are parentheses, ( ), braces, { }, brackets, [ ], and the bar (also called vinculum), $\overline{\quad}$.

For example, to indicate that 3 is to be subtracted from the difference 12 − 5, any one of the following symbolic expressions can be used:

$$(12-5)-3$$
$$\{12-5\}-3$$
$$[12-5]-3$$
$$\overline{12-5}\ -3$$

If the operations are performed as indicated, then first one obtains that 12 − 5 is 7, and then that 7 − 3 is 4. Therefore (12 − 5) − 3 results in the number 4.

If the parentheses or other grouping symbols were not used, the order in which the operations are to be performed would not be clear, and in some cases it would be possible to obtain as a result a different number than the one intended.

For example, consider 12 − 5 − 3. If 3 is first subtracted from 5, then the difference is 2. When 2 is subtracted from 12, the result is 10. Thus the expression 12 − 5 − 3 is ambiguous—that is, more than one number can be obtained as a final result, depending on how the expression is interpreted.

Grouping symbols are used to avoid ambiguity. Thus (12 − 5) − 3 results in 4 only and 12 − (5 − 3) results in 10 only since it is understood that the operation within the parentheses is to be performed first.

Several kinds of grouping symbols are used to promote clarity in reading an algebraic expression that involves more than two operations. For example, one way to indicate that the sum of 3 and the difference $8 - 2$ is to be subtracted from 12 is as follows:

$$12 - \{3 + (8 - 2)\}$$

This means that the operation within the innermost grouping symbols, the subtraction of 2 from 8, is to be performed first. Next, the result 6 is to be added to 3. Finally, the sum of 6 and 3, or 9, is to be subtracted from 12, giving a final result of 3.

This combination of operations could also have been written, using parentheses only, as follows:

$$12 - (3 + (8 - 2))$$

Note that the use of two kinds of grouping symbols causes the algebraic expression to be read more clearly and more rapidly.

The use of several kinds of grouping symbols becomes more advantageous as the number of operations increases. For example, compare

$$25 - \{3 + [10 - (2 + \overline{4 - 1})]\}$$

with

$$25 - (3 + (10 - (2 + (4 - 1))))$$

In reading an algebraic expression involving two or more sets of grouping symbols, it is understood that the innermost set indicates the operation that is to be performed first. After this operation has been performed, the innermost set remaining indicates the next operation that is to be performed, and so on.

EXAMPLE 1 Perform the indicated operations:

$$25 - \{3 + [10 - (2 + \overline{4 - 1})]\}$$

Solution

1. Perform the operation under the bar and obtain
   $$25 - \{3 + [10 - (2 + 3)]\}$$
2. Perform the operation within the parentheses and obtain
   $$25 - \{3 + [10 - 5]\}.$$
3. Perform the operation within the brackets and obtain
   $$25 - \{3 + 5\}$$
4. Perform the operation within the braces and obtain
   $$25 - 8$$
5. Subtract 8 from 25 and obtain 17 as the final result.

By adopting certain conventions, some grouping symbols can be omitted from certain expressions. This yields an expression which is simpler to read, and the intended meaning is still clear. The following convention is adopted:

CONVENTION

Unless the grouping symbols indicate otherwise, the operations are to be performed in the following order:

First: Taking square roots and/or cube roots as read from left to right
Second: Squaring and/or cubing as read from left to right
Third: Multiplication and/or division as read from left to right
Fourth: Addition and/or subtraction as read from left to right

Thus $5 + (2^3)$ can be written more simply as $5 + 2^3$, since the cubing must be done first, in agreement with the above convention. Thus $5 + 2^3$ means $5 + 8$, or 13, whereas $(5 + 2)^3$ means 7^3, or 343.

Similarly, $5 \cdot (2^3)$ can be written as $5 \cdot 2^3$, with $5 \cdot 8$, or 40, as the intended final result, since the cubing must be performed before the multiplication.

If one wants to indicate that 5 is to be multiplied by 2 and that the resulting product is to be cubed, grouping symbols must be used as follows: $(5 \cdot 2)^3$, which means 10^3, or 1000.

The number indicated by $5 \cdot 2 + 7$ is the sum of 10 and 7, or 17, since the convention requires that the multiplication be performed before the addition. Thus $5 \cdot 2 + 7$ is another name for 17.

To indicate that 2 is to be added to 7 and that the resulting sum is to be multiplied by 5, one writes $5(2 + 7)$, which names the number $5 \cdot 9$, or 45.

The product $5(2 + 7)$ could also have been written as $5 \cdot (2 + 7)$. However, since the numerals 5 and $(2 + 7)$ are written in juxtaposition (side by side), the operation of multiplication is clearly indicated and the dot is not necessary. Greater simplicity and clarity are achieved by writing only the symbols that are necessary.

EXAMPLE 2 Perform the indicated operation: $13 - (5 - 2)^2$.

Solution 1. Simplify the expression inside parentheses: $5 - 2 = 3$. Thus

$$13 - 3^2$$

2. Raise to power: $3^2 = 9$. Thus

$$13 - 9$$

3. Perform subtraction: $13 - 9 = 4$. Therefore

$$\begin{aligned} &13 - (5 - 2)^2 \\ &= 13 - 3^2 \\ &= 13 - 9 = 4 \end{aligned}$$

EXAMPLE 3 Simplify $5 + 2(3)^2 - (12 - 9)$.

Solution $5 + 2(3)^2 - (12 - 9)$

$= 5 + 2(3)^2 - 3$ (Simplifying parentheses)

$= 5 + 2 \cdot 9 - 3$ (Raise to power)

$= 5 + 18 - 3$ (Multiply)

$= 20$ (Add and subtract from left to right)

EXAMPLE 4 Simplify $\dfrac{8^2 + 8 \cdot 6}{2 \cdot 8 + 2 \cdot 6}$

Solution The bar used in division is a grouping symbol, so the operations in the numerator and in the denominator must be done before the division:

$$\frac{8^2 + 8 \cdot 6}{2 \cdot 8 + 2 \cdot 6} = \frac{64 + 8 \cdot 6}{2 \cdot 8 + 2 \cdot 6} \quad \text{(Squaring first)}$$

$$= \frac{64 + 48}{16 + 12} \quad \text{(Multiply)}$$

$$= \frac{112}{28} \quad \text{(Add)}$$

$$= 4 \quad \text{(Divide)}$$

EXAMPLE 5 Simplify $2\sqrt{5^2 - 3^2}$.

Solution The bar used in root extraction is also a grouping symbol, so the operations under the bar must be done first:

$$2\sqrt{5^2 - 3^2} = 2\sqrt{25 - 9}$$

$$= 2\sqrt{16}$$

$$= 2(4)$$

$$= 8$$

EXAMPLE 6 Translate into symbols: The product of 4 and the sum of x and 6.

Solution Since the entire expression is a product, multiplication is the last operation performed. Therefore, parentheses are needed to indicate that addition is done first:

The product of 4 and the (sum of x and 6)

The product of 4 and $(x + 6)$

$4(x + 6)$

EXAMPLE 7 Translate into symbols: The difference obtained by subtracting 8 from the quotient resulting when x is divided by 8.

Solution Since the entire expression is a difference, subtraction is the last operation to be done. First, abbreviating the words:

Difference subtracting 8 from x over 8

Difference subtracting 8 from $\dfrac{x}{8}$

$$\frac{x}{8} - 8$$

EXERCISES

In Exercises 1–50, perform the indicated operations.

1. $3 + (5 + 7)$
2. $(3 + 5) + 7$
3. $22 - (10 - 3)$
4. $(22 - 10) - 3$
5. $12 - (5 - 5)$
6. $(12 - 5) - 5$
7. $3(4)(5)$
8. $3 + (4)(5)$
9. $3(8 + 2)$
10. $3(8) + 2$
11. $(9 - 3)(6 - 4)$
12. $(15 - 2)(12 - 8)$
13. $9 - 3(6 - 4)$
14. $15 - 2(12 - 8)$
15. $15 - (10 + 3)$
16. $(15 - 10) + 3$
17. $(24 - 10) + 6$
18. $24 - (10 + 6)$
19. $15 - 3^2$
20. $(15 - 3)^2$
21. $3 + 7^2$
22. $(3 + 7)^2$
23. $2 \cdot 5^2$
24. $(2 \cdot 5)^2$
25. $\dfrac{\left(\dfrac{24}{6}\right)}{2}$
26. $\dfrac{24}{\left(\dfrac{6}{2}\right)}$
27. $\dfrac{2^3 + 3^3}{2 + 3}$
28. $\dfrac{2^3}{2} + \dfrac{3^3}{3}$
29. $\dfrac{5^2 - 4^2}{5 - 4}$
30. $\dfrac{5^2}{5} - \dfrac{4^2}{4}$
31. $30 - (2 \cdot 5 - 2)$
32. $30 - 2(5 - 2)$
33. $8 - 2(5 - [2 + 1])$
34. $(8 - 2)(5 - [2 + 1])$
35. $2(7^2 - 3^2) - (4^2 - 3^2)$
36. $10 - \{8 - [6 - (4 - 2)]\}$
37. $2([5^2 - 3\{4 + 2\}] + 1)$
38. $5\{(9 + 4)^2 - (9 - 4)^2\}$
39. $1 + \{1 - [1 - (1 - \sqrt{1 - 1})]\}$
40. $7 - [6 - \{5^2 - 4(2 + 3)\}]$
41. $8(3 + 2)^2$
42. $24 - (10 + 6) + 3$
43. $(24 - 10) + 6^2$
44. $4 + 2\{5 - 2[3 - (2 - 1)]\}$
45. $3\{(4 + 5)^2 - 41\}$
46. $(15 - 2)(7 - 2)^2$
47. $(5 - 4) - ([3 - 2] - 1)$
48. $7^2 - (6^2 - [5^2 - \{4^2 - (3^2 - 2^2)\}])$
49. $\dfrac{30 - 2(5 - 2)}{(30 - 25) - 2}$
50. $\dfrac{20 - [10 - 2(7 - 3)]}{20 - [10 + 2(7 - 3)]}$

Translate the verbal expressions in Exercises 51–65 into symbols.

51. The sum of x and twice y
52. Twice the sum of x and y
53. Twice the product of x and y
54. The product of 5 and the square of x
55. The difference obtained by subtracting the sum of x and 3 from y
56. The quotient obtained by dividing x by the sum of x and 3
57. 7 less than the square of the sum of y and 2
58. One-half the product of 3 and the sum of a and b
59. The result of adding y to 3 times x
60. 3 times the sum of x and y

61. The quotient obtained by dividing the sum of 7 and a by the product of 7 and a
62. The difference obtained when one-half the sum of a and b is subtracted from the square of b
63. The square root of the difference obtained by subtracting the square of 5 from the square of x
64. The cube of the product of 4 and y
65. One less than the remainder obtained by subtracting the square of 2 from the difference between the squares of 4 and 3

1.4 EQUALITY, SUBSTITUTION, FORMULAS

THE EQUALITY RELATION

An equation is a statement that has the form $A = B$, which is read "A equals B." The symbol = indicates that A and B are names of the same number.

As examples,

$12 + 3 = 15$

means that $12 + 3$ (the sum of 12 and 3) names the same number as the numeral 15, and

$12 \cdot 3 = 36$

means that $12 \cdot 3$ (the product of 12 and 3) names the same number as the numeral 36.

It is often convenient to use the symbol $\neq$, which means "does not equal." For example, $3 \neq 5$ is read "three does not equal five" and means that the numerals 3 and 5 do not name the same number.

SUBSTITUTION

Since the relation $r = s$ is understood to mean that the variables r and s are names of the same number, it seems reasonable that one name can replace the other in a given statement without changing the truth or falsity of the statement. Furthermore, if one name replaces the other in an algebraic expression, the number that is named by the algebraic expression remains the same. This property is called the **substitution axiom** for the equal relation. An axiom is a statement that is accepted without proof.

THE SUBSTITUTION AXIOM

If $r = s$, then r may replace s or s may replace r in an algebraic expression without changing the number that is being named, or in an algebraic statement without changing the truth or falsity of the statement.

For example, consider the statement $y = x + 5$.

Now if $x = 3$, then 3 can replace x in this statement, and one obtains $y = 3 + 5$. This substitution process may be repeated by using the fact that $3 + 5 = 8$. Replacing $3 + 5$ by its equal, 8, in the statement $y = 3 + 5$, one obtains $y = 8$.

The substitution axiom may be used to *evaluate* algebraic expressions. To evaluate an algebraic expression means to replace each letter by the numeral to which it is equal and then to perform the operations that are indicated, replacing the names of the numbers by simpler names that do not involve the operation symbols.

EXAMPLE 1 Evaluate $3(x + 4) - \frac{x}{2}$ for $x = 6$.

Solution

1. Rewrite the given expression:
   $$3(x + 4) - \frac{x}{2}$$
2. Remove the letter and hold its place with open parentheses:
   $$3((\ \ ) + 4) - \frac{(\ \ )}{2}$$
3. Insert the numeral to which the letter is equal within the parentheses:
   $$3((6) + 4) - \frac{(6)}{2}$$
4. Do the indicated operations:
   $$3(10) - 3$$
   $$30 - 3 = 27$$

FRANÇOIS VIETE: LAWYER, MATHEMATICIAN

The French lawyer François Viète (1540–1603) was one of the first persons to use letters to represent numbers. In 1591 he used capital vowels, such as *A*, *E*, *I*, for the variables. Viète is often called the "father of algebra" because of the improvements he made in the symbolism of algebra.

It is said that Viète helped Henry IV of France in his war against Spain by deciphering a Spanish code that contained hundreds of characters. So certain was King Philip II of Spain that no one could break his code, he complained to the pope that the French were violating the doctrines of the Christian religion by using magic against his country.

EXAMPLE 2 Evaluate $\dfrac{x^2 + 2xy - 3y^2}{x + 3y}$ for $x = 8$ and $y = 4$.

Solution

1. Rewrite the given expression:
$$\frac{x^2 + 2xy - 3y^2}{x + 3y}$$
2. Replace one letter, say x, by open parentheses:
$$\frac{(\quad)^2 + 2(\quad)y - 3y^2}{(\quad) + 3y}$$
3. Insert the value for x:
$$\frac{(8)^2 + 2(8)y - 3y^2}{(8) + 3y}$$
4. Replace the other letter, y, by open parentheses:
$$\frac{(8)^2 + 2(8)(\quad) - 3(\quad)^2}{(8) + 3(\quad)}$$
5. Insert the value for y:
$$\frac{(8)^2 + 2(8)(4) - 3(4)^2}{(8) + 3(4)}$$
6. Evaluate (do the operations):
$$\frac{64 + 2(32) - 3(16)}{8 + 12}$$
$$= \frac{64 + 64 - 48}{20}$$
$$= \frac{128 - 48}{20}$$
$$= \frac{80}{20}$$
$$= 4$$

FORMULAS

Many problems in mathematics, science, business, and other areas are most easily solved by using formulas.

A **formula** is a symbolic statement indicating what operations are to be performed on certain numbers with specialized meanings determined by the particular problem.

EXAMPLE 3 (Geometry: Perimeter of a Square) Express the following statement as a formula: The length of the perimeter of a square is obtained by multiplying the length of a side by 4.

Solution Let P represent the length of the perimeter. Let s represent the length of a side.

Formula: $P = 4s$.

EXAMPLE 4 Using the formula $P = 4s$, find P if $s = 3$ inches.
Solution $P = 4(3) = 12$ inches

EXAMPLE 5 (Geometry: Area of a Square) Express as a formula: The area A of a square is the square of the length of a side s.
Solution $A = s^2$

EXAMPLE 6 Evaluate $A = s^2$ for $s = 5$ centimetres.
Solution $A = (5)^2 = 25$ square centimetres

EXAMPLE 7 (Uniform Motion) Express as a formula: The distance d that an object travels is the product of the rate of speed r and the time t that is traveled. **Solution** $d = rt$

EXAMPLE 8 Given $d = rt$, find d if $r = 30$ mph and $t = 2$ hours.
Solution $d = 30 \cdot 2 = 60$ miles

EXAMPLE 9 (Resistance to an Electrical Circuit) Write a formula to express the following relation: The resistance R, measured in ohms, of an electrical circuit is the quotient obtained by dividing the electromotive force E, measured in volts, by the intensity I of the current, measured in amperes.

Solution $R = \dfrac{E}{I}$

EXAMPLE 10 Using $R = \dfrac{E}{I}$, find R if $E = 60$ volts and $I = 15$ amperes.

Solution $R = \dfrac{60}{15} = 4$ ohms

EXAMPLE 11 (Business Profit) Express as a formula: The profit P of a business transaction is obtained by subtracting the cost C from the selling price S. **Solution** $P = S - C$

EXAMPLE 12 Find the profit made on selling an end table for \$55 if the cost of the table was \$35.
Solution Using $P = S - C$ with $S = 55$ and $C = 35$, $P = 55 - 35 = 20$ dollars.

EXERCISES

Evaluate the algebraic expressions in Exercises 1–50.

1. $x^2 + 5x + 8$ for $x = 6$

2. $3x^2 + 2x + 11$ for $x = 5$

3. $4x^3 + 5x^2 + 7x + 6$ for $x = 3$

4. $3x^3 + 2x^2 - 10x + 4$ for $x = 3$

5. $3(x - 4)^2$ for $x = 4$

6. $4(x - 2)^2$ for $x = 5$

7. $\dfrac{x^2 - 25}{x - 5}$ for $x = 7$

8. $\dfrac{x^3 + 4}{x + 4}$ for $x = 2$

9. $x(x^2 - x)$ for $x = 6$

10. $x^2(x - 3)$ for $x = 4$

11. $\frac{y(y-1)}{2}$ for $y=10$

12. $\frac{a(a+1)}{3}$ for $a=5$

13. $(n+1)(n-1)$ for $n=11$

14. $(y+3)(y-3)$ for $y=7$

15. $x^2+2xy+y^2$ for $x=5$, $y=3$

16. $x^2+3xy+5y^2$ for $x=5$, $y=2$

17. x^2+y^2 for $x=5$, $y=3$

18. x^3+y^3 for $x=2$, $y=3$

19. c^2-a^2 for $c=13$, $a=12$

20. $\sqrt{x^2-y^2}$ for $x=25$, $y=24$

21. $\frac{a^3-b^3}{a-b}$ for $a=10$, $b=6$

22. $\frac{a^2-b^2}{a+b}$ for $a=3$, $b=2$

23. $\frac{3x}{5(x-7)}$ for $x=10$

24. $ab(a+b^2)$ for $a=3$, $b=5$

25. $a^3-\frac{a}{2}$ for $a=6$

26. $\frac{6x}{2x+4}$ for $x=4$

27. $\frac{a^3-8}{a-2}$ for $a=3$

28. $y^2-\frac{2y}{3}$ for $y=9$

29. $(y-2)(y^2+2y+4)$ for $y=3$

30. $\frac{y^3+8}{y+2}$ for $y=3$

31. $(x+y)^3$ for $x=2$, $y=3$

32. $(n-3)(n^2+3n+9)$ for $n=5$

33. $\frac{xy+x^2}{xy+y^2}$ for $x=8$, $y=2$

34. $(x+y)^2$ for $x=5$, $y=3$

35. $\frac{x^3+y^3}{x+y}$ for $x=5$, $y=2$

36. $\frac{xy}{x+y}$ for $x=10$, $y=15$

37. $5m^2-ms+6s^2$ for $m=4$, $s=3$

38. $\frac{a+b}{a-b}$ for $a=6$, $b=4$

39. $5ab^2-3a^2b$ for $a=3$, $b=5$

40. $3r^2-rs-2s^2$ for $r=7$, $s=3$

41. $(x+y)^2+(x+y)(x-y)+(x-y)^2$ for $x=4$, $y=1$

42. $\frac{x}{y}(x^2-y^2)$ for $x=10$, $y=5$

43. $\frac{x+y+z}{3}$ for $x=10$, $y=12$, $z=20$

44. $x^2+y^2+z^2$ for $x=3$, $y=4$, $z=12$

45. $\frac{a}{2}(b+c)$ for $a=8$, $b=6$, $c=9$

46. $a(b-c)^2$ for $a=5$, $b=12$, $c=3$

47. $r^2-(s^2+t^2)$ for $r=3$, $s=2$, $t=1$

48. $(r-s)^2+t^2$ for $r=3$, $s=2$, $t=1$

49. $5(m-n)^2$ for $m=10$, $n=7$

50. $\frac{m^3-n^3}{2m-n}$ for $m=6$, $n=5$

In Exercises 51–64 a relation is stated verbally, then written as a formula. Evaluate each formula using the indicated values.

51. The area A of a triangle is one-half the product of its base b and its height h.

$$A=\frac{1}{2}bh$$

for $b=18$ feet, $h=20$ feet

52. The perimeter P of a rectangle is twice the sum of the base b and the height h.
$P = 2(b + h)$
for $b = 10$ centimetres, $h = 14$ centimetres

53. The area A of a trapezoid is one-half the product of its height h and the sum of its bases a and b.
$A = \frac{1}{2}h(a + b)$
for $h = 7$ inches, $a = 13$ inches, $b = 5$ inches

54. The volume V of a pyramid with a square base is one-third the product of the height h and the square of a side b of the base.
$V = \frac{hb^2}{3}$
for $h = 5$ metres, $b = 6$ metres

55. In psychology, the intelligence quotient Q is obtained by dividing 100 times the mental age M by the chronological age C.
$Q = \frac{100M}{C}$
for $M = 18$, $C = 15$

56. The total resistance R in an electrical circuit with two resistances that have values S and T that are connected in parallel is obtained by dividing the product of the values of the two resistances by their sum.
$R = \frac{ST}{S + T}$
for $S = 20$ ohms, $T = 30$ ohms

57. The Celsius temperature C in degrees is equal to five-ninths the difference obtained by subtracting 32 from the Fahrenheit temperature F in degrees.
$C = \frac{5}{9}(F - 32)$
for $F = 212$ degrees

58. The Fahrenheit temperature F in degrees is equal to the sum of nine fifths of the Celsius temperature C in degrees and 32.
$F = \frac{9}{5}C + 32$
for $C = 20$ degrees

59. The amount of money A that results from investing a sum P at a simple interest rate r for n interest periods is the sum of P and the product of P, r, and n.
$A = P + Prn$
for $P = \$500$, $r = 0.06$, $n = 8$

60. The efficiency E of an engine is equal to the quotient when the difference, heat input I minus heat output O, is divided by the heat input.

$$E = \frac{I - O}{I}$$

for $I = 35$, $O = 30$

61. Neglecting air resistance, the distance d in metres that a dropped object falls in t seconds is equal to the product of 4.9 and the square of t.

$$d = 4.9t^2$$

for $t = 3$ seconds

62. The illumination E at a point on a surface in lumens is equal to the quotient obtained by dividing the intensity I of the source in candlepower by the square of the distance r between the point on the surface and the source of light.

$$E = \frac{I}{r^2}$$

for $I = 360$, $r = 6$

63. The focal length f of a camera lens is the quotient obtained by dividing the product of the distance a from an object to the lens and the distance b from the lens to the image by the sum of these two distances.

$$f = \frac{ab}{a + b}$$

for $a = 4$, $b = 0.05$

64. Using the straight-line depreciation method, the annual depreciation D is obtained by dividing the difference between the original cost C and the probable scrap value S by the number n of years representing the probable useful life of the article.

$$D = \frac{C - S}{n}$$

for $C = \$3000$, $S = \$600$, $n = 12$ years

65. In anthropology, the cephalic index C is obtained by dividing the product of 100 and the width of a head W by the length of the head L.

$$C = \frac{100W}{L}$$

for $W = 18$ centimetres, $L = 24$ centimetres

66. The amount of medication C for a child over one year of age can be obtained by dividing the product of the age of the child y in years and the adult dosage A by the sum of y and 12.

$$C = \frac{yA}{y + 12}$$

for $y = 8$, $A = 10$

1.5 REAL NUMBERS, NUMBER LINES

SPECIAL SETS OF NUMBERS

The answers to most number problems are found in a set of numbers called the set of real numbers. The set of real numbers and some of its important subsets will be introduced in this section. The set A is a **subset** of the set B if every element of A is an element of B. In symbols, $A \subset B$.

The counting numbers $\{1, 2, 3, 4, 5, \ldots\}$ were developed at a very early stage in our existence. By 3000 B.C. several numeral systems for these numbers had been invented. The early Egyptians had a simple grouping system something like our Roman numerals, and the early Babylonians had a positional system something like our modern Hindu-Arabic numerals.

DEFINITION

The set of counting numbers, $\{1, 2, 3, 4, 5, \ldots\}$, is also called the set of **natural numbers,** which may be designated by the letter N.

$$N = \{1, 2, 3, 4, 5, \ldots\}$$

As civilization progressed, people's requirements rose above the necessity of simply recording numbers of objects. In particular, they needed a technique for measuring quantities that were opposite in nature.

For example, in order to measure temperature, someone invented a thermometer on which a scale was established. The starting point was called 0 (zero) and then a unit of measurement, such as 1 degree Fahrenheit, was selected. Then equal units of measurement were marked off on one side of the zero point to obtain this scale, as in Fig. 1.1.

FIG. 1.1

To record temperatures below 0 degrees—that is, when the mercury fell lower than the zero point—units were marked off in the opposite direction.

To distinguish between a temperature above zero and one below zero, the numbers above zero were tagged with the symbol + (plus), and the ones below zero were tagged with the symbol − (minus) (Fig. 1.2).

Thus negative numbers, such as −1, −2, −3, and so on, came into existence as measures of quantities opposite in nature to other quantities.

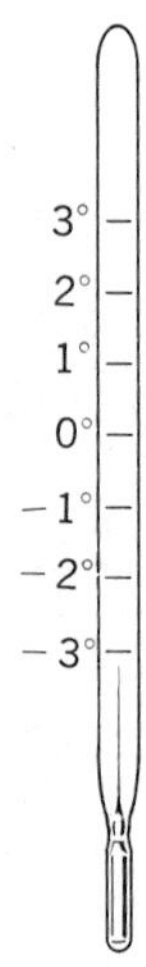

FIG. 1.2

Some examples of opposite quantities that can be measured by using negative numbers are shown in Table 1.2.

TABLE 1.2 QUANTITIES MEASURABLE WITH SIGNED NUMBERS

+30	−30
30 degrees above zero	30 degrees below zero
30 feet above sea level	30 feet below sea level
30 miles east	30 miles west
30 dollars bank deposit	30 dollars withdrawal

DEFINITION

The set of all natural numbers, their negatives, and the number zero is called the set of **integers,** which may be designated by the letter I.

$$I = \{. . . , -3, -2, -1, 0, 1, 2, 3, . . .\}$$

The natural numbers $\{1, 2, 3, . . .\}$ are also called the **positive integers.**

The numbers in the set $\{-1, -2, -3, . . .\}$ are called the **negative integers.**

The numbers in the set $\{0, 1, 2, 3, . . .\}$ are called the **whole numbers,** or the **nonnegative integers.**

The set of natural numbers, N, is a subset of the set of integers, I. In symbols, $N \subset I$.

When one natural number is divided by another natural number, the resulting quotient is not always a natural number. In arithmetic, these nonintegral quotients are called **fractions,** and each fraction is thought of as the number of subunits of a basic unit.

Many visual representations of fractions are possible, such as those in Fig. 1.3.

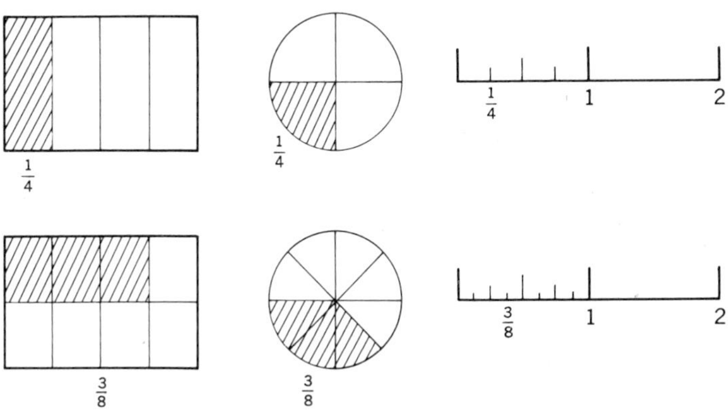

FIG. 1.3

In algebra this meaning of a fraction is retained. In addition to the fractions of arithmetic, called the *positive fractions, their negatives, called the negative fractions,* are also included in the number system of algebra.

DEFINITION

The set that includes all the integers and the positive and negative fractions is called the set of **rational numbers,** which may be designated by the letter Q.

The set Q may also be described as the set of numbers that can be expressed as the quotient of two integers, $\frac{p}{q}$, where p and q are integers and $q \neq 0$.

Examples of rational numbers are $\frac{2}{3}, \frac{5}{9}, \frac{-2}{3}, \frac{5}{-9}, -\frac{16}{17}$. In each of these numbers, the numerator and denominator is an integer, and no denominator is zero.

The set of integers can be identified as a subset of the rationals—that is, those quotients $\frac{p}{q}$ with $q = 1$.

This means, for example, that $\frac{5}{1}$ and 5 are the same number.

NUMBER LINES

A visual representation of numbers may be obtained by using the names of numbers as the names of points on a straight line.

A point is selected as the starting point. This point is called the **origin** and is given the name 0 (zero).

A unit of measurement and a direction, called the positive direction, are selected. Using this unit of length, points are marked off in succession in the positive direction, which is to the right in Fig. 1.4.

The arrow at the right indicates that the line continues indefinitely in this direction.

The negative integers $\{-1, -2, -3, \ldots\}$ are assigned to the points in the opposite direction in a similar manner. This direction is to the left in Fig. 1.4.

The arrow at the left indicates that the line continues indefinitely in this direction.

A line whose points are named by using numbers is called a **number line.**

The number that names a point is called the **coordinate** of the point.

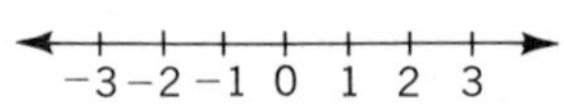

FIG. 1.4
A horizontal number line.

The point that is given a number name is called the **graph** of this number.

A number line does not have to be horizontal. A vertical arrangement is often used, as shown in Fig. 1.5. In this arrangement the positive direction is usually upward.

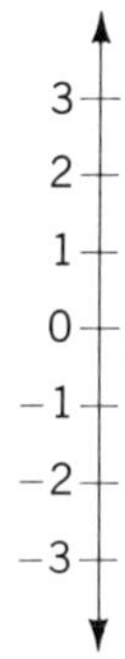

FIG. 1.5

All the rational numbers can be identified as coordinates on a number line by considering subdivisions of the basic unit and by using the concept of opposites (Fig. 1.6).

Thus it is observed that each rational number can be made to correspond to exactly one point on a number line.

One might be tempted to believe that the rational numbers exhaust the number line. However, this is not the case. For example, $\sqrt{2}$ is *not* a rational number.

The real number $\sqrt{2}$ is called an *irrational* number. Some other examples of irrational numbers are $\sqrt{3}$, $\sqrt{5}$, $\sqrt[3]{2}$, $-\sqrt{2}$, $-\sqrt{3}$, and π.

DEFINITION

An **irrational number** is a real number that is not rational—that is, it cannot be expressed as the quotient of two integers.

The totality of all the numbers that can be associated with points on a number line is called the set of **real numbers.** Thus a number line is called a **real number line.**

Each point on a real number line can be made to correspond to exactly one real number, and each real number can be made to correspond to exactly one point on a real number line. Thus there is a **one-to-one correspondence between the set of real numbers and the set of points on a real number line.** This important property of the set of real numbers is called the **axiom of completeness.** The set of real numbers is "complete" in the sense that all the real numbers are "used up" in naming the points on a number line, and every point has exactly one real number name.

The numbers associated with points to the right of 0 are called the **positive real numbers,** and those to the left of 0 are called the **negative real numbers** (Fig. 1.7).

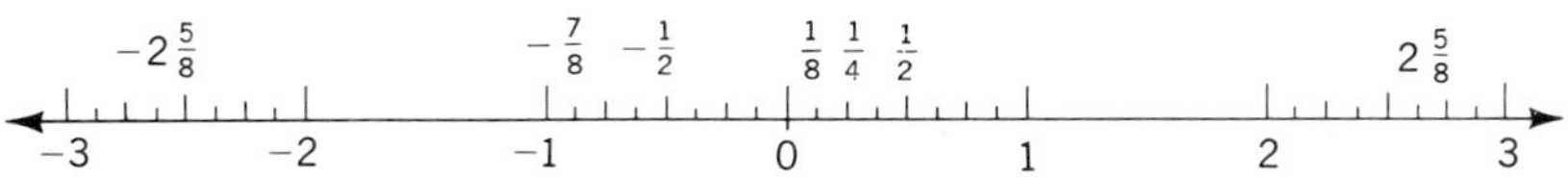

FIG. 1.6

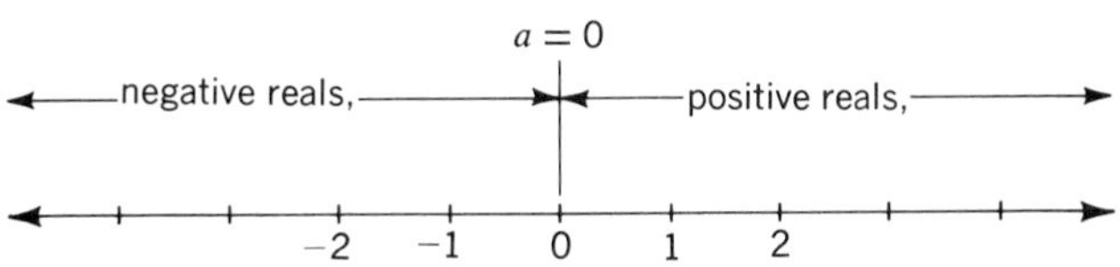

FIG. 1.7 Real number line.

Numbers that are tagged with a + or − sign are often called **signed numbers.** The numbers x and $-x$ are called **opposites** of each other. For example, the positive number 5 and the negative number −5 are opposites of each other. They are also called **additive inverses.**

EXERCISES

In Exercises 1–20, determine which of the following would best be measured by signed numbers and which by positive numbers alone.

1. Heights of people
2. Entries on a bank statement
3. Latitudes of cities
4. Historical dates from 4000 B.C. to now
5. Direction and speed of cars on a highway
6. Temperature of cities
7. Number of calories in various foods
8. Areas of plots of land
9. Daily changes in barometric pressure
10. Scores in a card game in which points can be gained or lost
11. Daily minimum temperatures at Glacier National Park
12. Volumes of containers
13. Populations of cities
14. Daily changes in stock prices
15. Weekly changes in the weight of a person on a diet
16. Longitudes of cities
17. Ages of people
18. Electric charges on ions
19. Freezing points of chemical compounds, in degrees centigrade
20. Barometric pressures

If each phrase in Exercises 21–40 is represented by a positive number, state what is represented by the corresponding negative number.

21. 35 degrees north latitude
22. 250 A.D.
23. 20 degrees above 0 Fahrenheit
24. A score of 35 in a pinochle game in which points may be won or lost
25. A force of 20 pounds toward an object
26. An acceleration of 32 ft/sec^2
27. A gain in heat of 150 Btu
28. An increase in price of $5
29. A counterclockwise rotation of 40 degrees

30. An image distance of 30 centimetres in front of a mirror
31. 80 degrees east longitude
32. 50 dollars profit
33. 70 feet above sea level
34. A gain of 5 yards by a football team
35. A 15-mph south wind
36. A velocity of 2800 mph upward, of a rocket
37. 6 steps upward
38. 8 hours later
39. 35 pounds overweight
40. An increase in volume of 20 cubic centimetres

For Exercises 41–60, name the coordinate of the point on the number line indicated by the dot.

41.
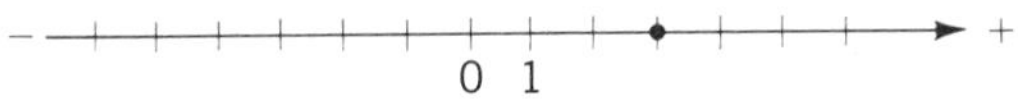

42.
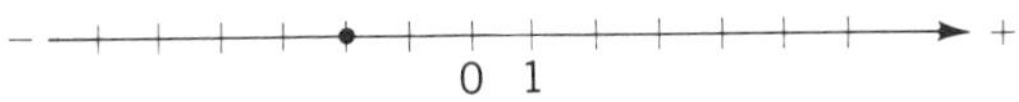

43.
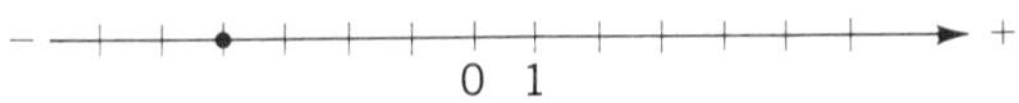

44.
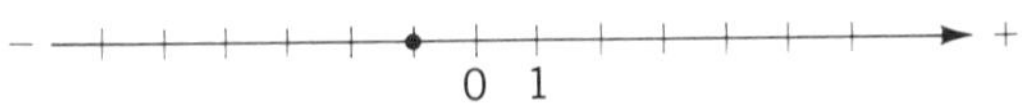

45.
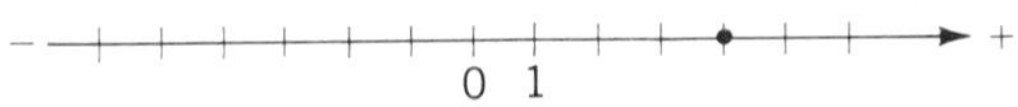

46.

47.
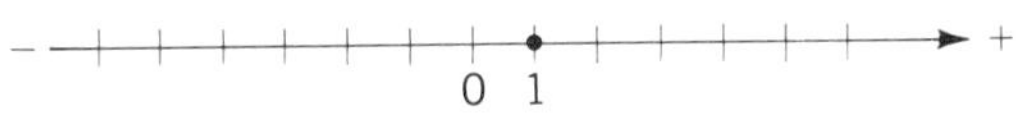

48.
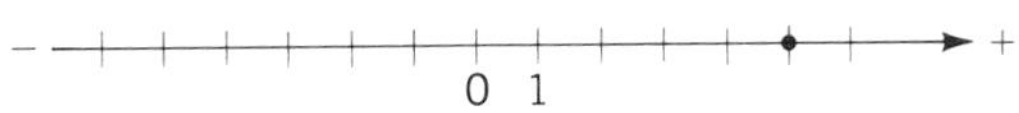

49.
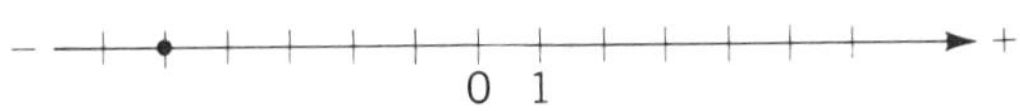

50.
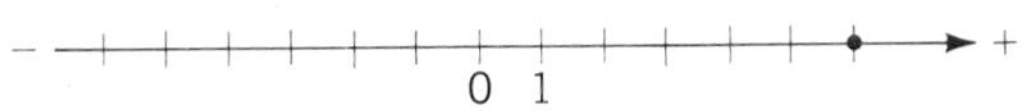

51. 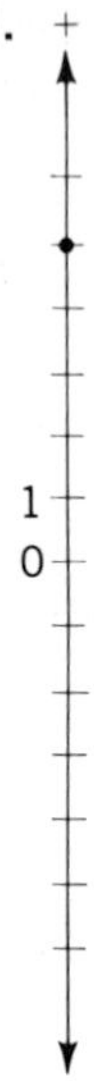

52. 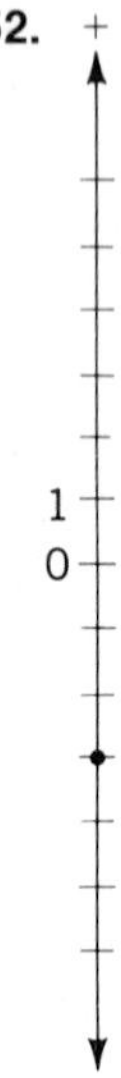

53. 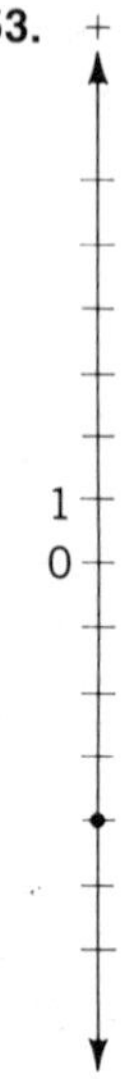

54. 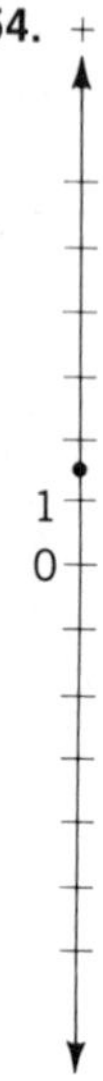

55. 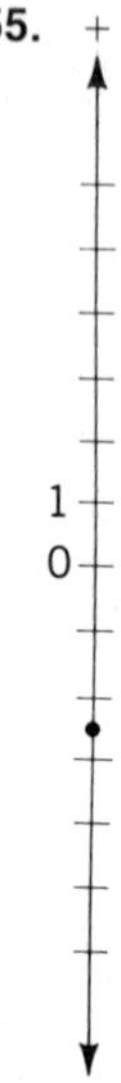

56. 

57. 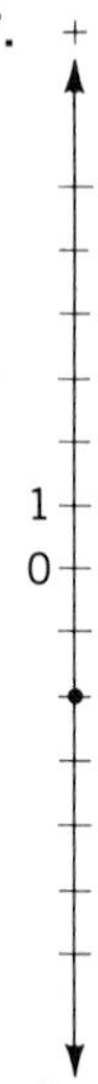

58. 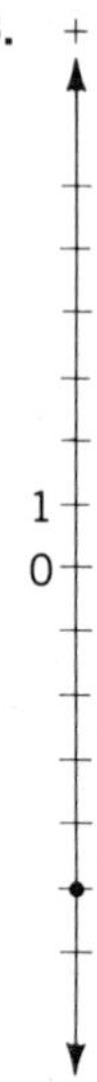

59. 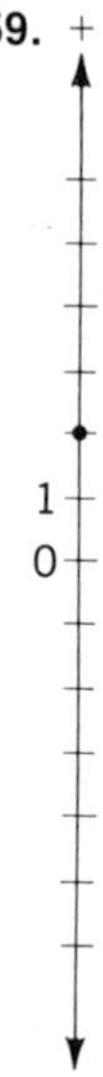

60. 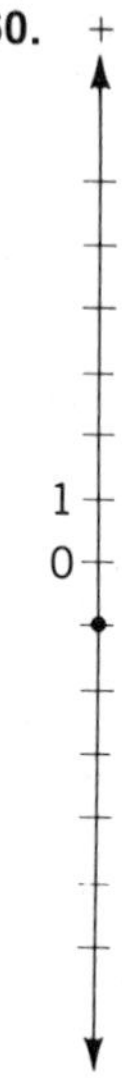

For Exercises 61–70, draw the graph of each of the following numbers on a horizontal number line whose positive direction is to the right.

61. 8

62. −8

63. 5

64. 0

65. −2

66. −4

67. 0

68. 4

69. −6

70. −10

For Exercises 71–80, draw the graph of each of the following on a vertical number line whose positive direction is upward.

71. -3

72. $2\frac{1}{2}$

73. $-2\frac{1}{2}$

74. $5\frac{5}{8}$

75. $-1\frac{3}{4}$

76. $4\frac{1}{2}$

77. $-2\frac{1}{3}$

78. $-\frac{3}{4}$

79. 0

80. $2\frac{3}{8}$

1.6 ABSOLUTE VALUE AND ORDER RELATIONS

ABSOLUTE VALUE

The number line provides a geometric model for the set of real numbers where points on the number line correspond to real numbers. Any point r and its opposite, or additive inverse, $-r$, are the same *distance* from the origin, but they are on opposite sides of the origin. The algebraic sign of a real number indicates on which side of the origin the corresponding point is located. The *distance* of the point from the origin, regardless of the side on which it is located, is called the *absolute value* of the number, denoted symbolically by $|r|$.

DEFINITION OF ABSOLUTE VALUE

If p is a positive real number, then $|p| = p$ and $|-p| = p$ and $|0| = 0$.

EXAMPLE 1 Simplify $|-6| + |3|$.

Solution $|-6| + |3| = 6 + 3 = 9$

EXAMPLE 2 Simplify $8\,|-5|$.

Solution $8\,|-5| = 8(5) = 40$

EXAMPLE 3 Simplify $2\,|7 - 7|$.

Solution $2\,|7 - 7| = 2\,|0| = 2(0) = 0$

ORDER RELATIONS

The symbols < and > are used to indicate that one number is less than (smaller than) another number and that one number is greater than (larger than) another number.

For example, $3 < 5$ means "3 is less than 5," and $5 > 3$ means "5 is greater than 3."

The expression $r < s$ means "the number r is less than the number s."

The expression $r > s$ means "the number r is greater than the number s."

The set of real numbers is an ordered set, and a number line provides a means to visualize this order. If points r and s correspond to two real numbers, r and s, then there are exactly three ways in which the placement of r and s can occur on a horizontal number line:

1. r is to the left of s
2. r is the same point as s
3. r is to the right of s

Symbolically, these three possibilities are expressed in Table 1.3.

TABLE 1.3 NUMBER RELATIONS

SYMBOLIC STATEMENT	*ALGEBRAIC MEANING*	*GEOMETRIC MEANING (for horizontal number line)*
1. $r < s$	r is less than s	r is to the left of s
2. $r = s$	r is equal to s	r is the same point as s
3. $r > s$	r is greater than s	r is to the right of s

RELATION SYMBOLS

The symbol =, which indicates equality, was introduced in 1557 by Robert Recorde in his work *The Whetstone of Witte* because, as he put it, "Noe 2 thynges can be moare equalle."

Descartes preferred ∝ or ꝏ, probably a modification of "ae," the first two letters of the Latin word *aequalis*, meaning "equal."

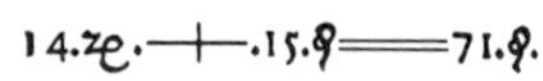

$14\,x \quad + \quad 15 \quad = \quad 71$

Thomas Harriot was the first to use the symbols < and >. These symbols appeared in his work *Artis Analyticae Praxis*, published in 1631, ten years after his death, but they were not immediately accepted, because other writers used ⊏ and ⊐, the symbols suggested by Oughtred, also in 1631.

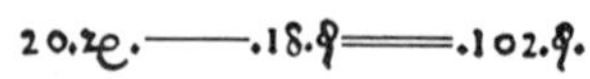

$20\,x \quad - \quad 18 \quad = \quad 102$

1.6 ABSOLUTE VALUE AND ORDER RELATIONS

Sometimes it is desirable to indicate that two numbers are related in one way or another. The combination of symbols $\leq$ is used to indicate that the number named on the left may be equal to or smaller than the one on the right. For example, $x + y \leq 25$ means that either the sum of x and y is equal to 25 or the sum is smaller than 25.

In general, $x \leq y$ means $x = y$ or $x < y$.

Similarly, $x \geq y$ means $x = y$ or $x > y$.

A slash drawn through an order symbol has the effect of the word "not." See Table 1.4.

TABLE 1.4 SUMMARY OF RELATION SYMBOLS

SYMBOL	*VERBAL TRANSLATION*
$=$	Equals, is equal to
$\neq$	Does not equal
$<$	Is less than
$>$	Is greater than
$\nless$	Is not less than
$\ngtr$	Is not greater than
$\leq$	Is less than or is equal to
$\geq$	Is greater than or is equal to

EXAMPLE 4 State the algebraic meaning and the geometric meaning of each of the following statements:

a. $2 > -5$ b. $-3 < -1$

Solution

a. 2 is greater than -5; 2 is to the right of -5 on a horizontal number line.

b. -3 is less than -1; -3 is to the left of -1 on a horizontal number line.

EXAMPLE 5 Insert either the symbol $<$ or the symbol $>$ between each pair of numbers so that the resulting statement is true:

a. $-7, 3$ b. $-7, -8$

Solution a. $-7 < 3$ b. $-7 > -8$

EXAMPLE 6 Translate into an algebraic statement: 5 times the sum of x and 4 is less than or equal to 6.

Solution $5(x + 4) \leq 6$

EXAMPLE 7 Translate into a verbal statement: $\dfrac{x-2}{5} \geq 9$

Solution The quotient obtained by dividing the difference of 2 subtracted from x by 5 is greater than or equal to 9.

In the preceding section it was shown that the number line can be used to graph points such as $x = 2$, $x = -\frac{1}{2}$, or $x = \sqrt{2}$.

Statements such as $x < 5$ or $x > 2$ can also be illustrated on a number line, but more than one point is involved. Consider the first statement: $x < 5$. Many numbers make this statement true: $3 < 5$, $0 < 5$, $-15 < 5$, $\frac{1}{2} < 5$; as a matter of fact, *all* numbers whose representation is to the left of 5 on a horizontal number line are less than 5. In the same manner it can be shown that *all* numbers to the right of 2 on a horizontal number line make $x > 2$ a true statement for x.

The following examples show how a set of real numbers described by an order relation can be graphed on a number line.

EXAMPLE 8 Graph $x > 3$ on a number line.

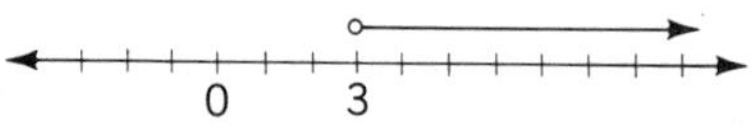

FIG. 1.8

Solution The set of all numbers x such that $x > 3$ is graphed as shown in Fig. 1.8. The circle above the numeral 3 indicates that 3 is excluded from the solution set; the solution set is indicated by the half-line starting at 3 (but not including 3) and including all values greater than 3, as shown by the direction of the line.

EXAMPLE 9 Graph $x \leq -2$ on a number line.

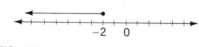

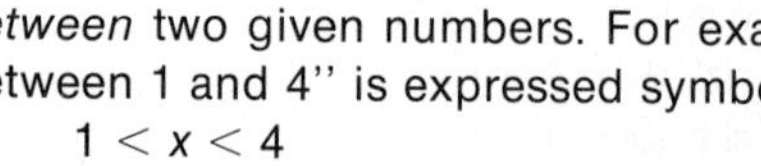

FIG. 1.9

Solution The set of all numbers x such that $x \leq -2$ is graphed as shown in Fig. 1.9. This time a solid dot over the -2 coordinate indicates that -2 is included in the solution set as well as all points to the left of -2, since x is less than or equal to -2.

Often it is desirable to indicate that x can be any number *between* two given numbers. For example, "x is any number between 1 and 4" is expressed symbolically as

$$1 < x < 4$$

where 1 and 4 are called the *end points* of the interval containing x. If either end point or both end points are to be included, the $\leq$ symbol is used to indicate this fact. For example,

$$1 \leq x \leq 4$$

means "x is between 1 and 4 and x may equal 1."

EXAMPLE 10 Graph $1 \leq x < 4$ on a number line.

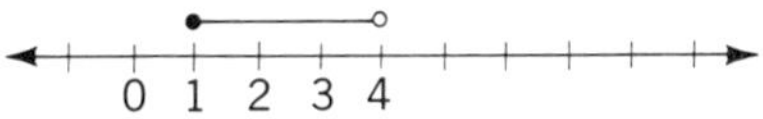

FIG. 1.10

Solution The set of all numbers x such that $1 \leq x < 4$ is shown in Fig. 1.10. A solid dot over the 1 indicates that 1 is included, whereas the circle over the 4 indicates that 4 is excluded.

EXERCISES

Simplify Exercises 1–36.

1. $|3|$
2. $|-3|$
3. $\left|-2\frac{1}{2}\right|$
4. $-|-3|$
5. $\left|-\left|\frac{1}{3}\right|\right|$
6. $|-3| + |2|$
7. $|-3| - |2|$
8. $|3 - 3|$
9. $2(|3| + |-2|)$
10. $|-7| - |4|$
11. $|-4| \cdot |-2|$
12. $3|-2|$
13. $4 + |-2|$
14. $6 - |-2|$
15. $2(|-4| - |+4|)$
16. $|8 - 2|$
17. $-|-|-5||$
18. $-(|6| \cdot |-2|)$
19. $|14 - 2|$
20. $14 - 2|-3|$
21. $|5| - |-3|$
22. $|-4|^2$
23. $|0|$
24. $|-1| \cdot |-3|$
25. $\left|-1\frac{3}{4}\right|$
26. $\left|7\frac{1}{2}\right|$
27. $|-6| + |6|$
28. $|-7| + |-2|$
29. $|8| + |-3|$
30. $3|-5|$
31. $|-6| \cdot |-4|$
32. $|12| - |-5|$
33. $|-15| - |8|$
34. $2(|-9| - |-1|)$
35. $4(|-8| - |8|)$
36. $|10 - 6|$

In Exercises 37–62 insert the symbol $<$, the symbol $>$, or the symbol $=$ between each pair of numbers so that the resulting statement is true.

37. 12, 5
38. 4, 9
39. -4, 2
40. 5, -6
41. 0, -3
42. 0, 8
43. -5, -7
44. -9, -7
45. -1, -2
46. 4, -1
47. -5, 0
48. 0, -2
49. $|-3|$, $|-6|$
50. $|3|$, $|6|$
51. $|-6|$, $|6|$
52. 6, $|-6|$
53. -6, $|6|$
54. $|6|$, -6

55. $|-5|, 0$

56. $|-2|, |1|$

57. $|-12|, |-4|$

58. $-4, |-12|$

59. $|-4|, -12$

60. $-12, -4$

61. $0, |-3|$

62. $0, -3$

Graph each of the sets of real numbers for Exercises 63–80 on a horizontal number line.

63. $x < 2$

64. $x > 2$

65. $x > -1$

66. $x \leq -3$

67. $x \leq -1$

68. $x > 0$

69. $x < 0$

70. $x > 4$

71. $x \geq 4$

72. $x < -5$

73. $x \geq 0$

74. $x \leq 0$

75. $-1 < x < 2$

76. $-1 \leq x < 2$

77. $2 < x \leq 5$

78. $-2 < x < 5$

79. $-5 \leq x \leq 3$

80. $0 < x \leq 2$

1.7 SUMS OF SIGNED NUMBERS

The meaning of the sum of two real numbers is motivated by the interpretation of a negative number as measuring a quantity opposite in nature to that measured by the corresponding positive number.

Since a \$5 gain followed by a \$3 gain results in a net gain of \$8, it is desirable to assign the meaning

$$5 + 3 = 8$$

Since a \$5 loss followed by a \$3 loss results in a net loss of \$8, it is desirable to assign the meaning

$$(-5) + (-3) = -8$$

Noting also that a \$3 gain followed by a \$5 gain results in a net gain of \$8 and that a \$3 loss followed by a \$5 loss results in a net loss of \$8, it follows that

$$5 + 3 = 3 + 5 = 8$$

and

$$(-5) + (-3) = (-3) + (-5) = -8$$

In other words, the order in which these numbers are added does not change the sum.

In general, the sum of two real numbers having the same sign is obtained by adding the absolute values of the numbers and prefixing their common sign.

1.7 SUMS OF SIGNED NUMBERS

Since a \$5 gain followed by a \$3 loss results in a net gain of \$2,

$5 + (-3) = 2$

Similarly, a \$3 loss followed by a \$5 gain results in a net gain of \$2,

$-3 + 5 = 2$

In other words,

$5 + (-3) = (-3) + 5 = 2$

On the other hand, since a \$5 loss followed by a \$3 gain results in a net loss of \$2,

$-5 + 3 = -2$

Also, since a \$3 gain followed by a \$5 loss results in a net loss of \$2,

$3 + (-5) = -2$

In other words,

$-5 + 3 = 3 + (-5) = -(5 - 3) = -2$

In general, the sum of two real numbers having opposite signs and unequal absolute values is obtained by subtracting their absolute values, the smaller from the larger, and prefixing the sign of the number having the larger absolute value.

Since the addition of zero can be interpreted as no change in measurement, for any real number x, $x + 0 = x$ and $0 + x = x$.

When a number is added to its opposite (also called additive inverse), the result is zero. For example, $4 + (-4) = 0$ and $(-4) + 4 = 0$. In general, $x + (-x) = 0$ and $(-x) + x = 0$.

There are two other important properties concerning the addition of real numbers.

THE LAW OF ORDER (COMMUTATIVE AXIOM)

The order in which real numbers are added does not change the sum. In symbols, $r + s = s + r$.

THE LAW OF GROUPING (ASSOCIATIVE AXIOM)

The way in which real numbers are grouped does not change the sum. In symbols, $(r + s) + t = r + (s + t)$.

Since $+5$ and 5 are simply different names for the same number, the $+$ sign is usually omitted for convenience in reading and writing. For example, the sum $(+9) + (-3)$ is usually written as $9 + (-3)$, and $(-8) + (+2)$ is usually written as $-8 + 2$.

EXAMPLE 1 Perform the indicated additions:

a. $(+8) + (+2)$ b. $(-8) + (-2)$
c. $(+8) + (-2)$ d. $(-8) + (+2)$

Solution a. $(+8) + (+2) = 8 + 2 = 10$
b. $(-8) + (-2) = -(8 + 2) = -10$
c. $(+8) + (-2) = +(8 - 2) = 6$
d. $(-8) + (+2) = -(8 - 2) = -6$

EXAMPLE 2 Perform the indicated additions:

a. $5 + 7$ b. $5 + (-7)$ c. $-5 + 7$ d. $(-5) + (-7)$

Solution a. $5 + 7 = 12$
b. $5 + (-7) = -2$
c. $-5 + 7 = 2$
d. $(-5) + (-7) = -12$

EXAMPLE 3 Find the indicated sum: $5 + [(-8) + 3]$

Solution $5 + [(-8) + 3] = 5 + (-5) = 0$

EXAMPLE 4 Find the indicated sum: $[(-6) + 6] + (-7)$

Solution $[(-6) + 6] + (-7) = 0 + (-7) = -7$

EXAMPLE 5 Find the indicated sum: $20 + (-30) + (-40)$

Solution $20 + (-30) + (-40)$
$= [(+20) + (-30)] + (-40)$
$= [-(30 - 20)] + (-40)$
$= (-10) + (-40)$
$= -(10 + 40) = -50$

Since the associative axiom for the addition of real numbers states that the way in which the numbers are grouped does not affect the sum, the sum may be obtained by grouping one way, and then this result may be checked by regrouping the other way.

Check $20 + (-30) + (-40)$
$= 20 + [(-30) + (-40)]$
$= 20 + [-(30 + 40)]$
$= 20 + (-70)$
$= -(70 - 20)$
$= -50$

EXERCISES

In Exercises 1–50 express each as a single integer.

1. $(+8) + (+3)$ **2.** $(-8) + (-3)$
3. $(+8) + (-3)$ **4.** $(-8) + (+3)$

5. $(-5) + 0$
6. $0 + (-8)$
7. $(-12) + (-18)$
8. $(-12) + (+18)$
9. $(+14) + (-9)$
10. $(-25) + (+15)$
11. $20 + (-5)$
12. $(-8) + (-7)$
13. $(-8) + 7$
14. $8 + (-7)$
15. $-4 + 4$
16. $0 + (-5)$
17. $-50 + 35$
18. $35 + (-50)$
19. $(-75) + (-25)$
20. $-25 + 75$
21. $(-6) + (-9) + (-5)$
22. $-12 + 4 + (-2)$
23. $50 + (-70) + 90$
24. $25 + (-35) + (-45)$
25. $-9 + [(-6 + 6)]$
26. $[7 + (-7)] + 8$
27. $8 + (-10 + 2)$
28. $-5 + (-4 + 9)$
29. $[20 + (-14)] + (-10)$
30. $20 + [(-14) + (-10)]$
31. $(-3) + [(-5) + (-2)]$
32. $[(-4) + (-5)] + (-6)$
33. $[10 + (-20)] + (-30)$
34. $15 + [(-25) + (-40)]$
35. $[(-8) + 8] + (-7)$
36. $9 + [(-12) + 3]$
37. $-(-5 + 17)$
38. $-(-20 + 6)$
39. $-(-7 + 8 + 14)$
40. $-(-30 + 50 + 0)$
41. $5 + (-10) + (-15)$
42. $(-7) + 8 + (-9)$
43. $12 + 4 + (-20)$
44. $(-60) + (-70) + 90$
45. $(-11) + (-9) + (-7)$
46. $18 + (-15) + 17$
47. $-1 + 1 + (-1)$
48. $5 + (-3) + (-2)$
49. $-2 + 5 + (-3)$
50. $-78 + 49 + 78$

51. A bank statement contains the following entries (a positive number means a deposit and a negative number means a withdrawal):

$+220, +70, -95, -22, +15, -84$

If the account originally contained \$300, how much was in the account after the above deposits and withdrawals were made?

52. In the card game of pinochle, it is possible to gain points and to lose points. Find the final score of a player whose scores on successive hands are listed as follows:

$+10, -25, +32, +8, -34$

53. The weekly changes in weight for 6 weeks of a person on a diet are recorded below:

$+2, -4, -2, +3, -5, +1$

If the person originally weighed 71 kilograms, find his weight at the end of the 6-week period.

54. Determine the net yardage for the following sequence of football plays, where a positive number (+) means a gain in yardage and a negative number (−) means a loss in yardage:

$+5, -3, -6, +15, +2, -10, +4$

55. Find the resulting speed of an object if its original speed was 40 mph and it was subject to the following successive accelerations (+) and decelerations (−):

$+15, -30, -10, +15, +20$

56. The following is a treasurer's report for a certain organization (a positive number indicates dollars received, and a negative number indicates dollars paid out):

Dues, +150; Stationery, −8; Stamps, −15; Food sale, +60; Gifts, −80; Party expenses, −75

Find the amount of money in the treasury.

57. A piston is moving upward and downward from a central position *C*. A positive number indicates the number of centimetres above *C*, and a negative number indicates the number of centimetres below *C*. Find the position of the piston with respect to the central position *C* after the following motions have taken place (the piston started at *C*):

−5, −3, +2, +6, −4, −1

In chemistry the valence of an atom (or a set of atoms) is an integer that determines how the atom (or set) will unite chemically as compared to the hydrogen atom, assigned a valence of +1. Find the valence (the sum of the component valences) for the ions in Exercises 58–62, whose component valences are given.

58. Sulfate ion, SO_4, where the valence of $S = +6$, of $O_4 = -8$

59. Hydroxyl ion, OH, where the valence of $O = -2$, of $H = +1$

60. Ammonium ion, NH_4, where the valence of $N = -3$, of $H_4 = +4$

61. Hydronium ion, H_3O, where the valence of $H_3 = +3$, of $O = -2$

62. Nitrate ion, NO_3, where the valence of $N = +5$, of $O_3 = -6$

63. A chemical compound is such that the sum of the valences of its components is zero. Find the valence of the component whose valence is not given.

a. Baking soda, $NaHCO_3$; $Na = +1$, $H = +1$, $O_3 = -6$

b. Ammonium sulfate (fertilizer), NH_4HSO_4; $H_4 = +4$, $H = +1$, $S = +6$, $O_4 = -8$

c. Jade (jadeite), $NaAlSi_2O_6$; $Na = +1$, $Si_2 = +8$, $O_6 = -12$

64. At the end of a week, the closing price of a certain stock was quoted in the newspaper as $57\frac{1}{4}$ (meaning $57\frac{1}{4}$ dollars, or $57.25). The changes in price for the next week were quoted as listed as follows, in dollars and fractions of dollars:

Monday $-1\frac{1}{4}$,

Tuesday $+\frac{3}{4}$,

Wednesday $+\frac{3}{8}$,

Thursday $-1\frac{1}{8}$,

Friday $-\frac{3}{4}$

Find the closing price of the stock at the end of this week.

1.8 DIFFERENCES OF SIGNED NUMBERS

In arithmetic the difference between two natural numbers (the numbers of arithmetic) is defined in terms of addition. For example, $12 - 3 = 9$, because $9 + 3 = 12$. In words, we ask: "What number, when *added* to 3, yields 12?" The answer, of course, is 9. The difference between two *real* numbers is defined in the same way.

For example, when looking for the answer to the problem $3 - 12$, we ask what number must be added to 12 to yield the answer 3. Since $12 + (-9) = 3$, $3 - 12 = -9$.

As another example,

$-3 - 12 = -15$ since $12 + (-15) = -3$

Similarly,

$3 - (-12) = 15$ because $-12 + 15 = 3$

Addition and subtraction are called **inverse operations.** There is an easy way to do subtraction problems by noting this relationship between addition and subtraction.

Note that

$$\begin{aligned} 12 - 3 &= 12 + (-3) = 9 \\ 3 - 12 &= 3 + (-12) = -9 \\ -3 - 12 &= -3 + (-12) = -15 \\ 3 - (-12) &= 3 + (+12) = 15 \\ -3 - (-12) &= -3 + (+12) = 9 \end{aligned}$$

GIROLAMO CARDANO: DOCTOR, GAMBLER, MATHEMATICIAN

Girolamo Cardano (1501–1576) was born in Pavia, Italy, the illegitimate son of a professor of jurisprudence and medicine. His father educated him to be a doctor of medicine, and he did achieve fame as a physician. He was a professor of mathematics and medicine at Milan, and later at Pavia and Bologna.

Cardano's life was stormy. He was an inveterate gambler who wrote a book on gambling, *Liber de ludo aleae* ("The Book on Games of Chance"). (An English version of this work, translated by Sydney H. Gould, was published by Holt, Rinehart and Winston, Inc., in 1961.) Deeply interested in astrology, Cardano also published a horoscope of the life of Christ, for which he was sent to prison. When he was released he resigned his professorship, moved to Rome, and became astrologer to the papal court, which post he held until he died.

As a generalization of these special examples, the following rule can be stated.

SUBTRACTION OF SIGNED NUMBERS

Change the sign of the subtrahend and add according to the rules for adding signed numbers.

In symbols, $r - s = r + (-s)$ and $r - (-s) = r + s$.

EXAMPLE 1 Perform the indicated subtractions:

a. $3 - 7$ b. $-3 - 7$ c. $3 - (-7)$ d. $-3 - (-7)$

Solution a. $3 - 7 = 3 + (-7) = -4$

b. $-3 - 7 = -3 + (-7) = -10$

c. $3 - (-7) = 3 + 7 = 10$

d. $-3 - (-7) = -3 + 7 = 4$

EXAMPLE 2 Subtract and check:

a. $15 - 8$ b. $15 - (-8)$ c. $-15 - 8$ d. $-15 - (-8)$

Solution a. $15 - 8 = 7$ (The answer is the same as it is in arithmetic.)

b. $15 - (-8) = 15 + 8 = 23$

c. $-15 - 8 = -15 + (-8) = -23$

d. $-15 - (-8) = -15 + 8 = -7$

Check $23 + (-8) = 15$

$-23 + 8 = -15$

$-7 + (-8) = -15$

EXAMPLE 3 Subtract:

a. $0 - 6$ b. $0 - (-6)$ c. $-6 - 6$ d. $-6 - (-6)$

Solution a. $0 - 6 = 0 + (-6) = -6$

b. $0 - (-6) = 0 + 6 = 6$

c. $-6 - 6 = -6 + (-6) = -12$

d. $-6 - (-6) = -6 + 6 = 0$

EXAMPLE 4 Write as a single integer: $-(2 - 3)$.

Solution $-(2 - 3) = -(2 + [-3])$

$= -(-1)$

$= 1$

EXERCISES

In Exercises 1–40, subtract and check.

1. $18 - 12$

2. $-9 - 4$

3. $10 - (-4)$

4. $(-15) - (-19)$

5. $(-17) - (-23)$

6. $0 - (-7)$

7. $2 - 9$

8. $-3 - 8$

9. $0 - 6$

10. $-2 - (-7)$

11. $10 - 9$
12. $6 - 10$
13. $50 - 15$
14. $40 - (-25)$
15. $(-3) - (-3)$
16. $5 - (-7)$
17. $7 - (-7)$
18. $(-7) - (-7)$
19. $0 - (-3)$
20. $0 - 3$
21. $7 - 3$
22. $3 - 7$
23. $7 - (-3)$
24. $-3 - 7$
25. $-6 - 4$
26. $-6 - (-4)$
27. $6 - 6$
28. $-4 - (-4)$
29. $-7 - 7$
30. $8 - (-8)$
31. $-20 - 8$
32. $-15 - (-10)$
33. $22 - 12$
34. $17 - 19$
35. $0 - 2$
36. $0 - (-5)$
37. $-8 - (-15)$
38. $8 - 15$
39. $-14 - 9$
40. $-12 - 7$

Perform the indicated operations in Exercises 41–60.

41. $(-5 + 5) - 9$
42. $(-1) - [(-2) - (-3)]$
43. $2 + (8 - 20)$
44. $0 - (6 - 12)$
45. $27 + [59 + (-27)]$
46. $(-38) + (38 - 26)$
47. $(-65) + [46 - (-65)]$
48. $(-6) + (7 - 10)$
49. $50 - (20 - 20)$
50. $[-(-8) - 2] - 3$
51. $20 - (10 - 5)$
52. $(20 - 10) - 5$
53. $-12 - (14 - 17)$
54. $-8 - (-4 + 4)$
55. $35 - [(-20) - (-20)]$
56. $[-65 - (-65)] - 40$
57. $-3 - (4 + [-2])$
58. $-3 - (4 - [-2])$
59. $(-3 - 4) + (-2)$
60. $(-3 - 4) - (-2)$

On a certain day a newspaper recorded the high and low temperatures (in degrees Celsius) for 6 cities, as shown in Exercises 61–66. Find the difference between the high temperature and the low temperature for each city.

	City	*High*	*Low*
61.	San Francisco	15	9
62.	New York	−4	−17
63.	Chicago	−12	−21
64.	Fairbanks	−26	−40
65.	Denver	−20	−25
66.	Honolulu	24	22

Determine the difference in latitudes between each pair of cities in Exercises 67–70 (a positive number means north of the equator, and a negative number means south of the equator).

67. Sacramento, California — +39 degrees
Lima, Peru — −12 degrees

68.	Los Angeles, California	+34 degrees
	Hanoi, North Vietnam	+21 degrees
69.	Johannesburg, S. Africa	−26 degrees
	Perth, Australia	−32 degrees
70.	Moscow, U.S.S.R.	+56 degrees
	Seattle, Washington	+48 degrees

Find the difference in elevation between each pair of geographic locations whose elevations are given in Exercises 71–75. A positive number indicates an elevation above sea level, and a negative number indicates an elevation below sea level.

71.	Mount Kilimanjaro (highest point in Africa)	+19,321 feet
	Qattara Depression, Egypt (lowest point in Africa)	− 436 feet
72.	Mount Whitney	+14,495 feet
	Death Valley (highest and lowest points in California)	− 282 feet
73.	Qattara Depression	− 436 feet
	Death Valley	− 282 feet
74.	Brawley, California	− 119 feet
	El Centro, California	− 45 feet
75.	Dead Sea (surface level)	− 1,292 feet
	Mount Everest (highest point in the world)	+29,028 feet

For Exercises 76–80 determine the number of years that elapsed between each pair of dates. A positive number means time A.D. *and a negative number means time* B.C. *(Note: There was no year* 0 *since the number* 0 *had not been invented when the calendar was reformed. In other words, the year* 1 A.D. *followed the year* 1 B.C. *For Exercises 78–80, calculate the difference in the usual way and then subtract one from the result to obtain the answer.)*

76. −2900, the building of the Great Gizeh Pyramid, to
−1650, date of the Rhind papyrus (mathematical work)

77. −550, during lifetime of Pythagoras, to
−300, during lifetime of Euclid

78. −212, fall of Syracuse to Rome, to
+400, fall of Rome (western part)

79. −425, Golden Age of Athens, to
+500, Golden Age of India

80. −2400, first historical records, to
+1980

1.9 PRODUCTS OF SIGNED NUMBERS

Although there are many practical applications that involve products of signed numbers, it is not easy to provide a simple geometric illustration of such a product.

In arithmetic the product $3(5)$, often read as "three fives," means the sum $5+5+5$, or 15. The rules for multiplying signed numbers are made to preserve this meaning and to preserve the laws of order and grouping.

THE LAW OF ORDER FOR MULTIPLICATION (COMMUTATIVE AXIOM)

The order in which numbers are multiplied does not change the product. In symbols, $rs = sr$.

THE LAW OF GROUPING FOR MULTIPLICATION (ASSOCIATIVE AXIOM)

The way in which the factors of a product are grouped does not change the product. In symbols, $(rs)t = r(st)$.

Considering $3(-5)$ as the sum of three negative fives,

$$3(-5) = (-5) + (-5) + (-5) = -15$$

Now $-3(5) = 5(-3)$ by the law of order, and therefore,

$$\begin{aligned} -3(5) &= 5(-3) \\ &= (-3) + (-3) + (-3) + (-3) + (-3) = -15 \end{aligned}$$

Note in these special cases that the product of a negative number and a positive number is negative.

The product $-3(5)$ can also be thought of as the subtraction of three fives, that is, as

$$-5 - 5 - 5 = (-5) + (-5) + (-5) = -15$$

Based on this idea, we can think of $(-3)(-5)$ as the subtraction of three negative fives, that is, as

$$-(-5) - (-5) - (-5) = 5 + 5 + 5 = 15$$

Accordingly $(-3)(-5)$ is 15.

These results can be summarized and generalized in the following rule.

THE BIRTH OF SYMBOLS

During the Middle Ages abbreviations began to be used to indicate the operations. The symbols gradually developed after the appearance of printed works. (The printing press was invented in 1438.)

The plus sign, +, is a contraction of the Latin word *et,* meaning "and." When *et* is written rapidly, it looks like *it*.

The minus sign, –, was used as an equivalent for "$\bar{m}$" and "m," abbreviations of the word minus.

The marks + and – were used in medieval warehouses on sacks, crates, or barrels to indicate whether the contents were more or less than what they were supposed to be. The signs + and – made their first appearance in print in Widman's *Commercial Arithmetic,* published in 1489.

The dot for multiplication was introduced in 1583 by Christopher Clavius of Germany (1537–1612), and established by the German mathematician Gottfried Wilhelm Leibniz (1646–1716).

The division notation of algebra can be traced to the Hindus through the works of Bhaskara, who in 1150 wrote $\begin{matrix}1\\3\end{matrix}$ for $\frac{1}{3}$. The bar appears in the works of Viète, who also indicated multiplication by juxtaposition.

The symbol $\sqrt{\ }$ for root extraction was introduced in 1525 by Christoff Rudolff because it resembles a small "r," the initial letter of *radix*, the Latin word for root.

Viète wrote *A*, *Aq*, and *Acu* for our modern x, x^2, and x^3. Pierre Herigone, in his *Cursus Mathematicus* (1634–1637), used $a2$, $a3$, and $a4$ for a^2, a^3, and a^4. Our modern notation is first found in Descartes' *La Géométrie* (1637), in which he used x^3, x^4, x^5, and so on. However, Descartes used both xx and x^2 to indicate the square of x. Until the latter part of the eighteenth century it was common to find xx for x^2 and xxx for x^3.

1.9 PRODUCTS OF SIGNED NUMBERS

MULTIPLICATION OF SIGNED NUMBERS

1. The product of two nonzero real numbers having the same sign is positive.
2. The product of two nonzero real numbers having different signs is negative. In symbols, if r and s are any real numbers,
   $r(-s) = -rs$, $-r(s) = -rs$, and $(-r)(-s) = rs$

The numbers one and zero are such special numbers that their properties need to be stated.

PRODUCTS INVOLVING 1 AND 0

The product of any real number and 1 is that number. In symbols, $x \cdot 1 = x$ and $1 \cdot x = x$.
The product of any real number and 0 is 0. In symbols, $x \cdot 0 = 0$ and $0 \cdot x = 0$.

EXAMPLE 1 Find the indicated products:
a. $7(4)$ b. $7(-4)$ c. $-7(4)$ d. $(-7)(-4)$

Solution a. $7(4) = 28$
b. $7(-4) = -28$
c. $-7(4) = -28$
d. $(-7)(-4) = 28$

EXAMPLE 2 Multiply:
a. $6(-1)$ b. $(-6)(1)$ c. $(0)(-6)$ d. $(-6)(0)$

Solution a. $6(-1) = -6$
b. $(-6)(1) = -6$
c. $(0)(-6) = 0$
d. $(-6)(0) = 0$

EXAMPLE 3 Find the product of $(-4)(59)(-25)$ in two different ways.

Solution
$(-4)(59)(-25) = (-236)(-25) = 5900$
$(-4)(59)(-25) = (59)(-4)(-25)$
$= 59(100) = 5900$

EXAMPLE 4 Perform the indicated operations:
a. -3^2 b. $(-3)^2$

Solution

a. -3^2 means $-(3^2)$, or the negative of 3^2, which is $-(3 \cdot 3)$; therefore, $-3^2 = -9$.
b. $(-3)^2$ means $(-3)(-3) = +9$; therefore, $(-3)^2 = 9$.

EXAMPLE 5 Perform the indicated operation: $(-9)^3$.

Solution $(-9)^3 = (-9)(-9)(-9)$
$= [(-9)(-9)](-9)$
$= (+81)(-9)$
$= -729$

EXERCISES

Perform the indicated operations in Exercises 1–60.

1. $(5)(7)$
2. $(5)(-7)$
3. $(-5)(-7)$
4. $(-8)(2)$
5. $(-8)(-2)$
6. $(4)(-25)$
7. $(-8)(125)$
8. $(-25)(-4)$
9. $(-125)(8)$
10. $(3)(-5)(-7)$
11. $(8)(125)$
12. $(11)(-8)$
13. $(-8)(11)$
14. $(-17)(-13)$
15. $(-35)^2$
16. $(-20)^3$
17. $(10)(-25)$
18. $(-25)(-100)$
19. $(0)(-19)$
20. $(-3)(6-6)$
21. $(-3)(6)+(-3)(-6)$
22. $(5)(2)(7)$
23. $(-2)(-5)(9)$
24. $(-5)(-8)(-2)$
25. $(4)(-25)(7)$
26. $(-4)(9)(-25)$
27. $4(-5)^2$
28. $4(-5)^3$
29. $(10-4)(4-10)$
30. $(5-8)(6-6)$
31. $(-2)(-4)(-6)$
32. $(-5)(46)(-2)$
33. $(9)(-2)(3)$
34. $(-4)(-4)(-4)$
35. $(-5)^3$
36. $(-6)^2$
37. $(-2)^3(-2)^2$
38. $4(-3)^2$
39. $2(-7)^3$
40. $(-2)(5-8)$
41. $3(4-9)$
42. $(7-8)(6-10)$
43. $(-4+8)(-7+7)$
44. $5[-3-(-5)]$
45. $(3-9)(9-3)$
46. $[-2-(-2)]\cdot(3-9)$
47. $(-3)(7-15)$
48. $(-3)(7)-(-3)(15)$
49. $8-4(3-9)$
50. $(8-4)(3-9)$
51. $8(4-9)$
52. $8(4)-8(9)$
53. $(-7)(10-15)$
54. $(-7)(10)-(-7)(15)$
55. $(-2)(-2)(-2)(-2)$
56. $(-2)(-5)(-2)(-5)(-2)(-5)$
57. $[(-2)(-5)]^3$
58. $(-7+3)^2-(-7-3)^2$
59. $-(6-5)(6-4)(6-3)$
60. $(10-1)(10-2)(10-3)(10-4)$

In physics the moment M of a force F is given by $M=Fd$, where d is the directed distance of the force from a fixed position. Find M in Exercises 61–65.

61. $F=+200$ pounds, $d=+15$ feet
62. $F=+200$ pounds, $d=-10$ feet
63. $F=-70$ pounds, $d=+8$ feet
64. $F=-120$ pounds, $d=-6$ feet
65. $F=-500$ grams, $d=-15$ centimetres

In chemistry a subscript at the lower right of a symbol for an atom indicates the number of atoms. For example, sulfuric acid is expressed in symbols as H_2SO_4, meaning 2 atoms of hydrogen (H), 1 atom of sulfur (S), and 4 atoms of oxygen (O). The valence of an *ion, a positive or negative integer indicating how the ion combines chemically, is the sum of the valences of the atoms composing the ion. For example, the valence of the sulphate ion,* SO_4, *equals (valence of S) + 4(valence of O) =* $(+6) + 4(-2) = 6 - 8 = -2$. *Find the valence of the ions in Exercises 66–70, given the valence of the component atoms.*

66. Nitrate ion, NO_3; valence of N = +5, valence of O = −2
67. Phosphate ion, PO_4; valence of P = +5, valence of O = −2
68. Bichromate ion, Cr_2O_7; valence of Cr = +5, valence of O = −2
69. Ammonium ion, NH_4; valence of N = −3, valence of H = +1
70. Permanganate ion, MnO_4; valence of Mn = +7, valence of O = −2

In a television set, the change c in the capacitance of a condenser is given by

$$c = kCT$$

where

k is the temperature coefficient
C is the capacitance of the condenser
T is the change in the temperature in degrees Celsius

Find c for each set of values in Exercises 71–75.

71. $k = \frac{-22}{100{,}000}$, $C = 0.002$, $T = +20$ degrees Celsius
72. $k = \frac{-75}{100{,}000}$, $C = 0.004$, $T = -10$ degrees Celsius
73. $k = \frac{3}{100{,}000}$, $C = \frac{1}{10{,}000}$, $T = -4$ degrees Celsius
74. $k = \frac{-47}{100{,}000}$, $C = 0.0006$, $T = -2$ degrees Celsius
75. $k = \frac{-33}{100{,}000}$, $C = 0.0005$, $T = +6$ degrees Celsius

1.10 QUOTIENTS OF SIGNED NUMBERS

Division may be defined for real numbers just as it is defined in arithmetic as the inverse operation to multiplication. For example, the quotient of 12 divided by 3 is defined to be 4, $\frac{12}{3} = 4$, because 4 is the only number such that $12 = 3 \cdot 4$.

DEFINITION OF DIVISION

If r and s are any real numbers such that $s \neq 0$, then $\frac{r}{s} = t$ if and only if there is exactly one real number t so that $r = st$.

EXAMPLE 1 Find the indicated quotients:

a. $\frac{12}{3}$ b. $\frac{-12}{-3}$ c. $\frac{12}{-3}$ d. $\frac{-12}{3}$

Solution

a. $\frac{12}{3} = 4$ because $12 = (3)(4)$

b. $\frac{-12}{-3} = 4$ because $-12 = (-3)(4)$

c. $\frac{+12}{-3} = -4$ because $12 = (-3)(-4)$

d. $\frac{-12}{3} = -4$ because $-12 = (3)(-4)$

EXAMPLE 2 Find the indicated quotients, if they exist:

a. $\frac{0}{5}$ b. $\frac{0}{-5}$ c. $\frac{5}{0}$ d. $\frac{0}{0}$

Solution

a. $\frac{0}{5} = 0$ because $0 = (5)(0)$

b. $\frac{0}{-5} = 0$ because $0 = (-5)(0)$

c. $\frac{5}{0}$ is undefined. There is no number t such that $5 = 0 \cdot t$ since $0 \cdot t = 0$ for all real numbers t.

d. $\frac{0}{0}$ is undefined. By definition, if $\frac{0}{0} = t$, then there must be exactly one real number t such that $0 = 0 \cdot t$. In this case, there are many possibilities since $0 = 0 \cdot t$ for all real numbers t.

The special cases shown in the preceding examples can be generalized as follows.

QUOTIENTS OF SIGNED NUMBERS

The quotient $\frac{0}{s} = 0$ for any real number s different from zero. The quotients $\frac{s}{0}$ and $\frac{0}{0}$ are undefined.

1.10 QUOTIENTS OF SIGNED NUMBERS

The quotient of two nonzero real numbers having the **same** sign is **positive.**
The quotient of two nonzero real numbers having **different** signs is **negative.**

EXAMPLE 3 Perform the indicated operations, if possible:

a. $\frac{7-22}{-5}$ b. $\frac{6-6}{3}$ c. $\frac{4-(-4)}{4-4}$ d. $\frac{8-2}{2-8}$

Solution

a. $\frac{7-22}{-5}=\frac{-15}{-5}=3$

b. $\frac{6-6}{3}=\frac{0}{3}=0$

c. $\frac{4-(-4)}{4-4}=\frac{4+4}{4+(-4)}=\frac{8}{0}$, undefined

d. $\frac{8-2}{2-8}=\frac{6}{-6}=-1$

EXERCISES

In Exercises 1–80, perform the indicated operations, if possible. If the expression is undefined, write "undefined."

1. $\frac{63}{9}$

2. $\frac{63}{-9}$

3. $\frac{-63}{9}$

4. $\frac{-63}{-9}$

5. $\frac{-1000}{125}$

6. $\frac{-1000}{-8}$

7. $\frac{100}{-5}$

8. $\frac{0}{-60}$

9. $\frac{-50}{0}$

10. $\frac{56}{7}$

11. $\frac{-56}{7}$

12. $\frac{56}{-4}$

13. $\frac{21}{-7}$

14. $\frac{-21}{7}$

15. $\frac{-21}{-7}$

16. $\frac{21}{7}$

17. $\frac{0}{-6}$

18. $\frac{-6}{0}$

19. $\frac{-56}{8}$

20. $\frac{63}{-7}$

21. $\frac{-55}{-11}$

22. $\frac{42}{-7}$

23. $\frac{-28}{4}$

24. $\frac{36}{4}$

25. $\frac{-132}{12}$

26. $\frac{169}{-13}$

27. $\frac{-100}{-4}$

28. $\frac{-1000}{8}$

29. $\frac{-125}{-25}$

30. $-\frac{15}{0}$

31. $\frac{0}{25}$

32. $\frac{0}{0}$

33. $\frac{7-2}{2-7}$

34. $\frac{4-12}{-4}$

35. $\frac{-120}{(-4)+6}$

36. $\frac{8-8}{8-(-8)}$

37. $\frac{120}{5-17}$

38. $\frac{10-30}{40-45}$

39. $\frac{25-15}{25-35}$

40. $\frac{0-9}{0+(-9)}$

41. $\frac{-132}{-22}$

42. $\frac{8-8}{8}$

43. $\frac{8-(-8)}{-8}$

44. $\frac{-3}{-3-(-3)}$

45. $\frac{18-25}{25-18}$

46. $\frac{96-39}{39-96}$

47. $\frac{(-5)^2}{-5}$

48. $\frac{(-5)^3}{-5}$

49. $\frac{40-55}{55-58}$

50. $\frac{60}{\left(\frac{-6}{2}\right)}$

51. $\frac{\left(\frac{60}{-6}\right)}{2}$

52. $\frac{-60}{\left(\frac{-10}{-2}\right)}$

53. $\frac{\left(\frac{-60}{-10}\right)}{-2}$

54. $\frac{(-4)+(-4)}{(-4)+(-4)}$

55. $\frac{(-1)+(-1)}{(-1)-(-1)}$

56. $\frac{(-7)^2-(-3)^2}{(-7)-(-3)}$

57. $\frac{12}{\left(\frac{-6}{2}\right)}$

58. $\frac{\left(\frac{12}{-6}\right)}{2}$

59. $\frac{-54}{\left(\frac{-6}{-3}\right)}$

60. $\frac{\left(\frac{-54}{-6}\right)}{-3}$

61. $\frac{(-10)^2}{-5}$

62. $\frac{56-89}{89-56}$

63. $\frac{95 - 48}{48 - 95}$

64. $\frac{(-10)^3}{125}$

65. $\frac{7 - (-7)}{-7}$

66. $\frac{-6}{6 - (-6)}$

67. $\frac{(-7)^2 - (5)^2}{-7 - 5}$

68. $\frac{(-3)^3 - (-2)^3}{-3 - (-2)}$

69. $\frac{(-10)^3 + (-5)^3}{(-10) + (-5)}$

70. $\frac{(5 - 1)(5 - 2)(5 - 3)}{(-1)(-2)(-3)}$

71. $\frac{(1 - 2)(1 - 4)(1 - 6)}{(-2)(-4)(-6)}$

72. $\frac{(-5)^2 + 2(-5)(-3) + (-3)^2}{(-5) + (-3)}$

73. $-\frac{-72}{-8}$

74. $-\frac{60}{-15}$

75. $-\frac{-154}{11}$

76. $\frac{(2 - 8)^3}{(8 - 2)^3}$

77. $(26 - 19)\frac{(2 - 6)}{(26 - 19)}$

78. $\frac{(3 - 9)(4 - 7)}{(4 - 7)(3 - 9)}$

79. $\frac{(5 - 1)(6 - 1)}{(1 - 6)(1 - 5)}$

80. $\frac{(-6)^2 - 2(-6)(-4) + (-4)^2}{(-6) - (-4)}$

1.11 COMBINED OPERATIONS: EVALUATION

Since the associative axiom for addition states that the way in which the numbers are grouped does not affect the sum, it is not necessary to use parentheses to indicate a sum of 3 or more terms. In other words,

$$x + y + z = (x + y) + z = x + (y + z)$$

for all real numbers x, y, and z.

On the other hand, subtraction is *not* associative. For example,

$$(10 - 5) - 2 \neq 10 - (5 - 2)$$

However, since by definition $x - y = x + (-y)$, it is convenient to use this idea and adopt certain conventions that reduce the number of symbols that must be written.

CONVENTIONS

For all real numbers r, s, and t

$$r + s - t = r + s + (-t)$$
$$r - s + t = r + (-s) + t$$
$$r - s - t = r + (-s) + (-t)$$

EXAMPLE 1 Use the preceding convention to calculate each of the following expressions in two ways, thus showing that the result is independent of the way in which the terms are grouped:

a. $7 + 6 - 5$ b. $12 - 8 + 3$ c. $10 - 5 - 2$

Solution

a.
$$\begin{aligned} 7 + 6 - 5 &= 7 + 6 + (-5) \\ &= (7 + 6) + (-5) \\ &= 13 + (-5) = 8 \\ 7 + 6 - 5 &= 7 + 6 + (-5) \\ &= 7 + [6 + (-5)] \\ &= 7 + 1 = 8 \end{aligned}$$

b.
$$\begin{aligned} 12 - 8 + 3 &= 12 + (-8) + 3 \\ &= [12 + (-8)] + 3 \\ &= 4 + 3 = 7 \\ 12 - 8 + 3 &= 12 + (-8) + 3 \\ &= 12 + [(-8) + 3] \\ &= 12 + (-5) = 7 \end{aligned}$$

c.
$$\begin{aligned} 10 - 5 - 2 &= 10 + (-5) + (-2) \\ &= [10 + (-5)] + (-2) \\ &= 5 + (-2) = 3 \\ 10 - 5 - 2 &= 10 + (-5) + (-2) \\ &= 10 + [(-5) + (-2)] \\ &= 10 + (-7) = 3 \end{aligned}$$

Certain expressions and formulas require the substitution of one or more negative values. This is illustrated in the following examples.

EXAMPLE 2 Evaluate $F = \frac{9C}{5} + 32$ for $C = -20$ degrees.

Solution
$$\begin{aligned} F &= \frac{9C}{5} + 32 \\ F &= \frac{9(\ \ )}{5} + 32 \\ F &= \frac{9(-20)}{5} + 32 \\ F &= 9(-4) + 32 = -36 + 32 = -4 \text{ degrees} \end{aligned}$$

EXAMPLE 3 Evaluate $\frac{100 + 2x - y}{5}$ for $x = -35$, $y = -15$.

Solution
$$\begin{aligned} \frac{100 + 2x - y}{5} &= \frac{100 + 2(-35) - (-15)}{5} \\ &= \frac{100 + (-70) + 15}{5} \\ &= \frac{30 + 15}{5} \\ &= \frac{45}{5} = 9 \end{aligned}$$

EXERCISES

Perform the indicated operations in Exercises 1–26.

1. $(8-2)+(2-8)$
2. $5-2(3-4)$
3. $8-(2+2)-8$
4. $(5-2)(3-4)$
5. $3(-2)^2+4(-2)$
6. $2(-3)^2-4(-3)$
7. $8-4+2$
8. $15-8-3$
9. $9+6-5$
10. $2-5-7$
11. $1-2+3$
12. $4+8-2-6$
13. $12-3-15$
14. $1-6+3$
15. $20+40-30$
16. $-15-25+5$
17. $4-7+3$
18. $6-5-4-3$
19. $15-17+19-21$
20. $8-2+2-8$
21. $50-40-30-20$
22. $75-64+25-36$
23. $27-3-2+24$
24. $15-22-6-2$
25. $5-2+3-6$
26. $-8-10+5+7$

Evaluate in Exercises 27–46.

27. $x+y+z$ for $x=7$, $y=-5$, $z=-9$
28. $x-y-z$ for $x=12$, $y=3$, $z=-8$
29. $x-y+z$ for $x=-6$, $y=-7$, $z=8$
30. $x+y-z$ for $x=-15$, $y=19$, $z=21$
31. $a^2+b^2-c^2$ for $a=2$, $b=-2$, $c=-1$
32. a^2-ab+b^2 for $a=7$, $b=-6$
33. $\dfrac{rs}{r-s-1}$ for $r=10$, $s=7$
34. $\dfrac{r^2+s^2+1}{r-s+1}$ for $r=4$, $s=-2$
35. $\dfrac{x+y+z}{3}$ for $x=20$, $y=-17$, $z=-15$
36. $2x+2y-1$ for $x=5$, $y=-4$
37. $\dfrac{c}{a}+\dfrac{d}{b}+\dfrac{a}{b}$ for $a=-6$, $b=-3$, $c=+18$, $d=-15$
38. $c^2-a^2-b^2$ for $c=11$, $a=2$, $b=6$
39. $\dfrac{ac+bd}{a+b}$ for $a=8$, $c=3$, $b=10$, $d=-6$
40. a^2-ab+b^2 for $a=-4$, $b=-5$
41. $\dfrac{p+q-w}{2}$ for $p=20$, $q=0$, $w=-25$
42. $\dfrac{xyz}{x-y-z}$ for $x=50$, $y=60$, $z=-20$
43. $xy+xz+yz$ for $x=5$, $y=-4$, $z=-2$
44. $a^2+b^2+c^2$ for $a=2$, $b=-3$, $c=-4$
45. $(n+1)^2-(n+1)(n-1)+(n-1)^2$ for $n=-5$
46. b^2-4ac for $a=-3$, $b=-5$, $c=-4$

47. (Temperature scales: Fahrenheit to Celsius)

$$C=\frac{5(F-32)}{9}$$

Find C for $F=-4$ degrees

48. (Temperature scales: Celsius to Fahrenheit)

$$F=\frac{9C}{5}+32$$

Find F for $C=-15$ degrees.

49. (Center of mass)

$$x=\frac{MD+md}{M+m}$$

Find x for $M=150$ grams, $D=40$ centimetres, $m=50$ grams, $d=-20$ centimetres.

50. Find x in Exercise 49 for $M=25$ pounds, $D=-6$ feet, $m=15$ pounds, $d=-2$ feet.

In Exercises 51–52 (mirrors),

$$f=\frac{pq}{p+q}$$

where

$f=$ *focal length of mirror (positive for concave mirrors and negative for convex mirrors)*

$p=$ *object distance from mirror (positive when object is in front of the mirror)*

$q=$ *image distance from mirror (positive when image is in front of the mirror and negative when image is behind the mirror)*

51. Find f for $p=45$ centimetres, $q=-180$ centimetres.

52. Find f for $p=6$ feet, $q=-3$ feet.

53. (Thermodynamics)

$$E=Q-W$$

where

$E=$ change in internal energy

$Q=$ change in heat (positive when added to the system and negative when removed)

$W=$ work done (positive when done by the system and negative when done on the system)

Find E for each of the following cases:

a. $Q=0$, $W=-6$ ft-lb

b. $Q=0$, $W=50$ joules

c. $Q=400$ joules, $W=-175$ joules

d. $Q=-20$ Btu, $W=0$

e. $Q=810$ Btu, $W=470$ Btu

54. (Corrective lenses) $P = \dfrac{100(p+q)}{PQ}$

where

P = power in diopters (positive for farsighted persons and negative for nearsighted)

p = object distance from lens (positive) in centimetres

q = image distance from lens (positive when on the opposite side of the lens as the object and negative when on the same side) in centimetres

Find P for each of the following cases:

a. $p = 20$, $q = -50$ b. $p = 300$, $q = -75$

55. (Flow of liquids) $P = \dfrac{d}{2}(V^2 - v^2)$

where

P = change in pressure (positive for increase and negative for decrease)

V = original speed of the liquid

v = new speed of the liquid

d = density of the liquid

Find P for each of the following cases:

a. $d = 62.5$, $V = 3$ feet per second, $v = 6$ feet per second

b. $d = 50$, $V = 4$ feet per second, $v = 2$ feet per second

56. (Acoustics) $F = \dfrac{fV}{V+v}$

where

F = observed frequency (pitch) of a moving source of sound waves

V = speed of sound in air

v = speed of the moving source (positive if moving away from the observer and negative if moving toward the observer)

Find F for $f = 460$ cycles per second, $V = 1100$ feet per second, $v = -88$ feet per second.

In Exercises 57–58 (chemistry: capillary tubes),

$$h = \frac{10SC}{49dr}$$

where

h = height in millimetres that the liquid rises (+) or is depressed (−)

S = surface tension in dynes per centimetre

C = constant depending on the liquid and the material of the tube

d = density of the liquid in grams per cubic centimetre

r = radius of the tube in millimetres

57. Find h for $S = 490$, $C = -0.68$, $d = 13.6$, $r = 2$ and state whether the liquid rises or is depressed (mercury in a glass tube).

58. Find h for $S = 72.8$, $C = 1$, $d = 1$, $r = 4$ (water in a glass tube).

REVIEW EXERCISES

In Exercises 1–10 perform the indicated operations.

1. $6[-3-(-5)]$
2. $(-2)(7-10)$
3. $-2(7)-10$
4. $(3-5)(5-3)$
5. $3-5(5-3)$
6. $3-(5)(5)-3$
7. $\dfrac{(-2)-(-2)}{(-2)+(-2)}$
8. $\dfrac{(-2)+(-2)}{(-2)-(-2)}$
9. $\dfrac{8-3}{3-8}$
10. $(-2)^2+(-2)^3$

Express the verbal expressions in Exercises 11–20 in symbols.

11. The sum of x and y.
12. The product of x and y.
13. The difference when 4 is subtracted from the product of 5 and x.
14. The quotient when twice the product of a and b is divided by the sum of a and b.
15. The sum of the square root of x and the square of x.
16. The product of 6 and x is greater than 12.
17. The quotient of r divided by 7 is less than or equal to 4.
18. Twice the sum of x and 7 is less than the product of 7 and x.
19. The sum of 9 and the product of 6 and x is greater than or equal to 8.
20. The square root of the sum of x and y is less than the square of y.

In Exercises 21–32, evaluate each.

21. $(x+2)(x-3)$ for a. $x=5$, b. $x=0$, c. $x=-5$
22. $\dfrac{4x}{6-x}$ for a. $x=8$, b. $x=0$, c. $x=-2$
23. $\dfrac{x^2-16}{x-4}$ for a. $x=2$, b. $x=0$, c. $x=-5$
24. $3x-(7-x)$ for a. $x=4$, b. $x=0$, c. $x=-2$
25. $x-[x-(x-2)]$ for a. $x=7$, b. $x=0$, c. $x=-1$
26. $10-2[x-(5-3x)]$ for a. $x=1$, b. $x=3$, c. $x=-2$
27. $\dfrac{(x-1)(x-2)(x-3)}{(-1)(-2)(-3)}$ for a. $x=9$, b. $x=1$, c. $x=-3$
28. $\dfrac{x^2+3xy-10y^2}{x-2y}$ for a. $x=3$, $y=2$
b. $x=-4$, $y=-5$
29. $x-y+z$ for a. $x=7$, $y=9$, $z=11$
b. $x=5$, $y=-2$, $z=-6$
30. $x-y-z$ for a. $x=25$, $y=15$, $z=35$
b. $x=-5$, $y=-10$, $z=+15$

31. xyz for a. $x = 7, y = -4, z = -25$
b. $x = -4, y = -3, z = -2$

32. $\frac{xy}{xz}$ for a. $x = -5, y = -8, z = +2$
b. $x = -6, y = +12, z = -9$

In Exercises 33–42, answer true or false.

33. $4 < 10$
34. $-4 < -10$
35. $8 > -3$
36. $0 > -6$
37. $-12 > -15$
38. $-7 > -6$
39. $|-5| < 0$
40. $|-5| > 0$
41. $|-8| = 8$
42. $|-5| < |-9|$

For Exercises 43–52, graph each on a horizontal number line.

43. $x < 4$
44. $x \leq -2$
45. $x > 0$
46. $x > -3$
47. $x \geq 5$
48. $x \leq 0$
49. $3 < x < 6$
50. $-2 \leq x < 0$
51. $1 < x \leq 5$
52. $-2 \leq x \leq 3$

53. (Slope of a line)

$$m = \frac{Y - y}{X - x}$$

Find m for $Y = 7$, $y = 10$, $X = -1$, $x = -7$.

54. (Flow of liquids)

$$P = p + \frac{d}{2}(v^2 - V^2)$$

Find P for $p = 50$, $d = 1$, $v = 20$, $V = 40$.

55. (Medication for child)

$$C = \frac{WA}{150}$$

Find C for $W = 60$ pounds, $A = 200$ milligrams.

56. (Radio and television)

$$r = \frac{R(E - G)}{E}$$

Find r for $R = 2$ megohms, $E = -12$ volts, $G = -9$ volts.

2 LINEAR EQUATIONS

THE RULE OF FALSE POSITION

The ancient Egyptians used a method called the *Rule of False Position* for solving certain types of linear equations. The following is a translated and simplified version of Problem 26 in the Rhind papyrus.

> A quantity and its fourth added together become 15. What is the quantity?
>
> Try 4. Then the sum of 4 and $\frac{1}{4}$ of 4 is 5.
>
> As many times as you must multiply 5 to get 15, so must you also multiply your trial number.
> Thus 4 times 3 is 12. Behold, see it is 12.
>
> 12 plus $\frac{1}{4}$ of 12 is 12 plus 3, 15.

In our modern notation this problem reads:

$$x + \frac{x}{4} = 15$$

A modern solution could be:

$$5\left(\frac{x}{4}\right) = 15;\ \frac{x}{4} = 3;\ x = 12$$

There are two main reasons for studying algebra:

1. To acquire a tool for the study of other disciplines, such as physics, biology, statistics, or economics.
2. To pursue algebra for its own sake as a branch of pure mathematics.

One of the most important skills needed for both purposes is the solution of equations. It is the aim of this chapter to introduce you to the solution of the simplest type of equation: the linear equation in one variable. In preparation for this, some preliminary axioms and theorems must be stated, some of which were introduced in the previous chapter.

There are three major categories of general statements in mathematics: definitions, axioms, and theorems. A **definition** is a precise explanation of the meaning of a term. An **axiom** is a statement that is assumed to be true. A **theorem** is a statement that is proved.

2.1 SOME AXIOMS

COMMUTATIVE AND ASSOCIATIVE AXIOMS

The commutative axioms (the laws of order) for addition and multiplication state that the order in which two numbers are added does not change the sum, and that the order in which two numbers are multiplied does not change the product.

The associative axioms (the laws of grouping) for addition and multiplication state that both the terms of a sum and the factors of a product may be regrouped without changing the result.

Two important consequences result from combining the commutative axiom with the associative axiom for the same operation:

1. The terms of a sum can be rearranged in any order without changing the value of the sum.
2. The factors of a product can be rearranged in any order without changing the value of the product.

There are certain conventions for writing the terms of a sum or the factors of a product. These conventions, stated as follows, are especially useful for comparing the results obtained by another person (such as checking the answers in the back of the book).

CONVENTIONS

The terms of a sum are written so that:

1. A numerical term is to the right of all literal terms.
2. The letters involved are written in alphabetical order whenever possible.

The factors of a product are written so that:

1. A numerical factor is to the left of all literal factors.
2. The letters involved are written in alphabetical order whenever possible.

EXAMPLE 1 Rearrange the terms of each sum and the factors of each product according to the sum and product conventions. Simplify each result if possible.

Given Expression	*Solution Rearrangement*	*Simplification*
a. $y + 5 + x$	$x + y + 5$	None possible
b. $-6 + n + 6$	$n + 6 + (-6)$	n
c. $a - 4 - b$	$a - b - 4$	None possible
d. $6x(-2)$	$(-2)(6)x$	$-12x$
e. $(-4xy)(-7x)$	$(-4)(-7)xxy$	$28x^2y$
f. $y(3x)$	$3xy$	None possible

THE DISTRIBUTIVE AXIOM

The distributive axiom is significant for many reasons. Three of these reasons are:

1. It links the operations of addition and multiplication.
2. It permits the collecting of "like terms" to simplify expressions, such as $2x + 3x$, which can be written as $5x$.
3. It permits the "removal of parentheses" needed in simplifying expressions and in solving equations.

THE DISTRIBUTIVE AXIOM

For all real numbers r, s, and t,

$$r(s + t) = rs + rt$$

In other words, multiplication "distributes" over addition. The factor r is distributed to *each* term of the sum.

EXAMPLE 2 Use the distributive axiom to remove the parentheses in $3(x+2)$.

Solution $3(x+2) = 3 \cdot x + 3 \cdot 2$
$= 3x + 6$

EXAMPLE 3 Express $5(y+z)$ as a sum by applying the distributive axiom.

Solution $5(y+z) = 5y + 5z$

The following immediate consequences of the distributive axiom are useful:

1. $a(b-c) = ab - ac$
2. $ab + ac = a(b+c)$
3. $ac + bc = (a+b)c$
4. $ac - bc = (a-b)c$
5. $ad + bd + cd = (a+b+c)d$
6. $-(b+c) = (-1)(b+c) = -b - c$
7. $-(b-c) = (-1)(b-c) = -b + c$

EXAMPLE 4 Express $2(x-5)$ as a sum, using the distributive axiom or one of its consequences.

Solution
$2(x-5) = 2(x) - 2(5)$ (By consequence 1)
$= 2x - 10$

EXAMPLE 5 Express $2x + 3x$ as a product by using consequence 3.

Solution $2x + 3x = (2+3)x = 5x$

EXAMPLE 6 Simplify $5z - 7z$.

Solution Expressing $5z - 7z$ as a product by using consequence 4,
$5z - 7z = (5-7)z = -2z$

EXAMPLE 7 Simplify $3y + 2y - 4y$.

Solution
$3y + 2y - 4y = (3+2-4)y$
$= 1y$
$= y$ (By consequence 5)

EXAMPLE 8 Remove the parentheses: $-(2x+8)$.

Solution Using consequence 6,
$-(2x+8) = -2x - 8$

EXAMPLE 9 Remove the parentheses: $-(5-3x)$.

Solution Using consequence 7,
$-(5-3x) = -5 + 3x$
$= 3x + (-5)$
$= 3x - 5$

EXAMPLE 10 Remove the parentheses: $-4(2x+5)$.

Solution $-4(2x+5) = -8x - 20$

One of the purposes of the distributive axiom, as stated at the beginning of this section, is to "collect *like* terms."

DEFINITIONS

Like terms are terms with identical literal factors.
A **literal factor** is a factor denoted by a letter.

As examples, $5x$ and $2x$ are like terms; $16x^2$ and $-4x^2$ are like terms; $39xy^2z$ and $-\frac{1}{2}xy^2z$ are like terms.

The terms $3x$ and $3y$ are *not* like terms, because the literal factors, x and y, are not identical. Similarly, $5x^2$ and $5x$ are *not* like terms, and xy and x are *not* like terms. Terms that are not like are called *unlike* terms.

The distributive axiom can be used to collect like terms, as shown in the preceding examples and also in the following examples. For convenience, the distributive axiom and all its consequences will be referred to simply as "the distributive axiom" from now on.

Simplify Examples 11–16 by collecting like terms.

EXAMPLE 11 $2x - 3x$ **Solution** $2x - 3x = (2 - 3)x = -x$

EXAMPLE 12 $4x^2 + 6x^2 - 2x^2$

Solution

$$4x^2 + 6x^2 - 2x^2 = (4 + 6 - 2)x^2 = 8x^2$$

EXAMPLE 13 $2x + 3 + 4x$ **Solution**

$$2x + 3 + 4x = (2x + 4x) + 3 = (2 + 4)x + 3 = 6x + 3$$

Note that $6x$ and 3 are unlike terms.

EXAMPLE 14 $x^2 + 2x^2$ **Solution**

$$x^2 + 2x^2 = 1x^2 + 2x^2 = (1 + 2)x^2 = 3x^2$$

EXAMPLE 15 $xy - 2y + xy + x$

Solution

$$xy - 2y + xy + x = (xy + xy) + x - 2y = 2xy + x - 2y$$

Note that $2xy$, x, and $2y$ are unlike terms.

EXAMPLE 16 $x^2 + 5x - 6x + 2$

Solution

$$x^2 + 5x - 6x + 2 = x^2 + (5x - 6x) + 2 = x^2 + (5 - 6)x + 2 = x^2 + (-1)x + 2 = x^2 - x + 2$$

EXAMPLE 17 Simplify $3(x + 2y) + 5(x - y)$.

Solution
$$\begin{aligned} 3(x + 2y) + 5(x - y) &= 3x + 6y + 5x - 5y \\ &= (3x + 5x) + (6y - 5y) \\ &= (3 + 5)x + (6 - 5)y \\ &= 8x + y \end{aligned}$$

EXAMPLE 18 Simplify $2(x + y) - (x - y)$.

Solution
$$\begin{aligned} 2(x + y) - (x - y) &= 2x + 2y - x + y \\ &= (2x - x) + (2y + y) \\ &= x + 3y \end{aligned}$$

With practice, you should be able to omit many of the steps shown in the examples.

EXERCISES

Rearrange the terms of each sum and the factors of each product in Exercises 1–20 according to the sum and product conventions stated in this section. Simplify each result if possible.

1. $y + 4 + x$
2. $4 + x - 7$
3. $(-8 - x) + 8$
4. $(y - 8) + (x + 4)$
5. $(-4xy)(-9xy)$
6. $(2 - x) + (x - 7)$
7. $8 + b(2a) - 12$
8. $3b(-4) + (-5a)(-6)$
9. $n - 7 + m$
10. $6 - n + m - 7$
11. $(3x)(-5x)$
12. $(-9x)(-3y)$
13. $(y - 6) + (x - 3)$
14. $(-6x)(5xy)$
15. $(x - 5) + (8 - x)$
16. $4 - y + x - 3$
17. $(4c)(-3b)(-2a)$
18. $d - b(-5a) - 4c$
19. $(-na)(-nb)(-nc)$
20. $(ka)(-kb)(-5b)(-7)$

For Exercises 21–40, remove parentheses by applying the distributive axiom or one of its consequences.

21. $2(x + 5)$
22. $-3(y + 2)$
23. $5(n - 7)$
24. $-6(2x - 3)$
25. $-(x - 5)$
26. $-(3x + 4)$
27. $-(6 - y)$
28. $3(x + y - 2)$
29. $-\frac{1}{2}(2x - 6y)$
30. $(a + b)x$
31. $(2a - b)3y$
32. $a - (b - c)$
33. $x - (y + 5)$
34. $-4(-2x + 3y - 4)$
35. $a - 2[b - (c - 3)]$
36. $y - [4z - 2(x + 5)]$
37. $3(a - 2b) + 4(x + 2y)$
38. $0 - (c - d)$
39. $4x^2(x - 1) - (x - 1)$
40. $a(x + 5) - 2(x + 5)$

Combine like terms and simplify by using the distributive axiom or one of its consequences in Exercises 41–66.

41. $3x + 2x$
42. $x + 4x + 5x$
43. $2x - x$
44. $3y - 3y$
45. $-4xy + 2xy$
46. $3z + 5z - 7z$
47. $3x + 5 - x$
48. $10k - 5k + 3k$
49. $6 - 4t - 3t$
50. $5x^2 + 5x - 8x - 2$
51. $3z^2 - z + 6z + 4$
52. $3p - q - 2p$
53. $6x^2 + 12xy - 5xy - 10y^2$
54. $x^2 - xy + xy - y^2$
55. $3z + 3z^2 - z$
56. $2k + 7 - 5k$
57. $x^2 + 2x - 3x + 5$
58. $2x + 5 + 3x - 7$
59. $4 - x + 2$
60. $5n + 4m + n$
61. $2s - t + 3s + 2t$
62. $2p + 3q + 3p$
63. $3x^2 - 6xy + 5xy - 10y^2$
64. $5xy - 6xz - 4xy - 2zx$
65. $9x^2 + 12xy - 12xy - 16y^2$
66. $ab + 2ac - 4ab - ac$

In Exercises 67–96, remove parentheses and collect like terms.

67. $3(x + 2) - 5$
68. $-(y - 3) + 2y$
69. $3x^2 - (5x - 2x) + 3$
70. $y^2 - (y + 3y) + 2(y^2 + 1)$
71. $6(x + y) + 2(x + y)$
72. $-7(c + d) - (c + d)$
73. $5(a - b) - 4(a - b)$
74. $3x(2x - 1) - 2x(3x + 2)$
75. $4x(2y - 3) - 3y(2x - 5)$
76. $10 - (x + 5)$
77. $6k - (4 + 5k)$
78. $2a(b - 8) - b(a - 6)$
79. $2(x + x) + 5$
80. $-(4 - 2k) + 3k$
81. $4y^2 - (3y + 5y) + 9$
82. $x^2 - (x - 2) + 3(x^2 + 5)$
83. $7(x + y) - 4(x + y)$
84. $-8(a - b) - (a - b)$
85. $2(x + y) - 2(x - y)$
86. $6x(5y - 2) - 3y(5x - 1)$
87. $7y(5y - 2) - 5y(7y + 2)$
88. $8x - (3x - 4)$
89. $6x - (6 + 7x)$
90. $a(b + 1) - 3b(5 - a)$
91. $5k - 2[4(2 - k) - (6 - k)]$
92. $x - 3[x - 3(x - 3)]$
93. $2(m - 4n) - 6(m - 4n) + (m - 4n)$
94. $2n - [3(n - 2) - 5(n + 3)]$
95. $2x - [2 - (x - 2) - 2(x - 2)]$
96. $3(c + 4d) - 5(c + 4d) - (c + 4d)$

2.2 EQUATIONS AND SOLUTIONS

BASIC CONCEPTS

An equation is a statement having the form $A = B$. However, an equation does not have to be a true statement. Consider the following examples of equations:

$2 + 4 = 6$	(True)
$7 - 3 = 8$	(False)
$x + 5 = 5 + x$	(Open, true for all values of x)
$x + 5 = x + 1$	(Open, false for all values of x)
$x + 5 = 9$	(Open, true for some value of x and false for some value of x)

An **open equation** is an equation containing one or more variables. An open equation is not classified as true or false, but becomes true or false when each variable is replaced by a numerical value.

The equation $2 + 4 = 6$ is called a *true equation* since it does not contain any variables and since it is known that the sum of 2 and 4 is 6.

The equation $7 - 3 = 8$ is called a *false equation* since it contains no variables and since it is known that the difference between 7 and 3 is 4 and not 8.

The open equation $x + 5 = 5 + x$ becomes true for all replacements of the variable. Such an equation is also called an **identity.**

The open equation $x + 5 = x + 1$ becomes false for all replacements of the variable. Equations such as these are sometimes called *contradictions.*

The open equation $x + 5 = 9$ is neither true nor false, but becomes true or false when the variable is replaced by a numerical value.

For example, if $x = 2$, then $x + 5 = 9$ becomes $2 + 5 = 9$, a false equation.

If $x = 4$, then $x + 5 = 9$ becomes $4 + 5 = 9$, a true equation.

An open equation that is sometimes true and sometimes false is also called a **conditional equation** because the equation becomes true on the condition that the variable is replaced by a certain numerical value. The conditional equation $x + 5 = 9$ is true on the condition that x is replaced by 4.

The number 4 is called a **solution** or **root** of the equation $x + 5 = 9$ because $x + 5 = 9$ becomes true when x is replaced by 4. The number 4 is also said to **satisfy** the equation $x + 5 = 9$.

An important concern of algebra is the process of finding all the solutions of an open equation. This process is called **solving the equation.**

DEFINITIONS

A **solution** or **root** of an open equation in one variable is a number that makes the equation true when the variable is replaced by this number.

The **solution set** of an open equation is the set of all solutions of the equation.

To **solve an equation** means to find the solution set of the equation.

One primitive method for solving an equation is the trial-and-error method. This method is illustrated in the following example.

EXAMPLE 1 Solve $2x^2 + 5x = 3$.

Trial-and-Error Solution First, try positive integers.

If $x = 1$, then $2x^2 + 5x = 2 \cdot 1^2 + 5 \cdot 1 = 2 + 5 = 7$;
$7 = 3$ is false.
If $x = 2$, then $2x^2 + 5x = 2 \cdot 2^2 + 5 \cdot 2 = 8 + 10 = 18$;
$18 = 3$ is false.
If $x = 3$, then $2x^2 + 5x = 2 \cdot 3^2 + 5 \cdot 3 = 18 + 15 = 33$;
$33 = 3$ is false.

Since the resulting numbers are getting larger and larger, it seems useless to continue trying positive integers. Thus negative integers are tried next.

If $x = -1$, then $2x^2 + 5x = 2(-1)^2 + 5(-1) = 2 - 5 = -3$;
$-3 = 3$ is false.
If $x = -2$, then $2x^2 + 5x = 2(-2)^2 + 5(-2) = 8 - 10 = -2$;
$-2 = 3$ is false.
If $x = -3$, then $2x^2 + 5x = 2(-3)^2 + 5(-3) = 18 - 15 = 3$;
$3 = 3$ is true.

At last a solution has been found! $x = -3$.

Have all the solutions to Example 1 been found? There is no way to know for certain by this method because all the integers have not been tried nor have any of the nonintegral rational numbers been tried.

As a matter of fact, it may be shown that $x = \frac{1}{2}$ is also a solution.

If $x = \frac{1}{2}$, then $2x^2 + 5x = 2\left(\frac{1}{2}\right)^2 + 5\left(\frac{1}{2}\right) = \frac{1}{2} + \frac{5}{2} = \frac{6}{2} = 3$;
$3 = 3$ is true.

The solution set of $2x^2 + 5x = 3$ is $\left\{\frac{1}{2}, -3\right\}$. However at this point there is no guarantee that the solution set has been found, that is, that $x = \frac{1}{2}$ and $x = -3$ are the *only* replacements that make the equation $2x^2 + 5x = 3$ true.

Finally, it seems reasonable that there must be a better method than the trial-and-error method for solving equations. Indeed, the next sections are devoted to the development of procedures that will be less time-consuming than the trial-and-error method and that will give assurance that the solution set has indeed been found.

EQUIVALENCE THEOREMS

DEFINITION

Equivalent equations are equations that have the same solution set.

For example, all the following equations are equivalent because each has $\{5\}$ for its solution set—that is, 5 is the only solution of each equation:

$$x + 2 = 7$$
$$2(x - 3) = 4$$
$$\frac{x}{3} = \frac{5}{3}$$
$$x = 5$$

The process of solving an equation involves the replacement of one equation by a simpler equivalent equation.

For example, a procedure is developed so that $2x - 6 = 4$ is replaced by the simpler equivalent equation $x = 5$. Not only does this technique find the solution, it also guarantees that all the solutions have been found, since it is known that 5 is the only replacement for x that makes $x = 5$ a true statement.

The following equivalence theorems are fundamental to the process of solving equations and are stated without proof.

THE EQUIVALENCE THEOREMS

1. **Addition theorem**
   If the same number is added to each side of an equation, the resulting sums are again equal, and the two equations are equivalent.
2. **Subtraction theorem**
   If the same number is subtracted from each side of an equation, the resulting differences are equal, and the two equations are equivalent.
3. **Multiplication theorem**
   If each side of an equation is multiplied by the same nonzero real number, the resulting products are equal, and the two equations are equivalent.
4. **Division theorem**
   If each side of an equation is divided by the same nonzero real number, the resulting quotients are equal, and the two equations are equivalent.

The following examples illustrate the use of the equivalence theorems.

EXAMPLE 2 Solve $x - 4 = 3$.

Solution $x - 4 = 3$ if and only if

$x - 4 + 4 = 3 + 4$ (Addition theorem—add 4 to both sides)

$x + 0 = 7$

$x = 7$

Thus 7 is the solution and $\{7\}$ is the solution set.

Check For $x = 7$, $x - 4 = 3$ becomes $7 - 4 = 3$, a true statement.

EXAMPLE 3 Solve $x + 2 = 4$.

Solution $x + 2 = 4$ if and only if

$x + 2 - 2 = 4 - 2$ (Subtraction theorem—subtract 2 from each side)

$x + 0 = 2$

$x = 2$

Thus 2 is the solution. The solution set is $\{2\}$.

Check For $x = 2$, $x + 2 = 4$ becomes $2 + 2 = 4$, true.

EXAMPLE 4 Solve $\frac{x}{2} = 3$.

Solution $\frac{x}{2} = 3$ if and only if

$2\left(\frac{x}{2}\right) = 2(3)$ (Multiplication theorem—multiply both sides by 2)

$x = 6$

Thus 6 is the solution.

Check For $x = 6$, $\frac{x}{2} = 3$ becomes $\frac{6}{2} = 3$, true.

EXAMPLE 5 Solve $4x = 20$.

Solution $4x = 20$ if and only if

$\frac{4x}{4} = \frac{20}{4}$ (Division theorem—divide both sides by 4)

$x = 5$

Thus 5 is the solution.

Check For $x = 5$, $4x = 20$ becomes $4(5) = 20$, true.

Equations such as $2x - 6 = 4$ and $5x + 10 = 0$ are called *linear equations.*

DEFINITION

A **linear equation in one variable, x,** is an equation that can be expressed in the form $ax + b = 0$ where $a \neq 0$.

By using the equivalence theorems, any linear equation can be solved by transforming the given equation into a simpler equation.

EXAMPLE 6 Solve $2x - 6 = 4$.

Solution

$$2x - 6 = 4$$
$$2x - 6 + 6 = 4 + 6 \qquad \text{(Addition theorem—add 6 to both sides)}$$
$$2x = 10$$
$$\frac{2x}{2} = \frac{10}{2} \qquad \text{(Division theorem—divide each side by 2)}$$
$$x = 5$$

Thus 5 is the solution.

Check For $x = 5$, $2x - 6 = 4$ becomes $2(5) - 6 = 4$

$$10 - 6 = 4$$
$$4 = 4, \text{ true}$$

Since $2x - 6 = 4$ is true for $x = 5$, 5 is the solution of $2x - 6 = 4$.

EXAMPLE 7 Determine if the indicated value of the variable is a solution of the given equation: $3(x - 2) = 5x + 2$; $x = 4$.

Solution For $x = 4$,

$$3(x - 2) = 3(4 - 2) = 3(2) = 6$$
$$5x + 2 = 5(4) + 2 = 20 + 2 = 22$$

Since $6 \neq 22$, 4 is *not* a solution.

THE HINDU METHOD OF INVERSION

Inversion was a favorite method among the Hindus for solving certain types of problems, such as those found in the works of the elder Aryabhata (ca. 500 A.D.). The following problem, while much simpler than those found in the Hindu works, illustrates this method.

> Beaming maiden with beaming eyes, tell me, as you understand the right method of inversion, what is the number which when multiplied by 3, then decreased by 29, then divided by 4, and then increased by 7, gives the number 26?

Operation	*Inverse Operation*	*Reversed Order*	*Calculations*
			26
Multiply by 3	Divide by 3	Subtract 7	-7
			19
Subtract 29	Add 29	Multiply by 4	$4(19) = 76$
Divide by 4	Multiply by 4	Add 29	$76 + 29 = 105$
Add 7	Subtract 7	Divide by 3	$\frac{105}{3} = 35$

The solution is 35.

Note that our modern solution of $\frac{3x - 29}{4} + 7 = 26$ parallels this method.

SOLVING LINEAR EQUATIONS

The examples of the previous section have shown how to find the solution of a linear equation systematically. The technique involves the use of the equivalence theorems to transform the given equation into one having the form $x = a$ where a is the solution desired.

The *operations* that are to be used in transforming the equation are determined by analyzing the original equation. The symbols indicate the order in which the operations were performed on the number named by the variable. The solution requires that the *inverse* operations be performed in the *reverse* order, as shown in the table in Example 8.

EXAMPLE 8 Solve $\frac{3(x-5)}{2} + 4 = 10$.

Analysis

(This work is usually done mentally.)

Order of Operations on x	*Inverse Operations*	*Reversed Order*
1. 5 was subtracted from x.	1. Add 5.	1. Subtract 4.
2. Result multiplied by 3.	2. Divide by 3.	2. Multiply by 2.
3. Result divided by 2.	3. Multiply by 2.	3. Divide by 3.
4. 4 was added.	4. Subtract 4.	4. Add 5.

Solution

(This work is written.)

$$\frac{3(x-5)}{2} + 4 = 10$$

$$\frac{3(x-5)}{2} = 10 - 4 = 6 \qquad \text{(Subtract 4 from each side)}$$

$$3(x-5) = 2(6) = 12 \qquad \text{(Multiply each side by 2)}$$

$$x - 5 = \frac{12}{3} = 4 \qquad \text{(Divide each side by 3)}$$

$$x = 4 + 5 = 9 \qquad \text{(Add 5 to each side)}$$

The solution is 9.

Check

If $x = 9$, then

$$\frac{3(x-5)}{2} + 4 = \frac{3(9-5)}{2} + 4$$

$$= \frac{3(4)}{2} + 4$$

$$= \frac{12}{2} + 4$$

$$= 6 + 4 = 10$$

EXAMPLE 9 Solve $3 - y = 6$.

Solution

$$3 - y = 6$$
$$-3 + 3 - y = -3 + 6 \quad \text{(Add } -3 \text{ to each side)}$$
$$-y = 3$$
$$(-1)(-y) = (-1)(3) \quad \text{(Multiply each side by } -1\text{)}$$
$$y = -3$$

The solution is -3.

Check If $y = -3$, then $3 - y = 3 - (-3) = 3 + 3 = 6$. Thus $3 - y = 6$ is true for $y = -3$.

Note in Example 9 that both sides were multiplied by -1 so that the final equivalent equation would have the form $y = a$ and *not* $-y = a$.

EXAMPLE 10 Solve $4(k + 3) = 10$.

Solution

$$4(k + 3) = 10$$
$$4k + 12 = 10 \quad \text{(Distributive axiom)}$$
$$4k + 12 - 12 = 10 - 12 \quad \text{(Subtraction theorem—subtract 12 from each side)}$$
$$4k = -2$$
$$\frac{4k}{4} = \frac{-2}{4} \quad \text{(Division theorem—divide each side by 4)}$$
$$k = -\frac{1}{2}$$

The solution is $-\frac{1}{2}$.

Check

$$4(k + 3) = 10$$
$$4\left(-\frac{1}{2} + 3\right) = 10$$
$$4\left(\frac{5}{2}\right) = 10$$
$$10 = 10, \text{ true}$$

EXAMPLE 11 Solve $8 = 8 - 5p$.

Solution

$$8 = 8 - 5p$$
$$8 + 5p = 8 - 5p + 5p \quad \text{(Addition theorem—add } 5p \text{ to each side)}$$
$$8 + 5p = 8$$
$$5p = 0 \quad \text{(Subtraction theorem—subtract 8 from each side)}$$
$$\frac{5p}{5} = \frac{0}{5} \quad \text{(Division theorem—divide each side by 5)}$$
$$p = 0$$

The solution is 0. The solution set is $\{0\}$. Note that this is *not* the empty set.

Check

$$8 = 8 - 5p$$
$$8 = 8 - 5(0)$$
$$8 = 8 - 0$$
$$8 = 8, \text{ true}$$

EXAMPLE 12 Solve $x + 2 = x + 5$.

Solution

$$x + 2 = x + 5$$
$$x + 2 - 2 = x + 5 - 2$$
$$x = x + 3$$
$$x - x = x - x + 3$$
$$0 = 3$$

But 0 can never equal 3. Therefore, there is no value of x which makes the equation true, and the solution set is the empty set, $\varnothing$.

EXAMPLE 13 Solve $5(x - 4) = 5x - 20$.

Solution

$$5(x - 4) = 5x - 20$$
$$5x - 20 = 5x - 20$$

Since the left side and the right side of the equation are identical, the statement is true regardless of the value of x; in other words, all real numbers satisfy the equation and the solution set is R, the set of real numbers.

EXERCISES

Solve and check the equations in Exercises 1–60.

1. $x + 3 = 5$
2. $x - 3 = 5$
3. $3 - x = 5$
4. $5 - x = 3$
5. $y + 3 = -4$
6. $z - 1 = -6$
7. $x + 5 = 12$
8. $x - 5 = 12$
9. $5 - x = 12$
10. $12 - x = 5$
11. $2 - k = 3$
12. $4 - m = -1$
13. $4 - p = 30$
14. $30 - p = 4$
15. $2m = 6$
16. $3p = 15$
17. $5x = -10$
18. $7x = 105$
19. $2p + 3 = 7$
20. $2y - 1 = 7$
21. $2 - 3x = 8$
22. $1 = t + 9$
23. $3m + 2 = 11$
24. $2x - 3 = 7$
25. $2 = 2s + 6$
26. $3 - 2n = 5$
27. $q + 2 = 0$
28. $2 - x = 0$
29. $t + 7 = 0$
30. $x - 5 = 0$
31. $4 - x = 0$
32. $-2 = s + 3$
33. $4 - 3y = 0 - 3y$
34. $6 - 2p = 2p - 6$
35. $5(t + 2) = 15$
36. $2(n - 1) = 8$
37. $3(x + 4) = -12$
38. $2(x + 3) = 16$
39. $3(k - 4) = 12$
40. $-2(y + 1) + 2 = 6$

41. $2 + 3(x + 1) = 11$
42. $3 - 2(x + 4) = 11$
43. $\frac{x}{4} = 5$
44. $\frac{z}{3} = 5$
45. $\frac{x}{5} = 1$
46. $\frac{x + 4}{2} = -1$
47. $2(4 - x) = 8 - 2x$
48. $\frac{x}{3} - 2 = 7$
49. $\frac{x + 3}{2} - 6 = 1$
50. $5 - x = x - 5$
51. $\frac{x + 2}{3} = -2$
52. $\frac{x - 1}{2} = 6$
53. $2x - 5 = -(5 - 2x)$
54. $\frac{x}{2} + 4 = 7$
55. $\frac{2(x + 5)}{3} = 4$
56. $2 - 2x = 2x - 2$
57. $-3(x - 1) = 12$
58. $\frac{-2(x + 1)}{5} + 1 = 3$
59. $2x + 2 = 2x - 2$
60. $2(x + 2) = 2x + 4$

2.3 MORE LINEAR EQUATIONS

The following examples illustrate the solution of more complicated linear equations in one variable.

EXAMPLE 1 Solve $2x + 9 = 5x - 12$.

Solution

$$\begin{array}{rcl} 2x + 9 &=& 5x - 12 \\ -9 & & -9 \\ \hline 2x &=& 5x - 21 \\ -5x & & -5x \\ \hline -3x &=& -21 \end{array}$$

(Subtract 9 from both sides)

(Subtract $5x$ from both sides)

$$\frac{-3x}{-3} = \frac{-21}{-3}$$

(Divide both sides by -3)

$$x = 7$$

Check Left side. $2x + 9 = 2 \cdot 7 + 9 = 14 + 9 = 23$
Right side. $5x - 12 = 5 \cdot 7 - 12 = 35 - 12 = 23$
Thus $23 = 23$, and $\{7\}$ is the solution set.

EXAMPLE 2 Solve $5(2-y) = 4y - (y+14)$.

Solution

$$\begin{aligned}
5(2-y) &= 4y - (y+14) & \\
10 - 5y &= 4y - y - 14 & \text{(Using the distributive axiom)} \\
10 - 5y &= 3y - 14 & \\
3y - 14 &= 10 - 5y & \text{(Exchanging sides)} \\
+14 \quad & \quad +14 & \text{(Add 14 to both sides)} \\
3y &= 24 - 5y & \\
+5y \quad & \quad +5y & \text{(Add } 5y \text{ to both sides)} \\
8y &= 24 & \\
\frac{8y}{8} &= \frac{24}{8} & \text{(Divide both sides by 8)} \\
y &= 3 &
\end{aligned}$$

Check

$$\begin{aligned}
5(2-y) &= 4y - (y+14) \\
5(2-3) &= 4(3) - (3+14) \\
5(-1) &= 12 - 17 \\
-5 &= -5
\end{aligned}$$

Since the resulting statement is true, $\{3\}$ is the solution set.

EXAMPLE 3 Solve $3x + 25 + 4x = 1 + x$.

Solution

It is usually desirable to simplify each side as much as possible before attempting the solution.

The left side of the equation is $3x + 25 + 4x$.

Combine like terms to obtain $7x + 25$. Thus

$$\begin{aligned}
3x + 25 + 4x &= 1 + x & \\
7x + 25 &= 1 + x & \text{(Combine like terms of left side)} \\
7x + 25 - 25 &= 1 + x - 25 & \text{(Subtract 25 from each side)} \\
7x &= -24 + x & \text{(Simplify right side)} \\
7x - x &= -24 + x - x & \text{(Subtract } x \text{ from each side)} \\
6x &= -24 & \\
\frac{6x}{6} &= \frac{-24}{6} & \text{(Divide each side by 6)} \\
x &= -4 &
\end{aligned}$$

Check

$$\begin{aligned}
3x + 25 + 4x &= 1 + x \\
3(-4) + 25 + 4(-4) &= 1 + (-4) \\
-12 + 25 - 16 &= 1 - 4 \\
-28 + 25 &= -3 \\
-3 &= -3, \text{ true}
\end{aligned}$$

The solution set is $\{-4\}$.

EXAMPLE 4 Solve $y + 7 - 4(y - 8) = 2(y + 2)$.

Solution

$$y + 7 - 4(y - 8) = 2(y + 2)$$

$$y + 7 - 4y + 32 = 2y + 4 \quad \text{(Distributive axiom to remove parentheses)}$$

$$-3y + 39 = 2y + 4 \quad \text{(Combine like terms on left side)}$$

$$-3y + 39 - 39 = 2y + 4 - 39 \quad \text{(Subtract 39 from each side)}$$

$$-3y = 2y - 35 \quad \text{(Simplify)}$$

$$-3y - 2y = 2y - 2y - 35 \quad \text{(Subtract } 2y \text{ from each side)}$$

$$-5y = -35 \quad \text{(Simplify)}$$

$$\frac{-5y}{-5} = \frac{-35}{-5} \quad \text{(Divide each side by } -5)$$

Thus, $y = 7$, and $\{7\}$ is the solution set.
The check is left for you to do.

EXAMPLE 5 Solve $\dfrac{2t - 4}{4} + 5 = t - (3 + t)$

Solution

$$\frac{2t - 4}{4} + 5 = t - (3 + t)$$

$$\frac{2t - 4}{4} + 5 = t - 3 - t \quad \text{(Remove parentheses on right side)}$$

$$\frac{2t - 4}{4} + 5 = -3 \quad \text{(Simplify right side)}$$

$$\frac{2t - 4}{4} + 5 - 5 = -3 - 5 \quad \text{(Subtract 5 from each side)}$$

$$\frac{2t - 4}{4} = -8 \quad \text{(Simplify)}$$

$$4\left(\frac{2t - 4}{4}\right) = 4(-8) \quad \text{(Multiply each side by 4)}$$

$$2t - 4 = -32 \quad \text{(Simplify)}$$

$$2t - 4 + 4 = -32 + 4 \quad \text{(Add 4 to each side)}$$

$$2t = -28 \quad \text{(Simplify)}$$

$$\frac{2t}{2} = \frac{-28}{2} \quad \text{(Divide each side by 2)}$$

$$t = -14$$

The solution set is $\{-14\}$. Verify this solution.

With a little practice, you can do several of the above steps mentally.

EXERCISES

Solve and check the equations in Exercises 1–60.

1. $5x + 1 = 4x - 4$
2. $x - 1 = 2x + 3$
3. $3x + 4 = 10 - 3x$
4. $2x - 2 = 3x + 5$
5. $7a + 7 = 4a - 2$
6. $3t + 1 - 2t = 0$
7. $4y - 3(y - 5) = 25$
8. $10p - 275 = 25(p + 1)$
9. $3y + 3(y - 1) = 21$
10. $2(m + 3) = 3(2 - m)$
11. $x - 20 = 5 + x$
12. $x + (x + 2) + (x + 1) = 0$
13. $x - 2(x + 1) + 1 = 0$
14. $5(m - 4) - 6(m + 1) = 4$
15. $10 + 2(3x + 4) = 3x + 21$
16. $4n + 9 - 5n = 0$
17. $2(y + 7) - 5 = -1 + 4(y - 2)$
18. $2(x - 1) + 4x - 3 = 6x - 5$
19. $3p - 6 = 3(p - 2)$
20. $2(x - 3) - 2(3 - x) = 0$
21. $2x - 5 - (4 - 3x) = 11$
22. $3(x + 20) - 2(x + 30) = 2x + 5$
23. $8x + (5 - x) + 30 = 0$
24. $4(t - 20) - 5(t - 22) = 2t$
25. $13y - 6 = 19y + 42$
26. $10t - 2(3t - 1) = 23 - 3t$
27. $4x - 1 = 2x - 5$
28. $2x - 4 = 2(x - 2)$
29. $2a = 7 - 3(a - 1)$
30. $3x + 4 = 5x - 2$
31. $x + 2(3x - 5) = 4$
32. $12 - 5(t - 2) = 2 - t$
33. $2x - 16 = 3(13 - 3x)$
34. $2n - (6 - n) = 4n - 13$
35. $5 + 3(2y + 1) = 6y + 8$
36. $5(3 - y) = 121 - 6(25 - y)$
37. $5(4p - 3) + 3(2p + 2) = 7p + 29$
38. $5(12 - x) = 7 - 2(6 - 4x)$
39. $30 - 3(2x - 3) = 5(3 - x)$
40. $12 = 8z - 3(7 - z)$
41. $4(2y - 5) - 8(y + 5) = 7$
42. $7 - 3x - (5 + 2x) = 12$
43. $p - 7 = 7 - p$
44. $p - 7 = p + 7$
45. $x - [1 - (x - 1)] = 3x$
46. $x - 2[x - 2(x - 2)] = 4$
47. $4t + 2(t - 6) = 0$
48. $4 = 2x + 10 + 4x$
49. $4x + (3 - 2x) = (4x + 3) - 2x$
50. $6(3y + 4) - 3(10y + 16) = 8(2y - 17)$
51. $6(y - 3) - 5(2y - 6) = 0$
52. $-2(t + 1) = 4(1 - 2t)$
53. $x + 4 = \dfrac{4(x - 1)}{4}$
54. $\dfrac{2 - 3z}{2} = 3 - (z + 2)$
55. $x + 2 = \dfrac{3x - 2}{5}$
56. $\dfrac{8y + 7}{5} = 2y - 3$
57. $\dfrac{4(y - 2)}{5} = y - 3$
58. $8 - \dfrac{7t + 3}{4} - 2(3 - t) = 0$
59. $\dfrac{2 - 5x}{4} = 1 - (x + 1)$
60. $\dfrac{5x + 2}{3} = 3x - 2$

2.4 LINEAR INEQUALITIES

Statements such as $x < 4$, $x \geq 7$, $2x - 1 \leq 9$, $3x > 2x + 5$, and $10 - (x - 3) < 24$ are called **inequalities.** There are many practical applications that involve inequalities.

Inequalities are said to have the **same sense** if they have the same order symbol. For example, $x < 4$ and $5 < 7$ are inequalities of the same sense.

On the other hand, $x < 7$ and $8 > 3$ are inequalities of the **opposite sense,** since their order symbols are different.

A **solution of an inequality** is a number that makes the inequality true when its variable is replaced by this number.

The **solution set** of an inequality is the set of all solutions of the inequality.

Two inequalities are equivalent if and only if they have the same solution set.

Solving an inequality is similar to solving an equation, but there are two important exceptions. One has to do with exchanging sides, and the other has to do with multiplying (or dividing) by a negative number.

THEOREM ON EXCHANGING SIDES

If one inequality is obtained from another one by exchanging sides and by changing the order symbol, then these two inequalities are equivalent.

For example
$3 < 8$ and $8 > 3$ are equivalent.
$x \geq 9$ and $9 \leq x$ are equivalent.
$12 - x > 3x$ and $3x < 12 - x$ are equivalent.

ADDITION THEOREM

If the same number is added to each side of an inequality, then the resulting inequality having the same sense is equivalent to the original one.

For example
$3 < 8$ and $3 + 4 < 8 + 4$ are equivalent. $x - 4 > 5$ and $x - 4 + 4 > 5 + 4$ (that is, $x > 9$) are equivalent.

MULTIPLICATION BY A POSITIVE NUMBER THEOREM

If each side of an inequality is multiplied by the same positive number, then the resulting inequality having the same sense is equivalent to the original one.

For example,
$5 > 2$ and $5(4) > 2(4)$ are equivalent.
$\frac{x}{4} \le 6$ and $x \le 24$ are equivalent.

MULTIPLICATION BY A NEGATIVE NUMBER THEOREM

If each side of an inequality is multiplied by the same negative number and if the order symbol is changed, then the resulting inequality, having the opposite sense, is equivalent to the original one.

For example,
$-2 < 8$ and $-2(-3) > 8(-3)$ (that is, $6 > -24$) are equivalent.
$-2x \ge 8$ and $x \le -4$ are equivalent.

EXAMPLE 1 Solve the inequality $2x + 3 < x + 5$ and graph the solution set.

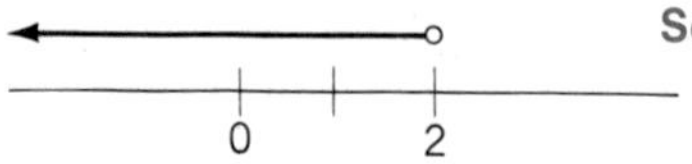

FIG. 2.1

Solution $2x + 3 < x + 5$
$2x < x + 2$ (Addition theorem—adding -3)
$x < 2$ (Addition theorem—adding $-x$)
See Fig. 2.1.

EXAMPLE 2 Solve for x and graph the solution set.

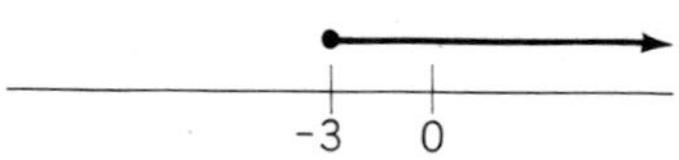

FIG. 2.2

Solution $2 - x \le 14 + 3x$
$2 - 4x \le 14$ (Adding $-3x$ to each side)
$-4x \le 12$ (Adding -2 to each side)
$x \ge -3$ (Multiplying each side by $-\frac{1}{4}$ and changing the order symbol)
See Fig. 2.2.

EXERCISES

Solve Exercises 1–40 and graph the solution sets.

1. $2x - 4 > 0$
2. $2x + 4 > 0$
3. $3x - 2 > 1 + 2x$
4. $3x + 5 < x + 7$
5. $2x + 1 < x - 5$
6. $6x + 10 < 2 + 4x$
7. $4 - 2x \le 0$
8. $8 - 2x \ge 0$
9. $15 - 3x \ge 0$
10. $15 - 3x \le 0$

11. $1 < 2x + 3$
12. $1 \leq 2x - 3$
13. $2x - 3(x + 1) > 0$
14. $2x - 3(x + 1) \leq 0$
15. $5 - x \leq 3 - (x - 2)$
16. $4x + 2 \leq 4x$
17. $x + 4 - 3x \leq 2x + 4$
18. $3x - (x + 4) \leq 4 - 2x$
19. $-2(x + 3) \geq 4(2x + 1)$
20. $2(x + 3) < -4(2x + 1)$
21. $33 - 9x \leq 2x$
22. $x - 12 \geq 0$
23. $12 - x \geq 0$
24. $\frac{x + 3}{2} < 0$
25. $\frac{x + 3}{5} \geq 0$
26. $2x - \frac{1}{3} \leq 0$
27. $\frac{x - 6x}{2} < -20$
28. $\frac{x - 6}{2} < -20$
29. $\frac{6 - x}{2} < -20$
30. $2(x + 3) \geq 8(2 - x)$
31. $\frac{x}{3} < 0$
32. $\frac{x}{3} > 0$
33. $x > 4 + x$
34. $x < 4 + x$
35. $x - 2 < 2 - x$
36. $x - 2 < 2 + x$
37. $-3(2 - 3x) < 15 - (x + 1)$
38. $15 - (x + 2) \leq 0$
39. $-2(x + 4) \geq -2(x + 4)$
40. $3 \leq \frac{x + 2}{5}$

2.5 LITERAL EQUATIONS

A formula is a general equation for the solution of a specific problem. For example, a formula for finding the area of a rectangle is $A = LW$, where A represents area, and L and W the length and width of the rectangle. The circumference of a circle can be expressed as $C = 2\pi r$, where C represents the circumference and r the radius of the circle. You are familiar with many formulas, some of which were presented in Chapter 1.

Often a formula is not in the form desired or is not convenient for the solution of a problem. Since a formula is an equation, it can be treated as such and changed to a desired equivalent equation by the methods shown in the preceding sections.

EXAMPLE 1 The formula for the perimeter of a rectangle is

$$P = 2L + 2W$$

where P stands for the perimeter, L stands for the length, and W for the width. Solve this formula for W in terms of the other letters.

Solution The technique for solution is to treat W as a variable and all other numerals and letters as constants.

$$P = 2L + 2W$$
$$2W + 2L = P$$
$$2W + 2L - 2L = P - 2L \qquad \text{(Subtract } 2L \text{ from each side)}$$
$$2W = P - 2L \qquad \text{(Simplify)}$$
$$\frac{2W}{2} = \frac{P - 2L}{2} \qquad \text{(Divide each side by 2)}$$
$$W = \frac{P - 2L}{2}$$

Now the equation is solved for W.

An equation involving more than one letter, some of which are constant, is called a **literal equation.**

EXAMPLE 2 Solve the formula for the circumference of a circle, $C = 2\pi r$, for r.

Solution
$$C = 2\pi r$$
$$2\pi r = C$$
$$\frac{2\pi r}{2\pi} = \frac{C}{2\pi} \qquad \text{(Divide each side by } 2\pi\text{)}$$
$$r = \frac{C}{2\pi}$$

Thus the radius of any circle is equal to the circumference of the circle divided by 2π.

EXAMPLE 3 $C = \frac{5}{9}(F - 32)$ is the formula for converting Fahrenheit temperature to degrees Celsius. Solve the formula for F—that is, rewrite it so that it can be readily used to convert Celsius temperature to Fahrenheit.

Solution
$$C = \frac{5}{9}(F - 32)$$
$$9C = 9\left(\frac{5}{9}\right)(F - 32) \qquad \text{(Multiply each side by 9)}$$
$$9C = 5(F - 32) \qquad \text{(Simplify)}$$
$$9C = 5F - 160 \qquad \text{(Distributive axiom)}$$
$$9C + 160 = 5F - 160 + 160 \qquad \text{(Add 160 to each side)}$$
$$5F = 9C + 160$$
$$F = \frac{9C + 160}{5} \qquad \text{(Divide each side by 5)}$$
$$F = \frac{9}{5}C + 32 \qquad \text{(Further simplification of right side)}$$

Thus $F = \frac{9}{5}C + 32$.

EXAMPLE 4 If $mx - y + b = 0$, solve for each of the following:

a. x b. y c. m d. b

Solution In each instance, consider all letters constant except the letter for which you are solving:

a. Solve for x:

$$mx - y + b = 0$$
$$mx - y + y + b = 0 + y \quad \text{(Add } y \text{ to each side)}$$
$$mx + b - b = y - b \quad \text{(Subtract } b \text{ from each side)}$$
$$mx = y - b \quad \text{(Simplify)}$$
$$x = \frac{y - b}{m} \quad \text{(Divide each side by } m \ [m \neq 0])$$

b. Solve for y:

$$mx - y + b = 0$$
$$mx - y + y + b = 0 + y \quad \text{(Add } y \text{ to each side)}$$
$$mx + b = y \quad \text{(Simplify)}$$
$$y = mx + b$$

c. Solve for m:

$$mx - y + b = 0$$
$$mx - y + b - b = 0 - b \quad \text{(Subtract } b \text{ from each side)}$$
$$mx - y + y = -b + y \quad \text{(Add } y \text{ to each side)}$$
$$mx = y - b \quad \text{(Commutative axiom, addition)}$$
$$m = \frac{y - b}{x} \quad \text{(Divide each side by } x \ [x \neq 0])$$

d. Solve for b:

$$mx - y + b = 0$$
$$mx + b = y \quad \text{(Add } y \text{ to each side)}$$
$$b = y - mx \quad \text{(Subtract } mx \text{ from each side)}$$

EXAMPLE 5 Solve $2x + y = 10$ for y.

Solution

$$2x + y = 10$$
$$-2x + 2x + y = 10 - 2x$$
$$y = 10 - 2x$$

or

$$y = -2x + 10$$

EXAMPLE 6 Solve $4x - y = 12$ for y.

Solution

$$4x - y = 12$$
$$-4x + 4x - y = -4x + 12$$
$$-y = -4x + 12$$
$$(-1)(-y) = (-1)(-4x + 12)$$
$$y = 4x - 12$$

EXERCISES

Solve the formulas in Exercises 1–40 for the indicated variables.

1. $A = LW$ (Area of rectangle); L
2. $V = LWH$ (Volume of a parallelepiped—box); W

3. $V = \pi r^2 h$ (Volume of a circular cylinder); h
4. $P = 2L + 2W$ (Perimeter of a rectangle); L
5. $D = rt$ (Uniform motion formula); t
6. $y = mx + b$ (Slope-intercept equation of a line); x
7. $A = \frac{bh}{2}$ (Area of a triangle); h
8. $A = \frac{1}{2}h(a + b)$ (Area of a trapezoid); a
9. $A = P + Prt$ (Simple interest); r
10. $W = Fd$ (Work); d
11. $C = 2\pi r$ (Circumference of a circle); r
12. $V = \frac{1}{3}bh$ (Volume of a cone); b
13. $A = a(a + 2s)$ (Surface area of a square pyramid); s
14. $P = I^2 r$ (Electric power); r
15. $F = \frac{9}{5}C + 32$ (Temperature conversion); C
16. $A = \frac{1}{2}h(a + b)$ (Area of a trapezoid); h
17. $A + B + C = 180$ (Sum of angles of a triangle); B
18. $P = a + b + c$ (Perimeter of a triangle); b
19. $D = A(n - 1)$ (Physics: law of small prisms); n
20. $D = A(n - 1)$ (Physics: law of small prisms); A
21. $Q = \frac{100M}{C}$ (Psychology); C
22. $E = \frac{I - O}{I}$ (Engineering); O
23. $R = \frac{C - S}{n}$ (Economics: depreciation); n
24. $R = \frac{C - S}{n}$ (Economics: depreciation); S
25. $\frac{S}{s} = \frac{d}{D}$ (Pulleys and gears); d
26. $\frac{S}{s} = \frac{d}{D}$ (Pulleys and gears); D
27. $\frac{PV}{T} = \frac{pv}{t}$ (Boyle's gas law); t
28. Solve Exercise 27 for P.
29. Solve Exercise 27 for p.
30. Solve Exercise 27 for V.
31. $C = \frac{100W}{L}$ (Anthropology: cephalic index); W
32. Solve Exercise 31 for L.
33. $r = c(x + a)$ (Biology and chemistry: growth rate); a
34. Solve Exercise 33 for x.

35. $C = \dfrac{yA}{y + 12}$ (Medical dosage); A

36. $C = \dfrac{WA}{150}$ (Medical dosage); W

37. $p = \dfrac{s}{s + f}$ (Probability; life insurance); f

38. $d = \dfrac{r}{1 + nr}$ (Discount rate); n

39. $r = \dfrac{R(E - G)}{E}$ (Radio, television); G

40. Solve Exercise 39 for R.

Solve the equations in Exercises 41–60 for the specified variables.

41. $x + y = 8;\ y$
42. $y - 2x = 5;\ y$
43. $3x - y = 6;\ y$
44. $5x - y = 20;\ y$
45. $x - 2y = 9;\ x$
46. $x + 7y = 4;\ x$
47. $2y - x + 4 = 0;\ x$
48. $8 - x - 4y = 0;\ x$
49. $2x - 7y = 8;\ x$
50. $5x + 4y = 20;\ y$
51. $y - 5x = 10;\ y$
52. $4x + y = 12;\ y$
53. $x + 4y = 12;\ x$
54. $x - 6y = 18;\ x$
55. $x + y + 1 = 0;\ x$
56. $x - 2y + 6 = 0;\ x$
57. $3x + 2y = 6;\ y$
58. $2x - 5y = 10;\ x$
59. $ax + by + c = 0;\ y$
60. $ax + by + c = 0;\ x$

2.6 APPLICATIONS: NUMERICAL PROBLEMS, AGE PROBLEMS, CONSECUTIVE INTEGERS

Numerical problems are very often stated in words. Besides mathematics, these problems may come from many other areas such as business or science. If the verbal problem can be translated into a linear equation in one variable, then it can be solved by the methods of the preceding sections.

Problems about numbers alone may have few practical applications, but they are useful in developing methods and techniques for solving applied problems. One needs to know how to translate "twice a number less 5 equals" no matter what the number represents. For example, a problem from chemistry might state, "Twice the number of grams of potassium sulfate less 5 grams yields . . ."

Techniques that are useful in translating a verbal problem into an equation are summarized as follows.

Verbal-Problem Techniques

1. Read the problem slowly at least two times.
2. Illustrate the problem with a simple picture or diagram, if possible.
3. Designate one of the unknown numbers by a variable, such as x.
4. Represent the other unknown numbers, if any, in terms of the variable selected.
5. Summarize the numerical information in a chart, if possible.
6. List any formula or formulas that might apply.
7. Find an equation relating the numbers of the problem.
8. Solve the equation.
9. Check the solution.

The expressions in Table 2.1 occur frequently in verbal problems.

TABLE 2.1 VERBALIZATION OF ALGEBRAIC TERMS

$a+b$	a plus b the sum of a and b a added to b a more than b a greater than b a increased by b	$a-b$	a minus b the difference between a and b (when b is subtracted from a) b subtracted from a b less than a a decreased by b
ab	a times b the product of a and b a multiplied by b	$\frac{a}{b}$	a divided by b the quotient when a is divided by b
$2x$	twice x the double of x	$\frac{x}{2}$	one-half of x
$\frac{3x}{5}$	three-fifths of x	$\frac{x}{3}$	one-third of x
$=$	equals, equal, is, is equal to, are equal to, is the same as, results in, becomes, was, will be		

EXAMPLE 1 Twice the difference obtained when 7 is subtracted from a certain number results in 20. Find the number.

Solution Let $x =$ the unknown number. Then

$$
\begin{aligned}
2(x-7) &= 20\\
2x-14 &= 20\\
2x &= 34\\
x &= 17
\end{aligned}
$$

Check

$$
\begin{aligned}
2(17-7) &= 20\\
2(10) &= 20\\
20 &= 20
\end{aligned}
$$

EXAMPLE 2 A man invests twice as much money in stock A as in stock B, and \$740 more in stock C than in stocks A and B combined. If his total investment is \$5000, how much did he invest in each stock? **Solution**

Let $x =$ the number of dollars invested in stock B

then

$2x =$ the number of dollars invested in stock A

and

$x + 2x + 740 =$ the number of dollars invested in stock C

The total investment, \$5000, $= x + 2x + (x + 2x + 740)$.

$$x + 2x + (x + 2x + 740) = 5000$$
$$6x + 740 = 5000$$
$$6x = 4260$$
$$x = 710$$

He invested \$710 in stock B.

He invested $2(710) =$ \$1420 in stock A.

He invested \$1420 + \$710 + \$740 = \$2870 in stock C.

Check $710 + 1420 + 2870 = 5000$

Another type of application involves consecutive numbers—specifically, integers. For example, if x stands for an integer, then $x + 1$ is the next or consecutive integer, followed by $x + 2$, $x + 3$, ... So if $x = 3$, then $x + 1 = 4$, $x + 2 = 5$, and $x + 3 = 6$, and 3, 4, 5, 6 are consecutive integers. Consecutive *even* integers are numbers such as 8, 10, 12, 14, whereas consecutive *odd* integers are numbers such as 9, 11, 13, 15, 17. Table 2.2 is a guide, assuming that x is an integer.

TABLE 2.2 CONSECUTIVE INTEGERS

$x, x + 1$	Two consecutive integers
$x, x + 1, x + 2$	Three consecutive integers
$x, x + 2$	Two consecutive even integers
$x, x + 2$	Two consecutive odd integers

EXAMPLE 3 Find three consecutive integers whose sum is 48.

Solution

Let $x =$ first integer

$x + 1 =$ second integer

$x + 2 =$ third integer

$$x + (x + 1) + (x + 2) = 48$$
$$3x + 3 = 48$$
$$3x = 45$$
$$x = 15$$

Therefore, $x = 15$, $x + 1 = 16$, and $x + 2 = 17$; the three consecutive integers are 15, 16, 17.

Check $15 + 16 + 17 = 48$

EXAMPLE 4 If 3 times the smallest of three consecutive *even* integers is 16 less than 5 times the largest, find the three integers.

Solution

Let $x =$ smallest integer

Then

$x + 2 =$ next consecutive *even* integer

and

$x + 4 =$ third consecutive *even* integer (the largest)

$$3x = 5(x + 4) - 16$$
$$3x = 5x + 20 - 16$$
$$-2x = 4$$
$$x = -2$$
$$x + 2 = -2 + 2 = 0$$
$$x + 4 = -2 + 4 = 2$$

Thus the three consecutive even integers are -2, 0, 2.

Problems involving ages of people or objects follow a pattern similar to that of consecutive integers.

EXAMPLE 5 Four years ago a father was twice as old as his son. The difference in their ages is 18 years. How old is each today?

Solution

	Now	*4 Years Ago*
Son	x	$x - 4$
Father	$x + 18$	$(x + 18) - 4$

$$(x + 18) - 4 = 2(x - 4)$$
$$x + 14 = 2x - 8$$
$$x = 22$$
$$x + 18 = 40$$

The father is 40 years old and the son is 22.

The following chart may be helpful.

	Age Problems
$x + k$	k years older than x
$x - k$	k years younger than x
$x + a$	Age a years from now, present age x
$x - a$	Age a years ago, present age x

EXERCISES

Solve and check Exercises 1–30.

1. Twice the sum of a number and 5 is 13 more than the number. Find the number.
2. Three more than twice a certain number is 7 less than 3 times the number. Find the number.
3. Four times a number decreased by 24 is 18 less than 5 times the number. Find the number.
4. Nineteen added to 3 times a number is 16 more than 4 times the number. Find the number.
5. The difference between 5 times a number and twice the number is 16 more than the number. Find the number.
6. The sum of two numbers is 28. Five times the smaller number is 4 less than 4 times the larger number. Find the numbers.
7. A resort owner has 100 rooms for rent, some double, some single, and some twin. At the end of one day the following rooms were rented: Double rooms, 3 more than twice the number of singles; twin rooms, half the number of singles. Six rooms were unrented. If all the unrented rooms were singles, how many rooms of each type are there for rent at the resort?
8. A small rental agency in a seaside resort has bicycles, motor scooters, and dune buggies for rent. The total storage area allows for 165 vehicles for maximum profit distributed in the following manner: motor scooters, 4 fewer than three times the number of bicycles; dune buggies, one-third the number of bicycles. How many vehicles of each type does the agency have?
9. A survey of the foreign language department of a certain college revealed the following facts about student enrollment in French, Spanish, Japanese, and Swahili: 6 fewer than twice the number of students taking French were enrolled in Spanish. The enrollment in Swahili topped the enrollment in French by 9, and the enrollment in Japanese was half of that in Spanish. If the total class enrollment was 460, how many students were enrolled in each language?
10. In a supermarket 3 types of refrigerators are used to store cases of perishable goods. If the first refrigerator holds 24 more cases than the second, and the third holds three-fourths as many cases as the first, find the storage capacity of each if their total capacity is 317 cases.
11. In a football game twice the number of points scored by the winning team was 14 less than 3 times the number of points scored by the losing team. If the winners won by 4 points, what was the final score in the game?
12. A jar of 62 coins contains pennies, nickels, and dimes. If there are 3 times as many dimes as nickels, and 6 more than 3 times as many pennies as nickels, how many coins are there in the jar? How much money is in the jar?

13. If x is the middle integer of three consecutive integers, write algebraic expressions involving x for the smallest and the largest of the three integers.

14. If the sum of the three consecutive integers in Exercise 13 is 159, what are the integers?

15. The sum of three consecutive integers is 42. Find the integers.

16. Find four consecutive integers so that the largest subtracted from 4 times the second is 53 more than the smallest.

17. Find three consecutive odd integers so that the sum of twice the largest and 3 times the smallest is 73.

18. Find three consecutive even integers so that the sum of twice the largest and 3 times the smallest is 8.

19. The largest of four consecutive odd integers is 5 less than twice the smallest. Find the integers.

20. Find three consecutive integers whose sum is the difference between 5 times the smallest and the largest.

21. The average of four consecutive even integers is -1. Find the integers.

22. The average of four consecutive odd integers is 34. Find the integers.

23. The average of six consecutive even integers is -9. Find the integers.

24. Of five increasing numbers, the three smallest are consecutive integers, and the second, fourth, and fifth numbers are consecutive odd integers. If their sum is 51, find the numbers.

25. A person bought a ranch 5 years ago. On this ranch was a barn and a farmhouse. At that time the barn was 3 times as old as the farmhouse. Now the barn is only twice as old. How old is the barn now? How old is the farmhouse now?

26. If the roof on a house will be twice as old in 6 years as it is now, how old is the roof now?

27. John's sister is 3 years younger than John, and John's father is 28 years older than John. Five years ago the father's age was one year more than twice the sum of his children's ages then. How old is each now?

28. Mike has a brother who is one-half his age and a sister who is twice his age. If the combined ages of the 3 siblings is 5 less than 4 times Mike's age, how old is Mike's sister?

29. In 12 years a building will be twice as old as it is now. In how many years will the building be 3 times as old as it is now?

30. When Mr. and Mrs. Anderson were married, Mr. Anderson was 3 years older than his wife. On their 25th wedding anniversary, the sum of their ages was 97 years. How old was each on his wedding day?

2.7 APPLICATIONS: GEOMETRIC PROBLEMS

The solution of geometric problems requires the application of formulas concerning geometric figures. In this type of problem it is useful to draw the figure discussed and mark it with the numerical information. The equation is obtained by substituting the numerical information into the appropriate formula.

Some geometric figures and their formulas are supplied in Fig. 2.3.

The rectangle	The square	The triangle (sides)	The triangle (angles)

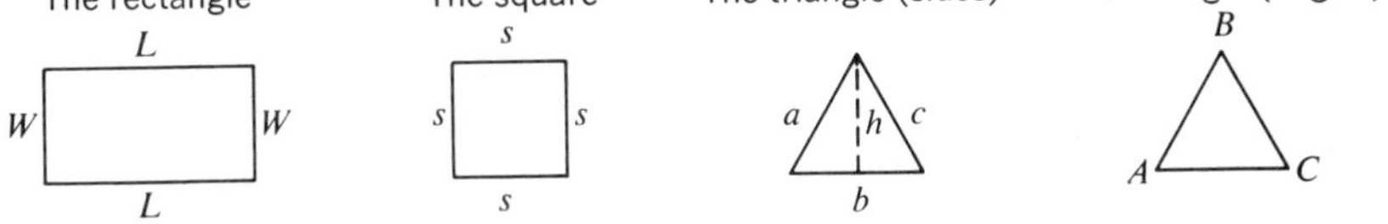

The rectangle	The square	The triangle (sides)	The triangle (angles)
$P = 2L + 2W$	$P = 4s$	$P = a + b + c$	$\angle A + \angle B + \angle C = 180^\circ$
$A = LW$	$A = s^2$	$A = \frac{bh}{2}$	

FIG. 2.3

EXAMPLE 1 A flower bed has the shape of a rectangle. The length of the rectangle is 4 times its width. The perimeter is unchanged if the width is doubled and the length is decreased by 9 feet. What are the original dimensions of the flower bed?

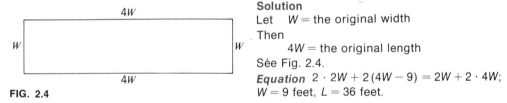

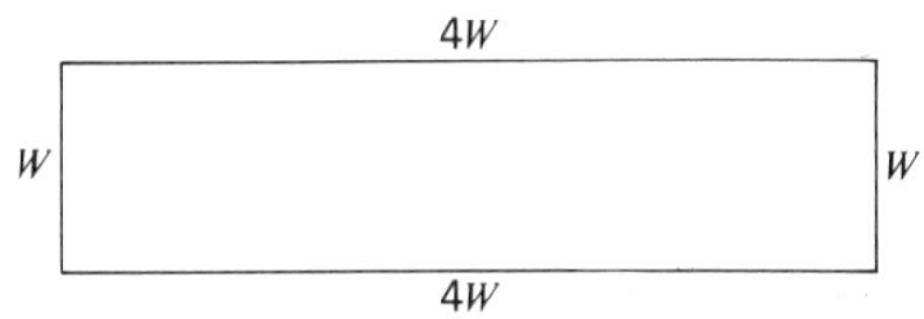

FIG. 2.4

Solution

Let $W =$ the original width

Then

$4W =$ the original length

See Fig. 2.4.

Equation $2 \cdot 2W + 2(4W - 9) = 2W + 2 \cdot 4W$; $W = 9$ feet, $L = 36$ feet.

EXAMPLE 2 One angle of a triangle is 10 degrees more than the second angle, and the third angle is 10 degrees less than the second angle. How many degrees are in each angle of the triangle?

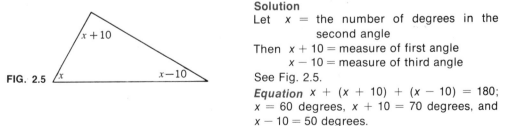

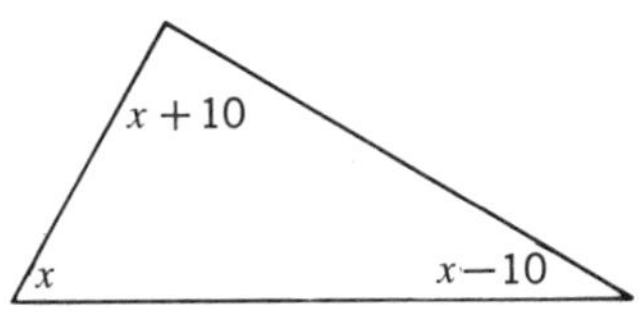

FIG. 2.5

Solution

Let $x =$ the number of degrees in the second angle

Then $x + 10 =$ measure of first angle

$x - 10 =$ measure of third angle

See Fig. 2.5.

Equation $x + (x + 10) + (x - 10) = 180$; $x = 60$ degrees, $x + 10 = 70$ degrees, and $x - 10 = 50$ degrees.

NUMBER PROBLEMS

Number and other word problems have a long history. They are found in ancient Egyptian manuscripts such as the Rhind papyrus written by the Egyptian scribe Ahmes around 1650 B.C. They occur on Babylonian clay tablets dated from 2100 B.C. to 1600 B.C.

The Greek Anthology, written around 500 A.D. by Metrodorus, is one of the best sources for ancient Greek algebraic problems.

Hindu problems are found in the works of Aryabhata (ca. 510 A.D.), Brahmagupta (ca. 628 A.D.), Mahavira (ca. 850 A.D.), Bhaskara (ca. 1150 A.D.), and in the Bakhshali manuscript, believed to have been written somewhere between 300 A.D. and 1000 A.D.

Algebraic knowledge passed from India to the Arabs and then to the Europeans. The famous *Liber abaci,* written in 1202 by the Italian Leonardo Fibonacci, was an important source by which the Hindu-Arabic numerals, arithmetic, and algebra were introduced into Europe.

EXERCISES

Solve and check Exercises 1–20.

1. A rectangular picture frame has a perimeter of 96 centimetres. If the width of the frame is 8 centimetres shorter than the length, find the dimensions of the frame.
2. The width of a rectangular garden is 2 metres more than one-third of its length. If the perimeter is 52 metres, find the dimensions of the rectangle.
3. The area of a square whose side is 8 feet is the same as the area of a rectangle with a 16-foot length. Find the width of the rectangle.
4. Find the area of a square whose perimeter is 40 inches.
5. If the length of a ping-pong table is 2 feet less than twice its width, find the length and width if the perimeter is 29 feet.
6. Two rectangular carpets have widths of 2.5 metres and 3 metres respectively. If the length of the first carpet is one metre longer than that of the second carpet, and if the sum of their areas is 24.5 square metres, find the length of each carpet.
7. A 12-inch-by-18-inch rectangular picture is to have a frame of uniform width. The perimeter of the framed picture determines the length of wood needed for the frame. Find the width of the frame if the perimeter of the framed picture is 84 inches.
8. A piece of copper tubing is to be bent into the shape of a triangle in such a way that one side of the triangle is 3 inches more than twice the second side, and the third side is 1.5 times the second side. If the piece of tubing is 48 inches long, find the dimensions of the triangle.
9. The measurements of the angles of a triangle can be obtained by multiplying each of three consecutive integers by 10. Find the number of degrees in each angle, recalling that the sum of the angles is 180 degrees.
10. What will be the cost of installing a hardwood floor to cover a rectangular area whose length is 6 feet less than twice its width if the cost is 80 cents a square foot and the perimeter is 78 feet?
11. In Fig. 2.6, the large rectangle is divided into four smaller rectangles. If the sum of the areas of the rectangles labelled I, II, and III is 5240, find the area of rectangle IV.

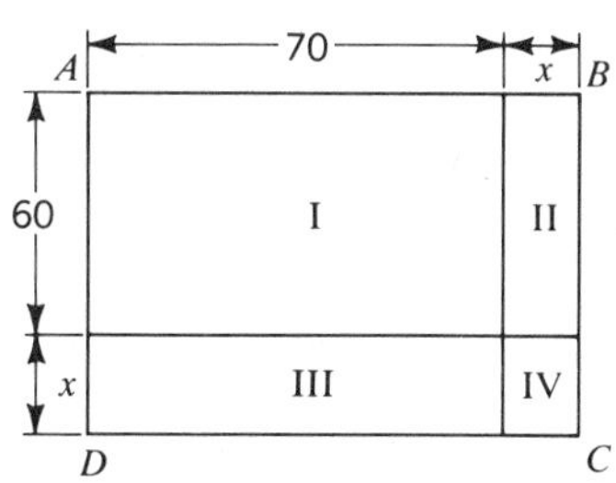

FIG. 2.6

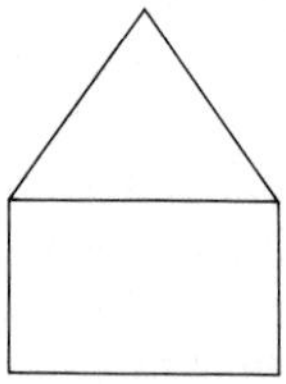

FIG. 2.7

12. A wood template has the shape of a rectangle surmounted by an equilateral triangle (three equal sides), as in Fig. 2.7. The height of the rectangle is 3 inches less than the base of the rectangle (also a side of the triangle). It takes a total length of 34 inches of metal stripping to go around the template. Find the length of a side of the triangle.

13. An isosceles triangle is a triangle with two equal sides and two equal angles. If each of the equal angles of an isosceles triangle is 5 degrees less than twice the third angle, how many degrees are there in each angle of the triangle?

14. Equilateral triangles (three equal sides) are cut off the three corners of a larger triangle to form a regular hexagon (six equal sides). (See Fig. 2.8.) If the perimeter of the hexagon is 54 centimetres, find the length of a side of the larger triangle.

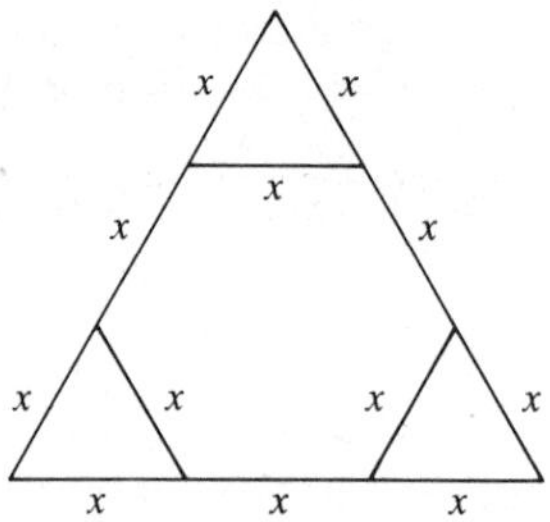

FIG. 2.8

15. The cross section of an irrigation ditch has the shape of a rectangle whose depth is one foot less than its width. By digging the ditch 2 feet deeper, the area of the cross section can be increased by 6 square feet. Find the width and the depth of the ditch before digging.

16. A man wants to build a 4-foot-high brick wall at a uniform distance from the two 24-foot sides of his house and from a 50-foot length of the house. If he uses 4-inch-by-8-inch bricks costing 10 cents apiece, how far from his house can he build the wall and keep the cost of the bricks at $212.40?

17. Each page of a book is 9 inches by 7 inches and is to have a one-inch margin along the two 9-inch sides. The margins at the other two sides of the page are equal in width. How wide should each of these margins be in order to have 40 square inches of printing?

18. A 4-by-5 portrait camera produces negatives that are 4 inches by 5 inches, rectangular in shape. A standard print from this negative is 8 inches by 10 inches.

a. How many prints can be made from a piece of paper 112 inches by 110 inches if no paper is wasted?

b. How many 11-inch-by-14-inch prints can be made from a piece of paper 112 inches by 110 inches if no paper is wasted?

19. A farmer planned to fence three sides of a rectangular area, the fourth side (a length) being along a river. He planned a rectangle whose length was 5 feet longer than the width. His son, who had studied algebra, told him that the area would be the same but less fencing would be needed if he increased the length by 15 feet and decreased the width by 10 feet. Following his son's advice, the farmer found that he used 120 feet of fencing. Find the amount of fencing that would have been needed for the original plan.

20. An owner building his home specified a triangular window whose height was 2 feet shorter than its base. However, in order to meet the city lighting requirements, it was necessary to increase the height by 4 feet to permit an increase in area of 6 square feet. Find the dimensions of the original window and the dimensions of the new window.

2.8 APPLICATIONS: MIXTURE PROBLEMS

Many problems can be classified as mixture problems. The essential feature of this type of problem is that two or more items each having a specified unit value are combined to form a mixture. The sum of the values of the components must equal the value of the final mixture.

In this type of problem, the chart or table is a very useful device for summarizing the information. From it the equation may be obtained very easily. The final entry in the last column is equal to the sum of the other entries in this column.

EXAMPLE 1 A piggy bank contains 23 coins, consisting of dimes and quarters. The total value is \$3.35. How many coins of each kind are there? **Solution**

Let $d =$ the number of dimes

Then $23 - d =$ the number of quarters

Item	*Unit Value* ·	*Number of Items* =	*Value*
Dimes	10 cents	d	$10d$
Quarters	25 cents	$23 - d$	$25(23 - d)$
Mixture		23	335 cents

Equation $10d + 25(23 - d) = 335$; $d = 16$ dimes, $23 - d = 7$ quarters.

EXAMPLE 2 How many pounds of candy worth 75 cents a pound should be mixed with 20 pounds of candy worth $1.30 a pound to obtain a mixture worth $1.00 a pound?

Solution

Let $x =$ the number of pounds of 75-cent candy.

Item	*Unit Value* ·	*Number of Items* =	*Value*
Candy	75 cents	x pounds	$75x$
Candy	130 cents	20 pounds	$20(130)$
Mixture	100 cents	$x + 20$	$100(x + 20)$

Equation

$75x + 20(130) = 100(x + 20)$, $x = 24$ pounds.

EXAMPLE 3 A businessman makes two types of investments: Type A, which yields a 5 percent annual return, and type B, which yields a 4 percent return. If his total investment is $10,000, and his income from the investment at the end of one year is $440, how much money did he invest in type A?

Solution

Let $d =$ amount invested in type A.

Item	*Unit Value (Percent Return)* ·	*Number of Items (Amount Invested) in Dollars* =	*Value (Income)*
Type A	0.05	d	$0.05d$
Type B	0.04	$10{,}000 - d$	$0.04(10{,}000 - d)$
Mixture (Totals)	–	10,000	440

Equation

$0.05d + 0.04(10{,}000 - d) = 440$, $d = 4000$ dollars.

EXAMPLE 4 Tickets to a certain event cost 75 cents for children and $2.00 for adults. A total of $2430 was collected. If there were 3 times as many adult tickets sold as children's tickets, how many adult tickets were sold?

Solution

Let x = the number of children's tickets

Then

$3x$ = the number of adult tickets

Item	*Unit Value* ·	*Number of Items* =	*Value*
Children's tickets	75 cents	x	$75x$
Adult tickets	200 cents	$3x$	$200(3x)$
Mixture			243,000

Equation

$75x + 200(3x) = 243{,}000$; $x = 360$, $3x = 1080$.

EXAMPLE 5 How many cubic centimetres (cc) of distilled water must be added to 30 cc of a 20 percent solution of ammonium sulfate to obtain a 15 percent solution of ammonium sulfate?

Solution

Let x = the number of cc of water

Item	*Unit Value* · (Percentage of sulfate)	*Number of Items* = (number of cc)	*Value*
Water	0	x	0
20% solution	0.20	30	$0.20(30)$
15% solution	0.15	$x + 30$	$0.15(x + 30)$

Equation

$0.15(x + 30) = 0.20(30)$; $x = 10$ cc

EXERCISES

Solve and check Exercises 1–20.

1. How many litres of high-octane gasoline worth 40 cents a litre should be blended with 300 litres of low-octane gasoline worth 35 cents a litre to produce a mixture worth 37 cents a litre?
2. A farmer combines seed worth 12 cents a pound with seed worth 20 cents a pound to obtain a 50-pound mixture worth 15 cents a pound. How many pounds of each type of seed does he use?
3. A cashier in a ticket booth starts the day with $100 worth of change. The change is in quarters, dimes, and dollar bills. If he has 50 times as many dimes as dollar bills and 60 more than 10 times as many quarters as dollar bills, how many dimes, quarters, and dollar bills did the cashier start with?
4. A jar at the checkout counter of a grocery store has a sign asking for contributions to a charitable cause. At the end of the week, the jar contains coins worth a total of $7.40. If there was 1 less than half as many dimes as nickels, and 4 more quarters than dimes, and these were the only types of coins, how many quarters were in the jar?
5. A grocer mixes 45 pounds of ordinary coffee beans worth $2.80 a pound with rare coffee beans worth $3.60 a pound. How many pounds of rare beans should he use to obtain a mixture worth $3.00 a pound?
6. Concrete is a mixture of cement and sand. How many pounds of cement worth 72 cents a pound and how many pounds of sand worth 12 cents a pound have been mixed to obtain 120 pounds of concrete worth 36 cents a pound?
7. How many doughnuts worth 12 cents each and how many worth 7 cents each are combined to produce an assortment of 3 dozen doughnuts costing $3.22?
8. A student attending a college which gives only A, B, and C grades on a 4, 3, 2 scale, respectively, is trying to compute his grade point average. For example, 3 units of A yield $3 \cdot 4 = 12$ grade points, and 4 units of C yield $4 \cdot 2 = 8$ grade points. The grade point average is the quotient of the number of grade points achieved, divided by the number of units taken. The student receives twice as many units of B as A, and 3 more units of C than of A. If his grade points totaled 54, how many units of A, B, and C did he receive? What was his grade point average?
9. On the basis of the information in Exercise 8, another student at the same school finds that she has 4 more units of B than of A, and one more unit of B than she has of C. If her total number of grade points is 45, how many units of A, B, and C did this student receive, and what was her grade point average?

10. The student association of a certain college decides to invest its building fund, since it cannot start construction of a student union for 3 more years. Some of the money is invested at 6 percent per year, and twice this amount is invested at $5\frac{1}{4}$ percent per year, yielding a total income at the end of the first year of \$825. How much money is invested at each rate?
11. A young couple (husband and wife, both working) managed to save \$8000. They decided to invest \$5000, part at $8\frac{1}{4}$ percent annual interest and part at 6 percent. If the $8\frac{1}{4}$ percent investment yielded an income of \$156 more than the 6 percent investment, how much did the couple invest at each rate?
12. A corporation invested \$100,000 in the following manner: 6 percent bonds, 8 percent stocks, and 9 percent mortgages. If the amount invested in bonds is the same as the amount invested in stocks, and if the total income per year from all three investments is \$7500, how much is invested in each of the three types of investment?
13. A businessman wishes to invest a part of \$7500 in stocks earning 10 percent dividends and the remainder in tax-exempt bonds earning 7 percent. How much must he invest in the stocks to receive an average return of 8 percent on the total amount of money?
14. At a movie theater on a Friday evening there were 420 paid admissions. If loge seats sold for \$2.50 each and general admission seats sold for \$1.75 each, how many tickets of each kind were sold if the day's receipts totaled \$817.50?
15. In constructing a state road, the county pays 40 percent as much as the state, and the city pays 65 percent as much as the county. What is the share of each for a road costing \$3071?
16. In football, a touchdown counts 6 points, a conversion 1 point, a field goal 3 points, and a safety 2 points. A team scored 49 points in a game by making the same number of safeties as field goals, 3 times as many touchdowns as field goals, and half as many conversions as touchdowns. How many scoring plays of each kind did the team make?
17. Six grams of a tranquilizer in powdered form and of normal strength is mixed with a double-strength tranquilizer to form a mixture which is 1.5 times normal strength. How many grams of the double-strength powder must be used to yield this new mixture?
18. How much water must be evaporated from a $2\frac{1}{2}$ percent salt solution weighing 50 kilos to obtain a 4 percent solution?

19. How many litres of water must be added to a 75 percent acid solution (75 percent acid and 25 percent water by volume) to obtain 100 litres of a solution that is 30 percent acid?

20. How many grams of sodium hydroxide consisting of 88 percent pure sodium hydroxide and 12 percent water are needed to make $5\frac{1}{2}$ litres of a 1 normal solution? (A 1 normal solution consists of 40 grams of sodium hydroxide per litre.)

2.9 APPLICATIONS: UNIFORM MOTION

If an object moves with a constant rate of speed, then the motion of the object is called *uniform motion*. The basic principle involved in such motion is the formula

rate × time = distance

(speed) $r \cdot t = d$

In solving problems of this type, it is useful to make a sketch illustrating the facts of the problem and also a chart organizing the facts.

EXAMPLE 1 At a certain time two trains start from the same depot and travel in opposite directions. If one travels 35 mph and the other travels 60 mph, in how many hours will they be 285 miles apart?

Solution

Chart

Formula:	r •	t =	d
One train	35	x	$35x$
Other	60	x	$60x$

See Fig. 2.9.

Equation

distance of one train + distance of other = total distance

$$35x + 60x = 285$$

$$x = 3 \text{ hours}$$

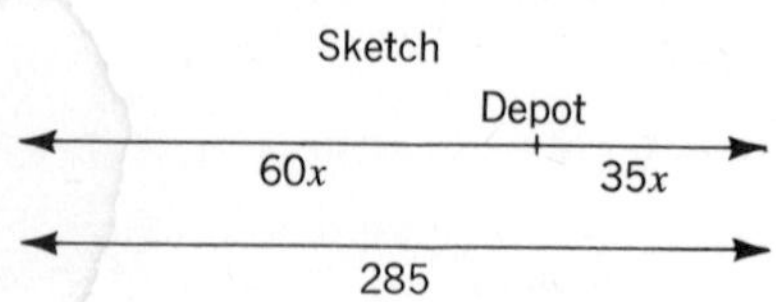

FIG. 2.9

EXAMPLE 2 A plane left an airport at 9 a.m. and traveled east at a uniform speed of 560 kph. At 10:30 a.m. a jet flying the same course left the same airport and overtook the first plane at noon. At what uniform rate did the jet fly?

Solution

Chart

Formula:	r	• t	= d
Plane	560	3	1680
Jet	x	$1\frac{1}{2}$	$\frac{3x}{2}$

FIG. 2.10

Sketch

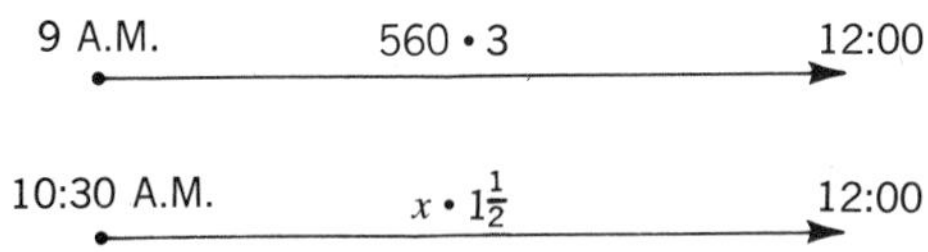

See Fig. 2.10.

Equation

distance of jet = distance of plane

$$\frac{3x}{2} = 1680$$

$$x = 1120 \text{ kph}$$

It is important when working this type of problem to keep the *units* consistent. For example, if the distance is in *miles* and the time in *hours,* then the rate must be in miles per hour. If the distance is in feet and the rate in feet per second, then the time must be expressed in seconds. If the distance is in kilometres and the time in hours, then the rate must be in kilometres per hour.

(1.) rate (miles per hour) X time = distance

EXERCISES

Solve and check Exercises 1–20.

1. A car and a motorcycle stop at a rest stop on the highway. The car travels north at 55 mph and the motorcycle goes south at 50 mph. If the two vehicles leave the rest stop at the same time, how long will it take them to be 210 miles apart?
2. How far apart will the car and the motorcycle from Exercise 1 be at the end of 40 minutes?
3. Two trains, 465 miles apart, travel toward each other, one traveling 15 mph faster than the other. They pass each other in 3 hours. What is the rate of the slower train?
4. At noon two cars leave Sacramento. One car, southbound for Fresno, travels 22 kph faster than the other car, northbound for Portland, Oregon. If the two cars are 712 kilometres apart at the end of 4 hours, find the rate of speed of each car.

5. A plane took 4 hours to fly to Chicago from San Francisco. The return trip from Chicago to San Francisco took one hour longer because strong headwinds reduced the plane's speed by 100 kph. Find the rate of the plane going to Chicago.
6. A car speeding at 80 mph is 3 miles beyond a police car when the police car starts in pursuit at 90 mph. How long does it take the police car to overtake the speeding car?
7. Two men drive from Los Angeles to San Francisco by different routes. The journey is 630 kilometres by one route and 585 kilometres by the other route. The man taking the shorter route drives 15 kph faster than the second man, and arrives in San Francisco $6\frac{1}{2}$ hours after leaving Los Angeles. How long does it take the second man to get from Los Angeles to San Francisco?
8. At 8 a.m. a truck leaves a depot, traveling west at 45 mph. Two hours later a car starts from the same depot and travels at 60 mph until it overtakes the truck. At what clock time does the car overtake the truck? (It is assumed that the truck driver does not stop for lunch.)
9. Two planes leave an airport at the same time and travel in opposite directions. One plane travels 80 mph faster than the other plane. What is the rate of each plane if the planes are 2190 miles apart at the end of 3 hours?
10. At 6 a.m. two trains leave the same depot and travel in opposite directions. They are 972 kilometres apart at the end of 6 hours. Find the rate of each train if one travels 18 kph slower than the other.
11. A police car moving at 60 mph pursues a traffic offender driving at 40 mph. If the offender was 0.5 mile ahead when the police car started, how long does it take for the police car to overtake the offender?
12. A fisherman drove from his home to a mountain lake in 4 hours. Returning by the same route, he took 1 hour longer because heavy traffic forced him to drive 12 kph slower. Find his average rate going to the lake.
13. A passenger train and a freight train leave the same station at the same time and travel in opposite directions. The average rate of the passenger train is 20 mph faster than the freight train. The trains are 520 miles apart at the end of 5 hours. Find the average rate of each train.
14. A Coast Guard boat averaging 30 mph starts one-half hour later from the same dock to overtake another boat, moving at 18 mph. How long does it take the Coast Guard boat?
15. How far can a boat travel out to sea at 30 mph and return at 20 mph if the boat has just enough fuel for a 6-hour trip?

16. A man walks from his home into the countryside at 4 mph. He visits with friends for an hour and they drive him home, at a rate of 36 mph. If the man returns 6 hours after he started, how far from his home is his friend's house?
17. A couple attends an out-of-town wedding. The trip to the wedding takes 3 hours, the wedding and reception last 2 hours, and as a result of the celebration, the trip home takes 4 hours, at a rate of 15 mph less than the going rate. What was the couple's rate of travel on the way home?
18. Mr. Lately has a business appointment in Redding, California. He leaves Sacramento, a town 225 kilometres south of Redding, and drives at a rate of 75 kph. Suddenly he realizes that he will be late if he does not speed up, so he increases his rate to 90 kph. If his total driving time is 2 hours and 50 minutes, how far did he travel at 75 kph?
19. A ship is heading due west out of San Francisco at a rate of 35 mph (*not* knots). A passenger on board realizes he has forgotten to bring his medicine. A helicopter, flying at a rate of 95 mph, is sent to deliver the medicine to the ship. If the helicopter starts out when the ship has been underway for 6 hours, how far from San Francisco is the ship when the helicopter reaches it?
20. Jim's home town is 340 miles from his college. Jim leaves college at 8 a.m. to drive home for Christmas vacation. His girlfriend, Debbie, who lives in his home town, decides to drive to meet him. Debbie leaves at 11 a.m. and drives along the same highway as Jim. If Jim drives 10 mph faster than Debbie and they meet at noon, what was Jim's speed?

REVIEW EXERCISES

Solve and check the equations in Exercises 1–40.

1. $x + 7 = 12$
2. $3x - 2 = 13$
3. $2 - 3x = 23$
4. $x + 7 = x - 3$
5. $x + 7 = 3 - x$
6. $5x = 2x + 6$
7. $3x = 8x - 20$
8. $5x - (x - 2) = 18$
9. $6x + 7 - 5x = 2$
10. $2x - 5 = 7$
11. $x + 5 = -7$
12. $3x + 2 = x + 4$
13. $5 - 2y = 15$
14. $3 + 4x - 2 = 4 + 2x$
15. $2(x - 4) = 3x - 16$
16. $3(y + 2) + 4 = 5y - 2$
17. $4 - (3x + 8) = 17$
18. $5(z - 1) - (1 - 4z) = 30$
19. $5t + 7t - 2 = 5 + 7 - 2t$
20. $x + 2 = x + 3$
21. $2(x - 5) = 2x - 10$
22. $6 - \dfrac{x + 2}{3} = 4$
23. $4 = 2x + 3$
24. $4x - (x - 5) = 4 - (x + 7)$

25. $0 = \frac{x+5}{2}$

26. $7x - 5(x-2) = 20$

27. $9 - 6(2-x) = 7x$

28. $x + 4 = 2x - 3$

29. $z + 1 = z$

30. $3 - x = x - 3$

31. $4(x+3) = 12$

32. $2(x-3) - 3(x+1) = 0$

33. $y - 2 = 2 - y$

34. $4 - 3(x+2) = 7$

35. $3(x+2) = 3x + 6$

36. $0 = 2(x+5)$

37. $\frac{t+7}{2} = 5$

38. $5 - \frac{x+3}{2} = 6$

39. $2(x-3) + 3(x+2) = x + 8$

40. $x - 3[x - 3(x-3)] = 1$

Solve the equations in Exercises 41–60 for the specified variables.

41. $3x - y = 5;\ y$

42. $3x - y = 5;\ x$

43. $2x + 5 + y = 0;\ y$

44. $2x + 5 + y = 0;\ x$

45. $5x - 2y = 10;\ x$

46. $5x - 2y = 10;\ y$

47. $y = 3x + 2;\ x$

48. $x = 3y + 2;\ y$

49. $ax + by = c;\ y$

50. $ax + by = c;\ x$

51. $C = \pi d;\ d$

52. $A = P + Prt;\ t$

53. $P = x + y + z;\ y$

54. $S = 2a + 2b;\ b$

55. $R = \frac{g}{T-t};\ t$

56. $M = n(n + 2d);\ d$

57. $B = 15 - \frac{A}{2};\ A$

58. $W - 5H + 190 = 0;\ H$

59. $A + 2B - 3C = 20;\ B$

60. $A + 2B - 3C = 20;\ C$

Solve and check Exercises 61–69.

61. Six more than twice a number is equal to 5 times the difference obtained when 3 is subtracted from the number. Find the number.

62. A bus and a train leave the same station at the same time and both travel north. The rate of the train is 15 kph less than twice the rate of the bus. At the end of 3 hours, the train is 135 kilometres farther north than the bus. Find the rate of each.

63. How many grams of copper must be added to 18 grams of an alloy composed of 40 percent copper to make an alloy composed of 50 percent copper?

64. How much paint is required to paint 3 walls of a room if each wall is a rectangle with a length 2 feet less than twice the height? The perimeter of each wall is 50 feet and one gallon of paint covers about 400 square feet.

65. A woman paid \$2.21 for some fruit consisting of peaches costing 29 cents a pound, plums at 25 cents a pound, and bananas at 10 cents a pound. If she bought twice as many pounds of plums as peaches, and one pound less bananas than plums, how many pounds of each kind of fruit did she buy?

REVIEW EXERCISES

66. A corner lot has the shape of a right triangle (one angle is 90 degrees). The sides forming the 90-degree angle are along the streets, and one of these sides is 11 feet longer than the other side. To widen the street along the longer side, a strip 10 feet wide is removed from the lot, thus reducing the length of this side by 11 feet. The area of the lot was decreased by 2310 square feet. Find the original length of the shorter side along the street.

67. During an average life of 70 years, it is estimated that a person sleeps 3 years more than he works; that he spends one-half the years he works on recreation and church functions; 7 years eating and drinking; 5 years traveling, 2 years dressing, and 3 years being ill. How many years does he work?

68. A person traveling on a plane is allowed 20 kilos of baggage free but must pay \$1.50 per kilo for all excess baggage. A wife had 5 kilos of baggage more than her husband had. Together they paid \$28.50 for excess baggage. How much baggage did each have?

69. A rush order is received in Boomtown for some machine parts that must be delivered from Bolttown, 280 miles away. To speed the delivery, a station wagon traveling 65 mph leaves Boomtown at 11 a.m. to intercept the delivery truck traveling 50 mph. If the delivery truck left Bolttown at 10 a.m., at what clock time is the delivery truck intercepted?

In Exercises 70–75, solve and graph on a number line.

70. $3x + 5 > x - 3$

71. $5 - x \leq x - 5$

72. $0 \leq 4x - 12$

73. $2x + 3 - x < 5 + x$

74. $2x + 3 > 5 + 2x$

75. $12 \geq -3(4x - 2)$

3 OPERATIONS ON POLYNOMIALS

A fundamental concept in the study of algebra is the class of algebraic expressions known as polynomials. The applications of polynomials to real-world situations are too numerous to list. For instance, the distance a missile travels when thrown into the air and allowed to fall back to earth can be expressed in terms of a polynomial; so can the velocity of the same missile, and its acceleration. In business, revenue obtained from the sale of a commodity is often expressed by a polynomial, and so are marginal revenue, supply and demand, efficiency of investment, and so forth. A study of any of the fields of application of mathematics will surely convince you of the importance of polynomials.

It is the object of this chapter to introduce polynomials, to define operations on polynomials, to present some basic factoring techniques, and to show the solution of factorable quadratic equations in one variable.

3.1 PRODUCTS OF MONOMIALS

DEFINITION

A **monomial** is:

1. A constant;
2. A term of the form cx^n,
   where c is a constant, x is a variable, and n is a natural number; or
3. A product of terms as described in (2).

Each of the following is an example of a monomial:

$3,\ x^2,\ 5x^3,\ \sqrt{2}xy,\ x^2y^9,\ \frac{1}{2}xyz^5$

$\sqrt{x}$ is *not* a monomial; neither is $\frac{1}{x}, \frac{5}{x^2}$, or any other term which does not fit the description of being a constant or of the form cx^n, where c is constant and n is a natural number.

A monomial that has only one variable is called a **monomial in one variable.** For example, $3x$, $15x^3$, and $-2y^2$ are each a monomial in one variable. The monomial $4x^2y^3$ is not a monomial in one variable but a **monomial in two variables.**

A definition is needed here to explain what is meant by x^n, where n is a natural number. In Chapter 1 the operation "raising to a power" was discussed. For example,

$x^2 = x \cdot x$
$x^3 = x \cdot x \cdot x$

DEFINITION OF x^n

If x is a real number and n is a natural number, then

$$x^1 = x \text{ and } x^n = \overbrace{x \cdot x \cdot x \cdot \ .\ .\ .\ \cdot x}^{n \text{ factors}} \text{ if } n > 1$$

EXAMPLE 1 $x^2 \cdot x^3 = (x \cdot x) \cdot (x \cdot x \cdot x)$
$= x \cdot x \cdot x \cdot x \cdot x$
$= x^5$

EXAMPLE 2
$3x^2 \cdot 2x^3 = (3 \cdot x \cdot x) \cdot (2 \cdot x \cdot x \cdot x)$
$= (3 \cdot 2) \cdot (x \cdot x \cdot x \cdot x \cdot x)$ (Associative and commutative axioms, multiplication)
$= 6x^5$

The preceding examples lead to the following theorem.

THE FIRST THEOREM OF EXPONENTS

The product of two powers having the same base is a power whose base is this common base and whose exponent is the sum of the exponents. In symbols, $x^m x^n = x^{m+n}$.

EXAMPLE 3 $x^2 \cdot x^3 = x^{2+3} = x^5$

EXAMPLE 4 $3x^2 \cdot 2x^3 = (3 \cdot 2) \cdot (x^2 \cdot x^3) = 6(x^{2+3}) = 6x^5$

EXAMPLE 5 $3^2 \cdot 3^3 = 3^{2+3} = 3^5 = 243$

EXAMPLE 6 $2^3 \cdot 3^2 \cdot 2^4 = 2^{3+4} \cdot 3^2 = 2^7 \cdot 3^2$

$$= 128 \cdot 9$$
$$= 1152$$

It should be emphasized that the variable need not be the letter x but can be any letter that designates a real number.

EXAMPLE 7 $y^5 \cdot y^9 = y^{5+9} = y^{14}$

EXAMPLE 8 $5z^2 \cdot 6z = 5 \cdot 6 \cdot z^2 \cdot z = 30z^{2+1} = 30z^3$

Now consider raising a power to a power. For example,

$$(x^3)^2$$

By the definition of x^n,

$$(x^3)^2 = x^3 \cdot x^3$$

and by the first theorem of exponents,

$$x^3 \cdot x^3 = x^{3+3} = x^6$$

Therefore, $(x^3)^2 = x^6$. Also,

$$(x^2)^4 = x^2 \cdot x^2 \cdot x^2 \cdot x^2 = x^{2+2+2+2} = x^{4 \cdot 2} = x^8$$

The problem of raising a power to a power can be generalized by the following theorem of exponents:

THE SECOND THEOREM OF EXPONENTS

The power of a power is a power having the same base and an exponent that is the product of the exponents. In symbols, $(x^m)^n = x^{mn}$.

EXAMPLE 9 $(2^3)^2 = 2^6 = 64$

EXAMPLE 10 $(x^3)^4 = x^{3 \cdot 4} = x^{12}$

Note: Because multiplication is commutative, $x^{mn} = x^{nm}$; therefore, $(x^m)^n = (x^n)^m$.

EXAMPLE 11 $(y^5)^m = y^{5m}$, m is a natural number.

Use caution when applying the first theorem of exponents. For example, $5x^2 \cdot 7y^3 = 35x^2y^3$.

The theorem does not apply to the variables x and y, since they are different. However, the following example illustrates that the theorem *may* be used for monomials in more than one variable when it applies.

EXAMPLE 12 $(5x^2yz^3)(3xy^4) = 15x^2xyy^4z^3$
$= 15x^3y^5z^3$

EXERCISES

Simplify Exercises 1–40.

1. $z^3 \cdot z^4$
2. $5y \cdot y^3$
3. $3x^2 \cdot 4x^4$
4. $7a \cdot 5a^5$
5. $x^3 \cdot x^2$
6. $3x \cdot x^4$
7. $2y^2 \cdot 3y^4$
8. $5z^2 \cdot 7z^9$
9. $(-2x^4)(3x^2)$
10. $(-x^{11})(-5x^2)$
11. $\left(\frac{1}{2}y^3\right)(4y^5)$
12. $(x^2)(3x)(-x^3)$
13. $(-4x^3)(6x^2)$
14. $(-y^5)(-3y^2)$
15. $(-a^2)(-a)(-a^3)$
16. $(ab)(-a^2b)$
17. $(x^2)(-3x)(5x^4)$
18. $(x^2y)(2xy^2)$
19. $(3ab)(-2a)(-4b)$
20. $(rst)(rs)(st)$
21. $(-z)(-z^2)(-z^3)$
22. $(xy^2)(3xy)$
23. $(5xz)(3x^2y)$
24. $(abc)(a^2b^2c^2)$
25. $(x^2)^4$
26. $(x^4)^2$
27. $(x^3)^2$
28. $(x^2)^3$
29. $5(z^2)^3$
30. $x(x^2)^3$
31. $(y^3)^4$
32. $(x^3)^2 \cdot x^2$
33. $xy(y^2)^5$
34. $(-x)^2$
35. $(-x^2)^3$
36. $(2xy)(xz^2)(-yz)$
37. $ab(b^4)^5$
38. $(-y^2)^2$
39. $-(y^2)^2$
40. $2(-3x)(xy)(y^2)^4$

In Exercises 41–54, use the first or second theorem of exponents to simplify each expression.

41. $2^3 \cdot 2^2$
42. $3^3 \cdot 3^2$
43. $(2^2)^3$
44. $(3^3)^2$
45. $(3^2)^3$
46. $(-2^2)^3$
47. $[(-2)^2]^3$
48. $(-2)^3(-2)^2$
49. $4^2 \cdot 4$
50. $4^2 \cdot 4^3$
51. $3 \cdot 3^2$
52. $5^2 \cdot 5$
53. $4^2 \cdot 2^3$
54. $9 \cdot 3^3$

Use the first or second theorem of exponents to simplify the expressions in Exercises 55–74. Assume all exponents to be natural numbers.

55. $x^3 \cdot x^a$
56. $5y \cdot y^m$
57. $(x^a)^b$
58. $x^{2a}y^a \cdot x^a y^2$
59. $x^2 \cdot x^m$
60. $2x^p \cdot x^q$
61. $(x^3)^n$
62. $(x^n)^3$
63. $x^n y^m \cdot xy^{2n}$
64. $y^{n+1}y^{n-1}$
65. $x^b(xy^2)$
66. $(rs^2)(r^a s^a)$
67. $t^{n+2}t^{n-3}$
68. $(y^3)^b(z^b)^2$
69. $[(y^p)^q]^2$
70. $(x^2)^{3n}(x^{2n})^3$
71. $(rt^k)(r^k t^k)$
72. $(r^{n-1}t^n)(rt^{n-2})$
73. $(x^n)^2(y^2)^n$
74. $[(t^a)^b]^c$

3.2 SUMS AND DIFFERENCES OF POLYNOMIALS

DEFINITION

A **polynomial** is a monomial or an algebraic sum of monomials.

EXAMPLE 1 Each of the following is an example of a polynomial:

a. $x^2 + 3x + 2$ is a polynomial in one variable.
b. $15y^9 - y$ is a polynomial in one variable.
c. $x^2 - 3xy + 2y^2$ *is a polynomial in two variables.*
d. $9x^5 - 3x^4 + 2x^2 + 5x - 1$ is a polynomial in one variable.
e. $x^2 + y^2 + z^2 - 4xyz$ is a polynomial in three variables.

Some common types of polynomials have special names. A **monomial** is a polynomial of one term, a **binomial** is a polynomial of two terms, and a **trinomial** is a polynomial of three terms.

Each of the following is an example of a binomial:
$x + 1$, $3y^2 + y$, $-5x^2 - 2$, $a + b$, $x^2 - y^2$

Each of the following is an example of a trinomial:
$x^2 + 2x + 1$, $5y^3 - 3y + 2$, $a + b + c$, $x^2 - 6xy + 9y^2$

Polynomials are added or subtracted by using the commutative and associative axioms to rearrange the terms and by using the distributive axiom to combine similar terms.

EXAMPLE 2 Add $8x^2 - 5x + 7$ to $x^2 + 3x - 4$.

Solution

$$
\begin{aligned}
& (8x^2 - 5x + 7) + (x^2 + 3x - 4) \\
&= (8x^2 + x^2) + (-5x + 3x) + (7 - 4) \\
&= (8 + 1)x^2 + (-5 + 3)x + (7 - 4) \\
&= 9x^2 - 2x + 3
\end{aligned}
$$

Most of these steps can be performed mentally, and, as a rule, the final result can be written immediately after inspection of the problem.

EXAMPLE 3 Simplify by performing the indicated operations: $(4x + 8y + 9) + (3x - 9y - 2)$.

Solution $(4x + 8y + 9) + (3x - 9y - 2) = 7x - y + 7$

To subtract one polynomial from another, the subtraction problem must be changed to an addition problem by using the definition of subtraction: $r - s = r + (-s)$.

It is important to remember that the sign of each term of the subtrahend must be changed, as shown in the following example.

EXAMPLE 4 Subtract $4x^2 + xy - 6y^2$ from $2x^2 + 3xy - 9y^2$.

Solution

$(2x^2 + 3xy - 9y^2) - (4x^2 + xy - 6y^2)$ (Recalling that "subtract a from b" is translated as "$b - a$")

$= (2x^2 + 3xy - 9y^2) + (-4x^2 - xy + 6y^2)$ (Using the definition of subtraction)

$= (2x^2 - 4x^2) + (3xy - xy) + (-9y^2 + 6y^2)$ (Using the associative and commutative axioms several times)

$= (2 - 4)x^2 + (3 - 1)xy + (-9 + 6)y^2$ (Using the distributive axiom)

$= -2x^2 + 2xy - 3y^2$

Again, it is usually possible to write the final result immediately after inspection of the problem. Thus, by performing much of the work mentally, the solution would be written as illustrated in Example 5.

EXAMPLE 5 Subtract $5x - 2y + 4$ from $-3x + 2y + 4$.

Solution

$$
\begin{aligned}
& (-3x + 2y + 4) - (5x + 2y + 4) \\
&= (-3x + 2y + 4) + (-5x + 2y - 4) \\
&= -8x + 4y
\end{aligned}
$$

It is quite simple to check the addition or subtraction of polynomials by assigning a value to each variable.

EXAMPLE 6 Check the result of Example 5 by letting $x = 3$ and $y = 4$.

Solution If $x = 3$ and $y = 4$,

$$5x - 2y + 4 = 5(3) - 2(4) + 4$$
$$= 15 - 8 + 4 = 11$$
$$-3x + 2y + 4 = -3(3) + 2(4) + 4$$
$$= -9 + 8 + 4 - 3$$

Now

$$(-3x + 2y + 4) - (5x - 2y + 4) = 3 - 11 = -8$$

and

$$-8x + 4y = -8(3) + 4(4) = -24 + 16 = -8$$

Therefore, for $x = 3$ and $y = 4$,

$$(-3x + 2y + 4) - (5x - 2y + 4) = -8x + 4y$$

From the check in Example 6 it is reasonable to conclude that $-8x + 4y$ is the correct difference for Example 5. However, there is a danger involved. Special values of the variables may produce a "check" even though the answer is wrong. This can usually be prevented by avoiding the use of the special numbers 0, 1, and -1 as replacement values.

It is conventional to express a polynomial in **descending powers** of a variable. This means that the term containing the highest power of the variable is written first, at the left; the next highest power is written second; and so on, with the lowest power written last, at the right. For example,

$$5x^4 - 6x^3 - 2x^2 + 8x - 4$$

is written in descending powers of the variable x. As another example,

$$y^3 + 3y^2z - z^4$$

is written in descending powers of the variable y.

If the order just described is reversed, then the polynomial is said to be written in **ascending powers** of the variable. For example,

$$1 - 2x - x^2$$

is written in ascending powers of the variable x.

Some problems are more easily done if each polynomial in the problem is arranged in either descending powers of a variable or ascending powers of a variable.

EXAMPLE 7 Simplify $(3y - 6 - 2y^2) + (5y^2 + 9 - 2y)$.

Solution First rearrange each polynomial in descending powers of the variable y:

$$(3y - 6 - 2y^2) + (5y^2 + 9 - 2y)$$
$$= (-2y^2 + 3y - 6) + (5y^2 - 2y + 9)$$

and then combine like terms:

$$= (-2y^2 + 5y^2) + (3y - 2y) + (-6 + 9)$$
$$= 3y^2 + y + 3$$

EXERCISES

Simplify the expressions in Exercises 1–20.

1. $(3x^2 + 2x) + (4x^2 + 3x + 1)$
2. $(y^2 + 3) - (y^3 - 1)$
3. $(x^3 + 2x - 1) + (x^2 + 3x + 2)$
4. $(4z^2 + 2z + 6) + (3z^2 + 5z + 9)$
5. $(2x^2 + y - z) + (3x - y + 2z)$
6. $(7x^2 - 5x + 2) + (x^2 + x - 6)$
7. $(3a + 5b - 7) + (2a - 5b + 7)$
8. $(-2x - 3y - 4) + (2x - 3y - 4)$
9. $3(2a - 5) + 4(7 - 3a)$
10. $(5y^2 - 6y + 9) + (5y - 8 - 4y^2)$
11. $(2a - b - c) - (a + b + c)$
12. $(-r - s + t) + (r + s + t)$
13. $(8 - 2x + y) - (9 - 2x + y)$
14. $(1 + x - x^2) - (2 - x^2 + x^4)$
15. $3(2a - b) - 4(b - 2a)$
16. $(y^2 + 6y + 9) - (y^2 - 4y + 4)$
17. $(25x^4 - 10x^2 + 1) - (9x^2 + 6x + 1)$
18. $(x^3 - x^2 + x) + (x^2 - x + 1)$
19. $[(x^2 + xy + y^2) - (x^2 - xy - y^2)] - (3x^2 + 2xy - y^2)$
20. $(a - b + c) - [(a + b - c) - (a - b - c)]$

In Exercises 21–40, perform the operations as directed.

21. Add $3x^2 + 5 - x$, $x - 8$, $x^2 + 4$. Check, using $x = 6$.
22. Subtract $2a^2 - 5b^2 - 4$ from $a^2 - b^2 + 1$. Check, using $a = 3$, $b = 2$.
23. From $-t^2 - 3t - 5$ subtract $-t^2 - 5t + 4$. Check, using $t = 5$.
24. Find the sum of $c^3 - 3c^2 - c - 7$ and $4c - 3c^2 - 6c^3 + 6$. Check, using $c = 1$.
25. Find the sum of $x^3 - 3x^2 + x - 5$ and $x^2 - 3x + 4$. Check, using $x = 2$.
26. From the sum of $3x^2 + 5x + 9$ and $x^2 - 7x + 14$ subtract $2x^2 - 3x + 5$.
27. Subtract $3a^2 + 5ab - 6b^2$ from the sum of $2a^2 - 3ab + 4b^2$ and $5ab - 6b^2$.
28. Add $4 - 3x^2$, $2 + 3x + 8x^2$, $3 - 2x^2 - 5x$. Check, using $x = 3$.
29. From $4a + 2b - 4c$ subtract $3a - 3b - 3c$. Check, using $a = 2$, $b = 3$, $c = 5$.
30. Subtract $2y^3 - 5y^2 - 3y + 9$ from $-4y^3 - 3y^2 - 4$. Check, using $y = 4$.
31. Subtract $2x^2 - 6$ from the sum of $-3x^2 + 5x$ and $4 - 7x$. Check, using $x = 1$.
32. Find the number that must be added to $2x^2 - 3xy - y^2$ to obtain $y^2 + xy + x^2$. Check, using $x = 5$, $y = 1$.
33. Subtract $x^3 - 17x + 1$ from the sum of $x^4 + 3x^3 - x^2 + 2$ and $5x^4 - x^3 + 4x - 7$.

34. From the sum of $a^2 + 3ab + 4b^2$ and $2a^2 - 4ab + 5b^2$ subtract $3a^2 - 7ab + 8b^2$.

35. Subtract the sum of $x^4 + 3x^2 + 2$ and $2x^4 - 5x^3 + x^2 - 1$ from $6x^3 - 7x^2 + x$.

36. From $2x^3 - 4x^2y + 8xy^2 + 11y^3$ subtract the sum of $x^3 + y^3$ and $3x^2y - 5xy^2 - 7y^3$.

37. Find the sum of $a^3 + b^3 - a^2b + ab^2$, $a^2b + b^3 - 3a^3$, and $b^3 - 5ab^2 + a^2b$.

38. From $x^3 - x^2 - 3x + 2$ subtract the sum of $x^4 + 5x - 1$ and $x^3 + 3x^2 - 6x + 2$.

39. Subtract the sum of $x^3 + 2x^2y - xy^2 + y^3$ and $5x^2y + 6xy^2 - 2y^3$ from $4x^3 - 3x^2y + 3xy^2 + 4$.

40. Find the sum of $a^3 - 3a^2b + 5ab^2 - b^3$, $2a^3 + 5a^2b - 2ab^2$, and $6a^2b + 15ab^2 - 9b^3$.

3.3 PRODUCTS OF POLYNOMIALS

In order to find the products of polynomials, the distributive axiom is used. It is restated below for emphasis.

THE DISTRIBUTIVE AXIOM

If r, s, and t are real numbers, then

$$r(s + t) = rs + rt$$

This axiom can be applied for multiplying a monomial by a binomial, and it can be extended to multiplying a binomial by a binomial, a monomial by a trinomial, and so on.

When parentheses are removed in the multiplication of a polynomial by a monomial, it is important to remember that each term of the polynomial must be multiplied by the monomial.

EXAMPLE 1 Multiply $x(2x^2 + 1)$.

Solution $x(2x^2 + 1) = x \cdot 2x^2 + x \cdot 1$ (Distributive axiom)

$= 2x^3 + x$

Therefore

$$x(2x^2 + 1) = 2x^3 + x$$

EXAMPLE 2 Multiply $3x^3(2x^2 + 4x)$.

Solution $3x^3(2x^2 + 4x) = 3x^3 \cdot 2x^2 + 3x^3 \cdot 4x$

$= 6x^5 + 12x^4$

3.3 PRODUCTS OF POLYNOMIALS

The product of a polynomial multiplied by a polynomial is obtained by applying the distributive axiom several times.

EXAMPLE 3 Multiply $(2x+5)(3x+2)$.

Solution $(2x+5)(3x+2)$

$= (2x+5)(3x) + (2x+5)(2)$	(Distributive axiom)
$= 3x(2x+5) + 2(2x+5)$	(Commutative axiom)
$= 6x^2 + 15x + 4x + 10$	(Distributive axiom)
$= 6x^2 + 19x + 10$	(Distributive axiom)

EXAMPLE 4 Write $(x^2+2)(3x^2+x+1)$ as a single polynomial (multiply).

Solution $(x^2+2)(3x^2+x+1)$

$$= (x^2+2)(3x^2) + (x^2+2)(x) + (x^2+2)(1)$$
$$= 3x^4 + 6x^2 + x^3 + 2x + x^2 + 2$$
$$= 3x^4 + x^3 + 7x^2 + 2x + 2$$

Note that the answer was stated in descending powers of the variable—that is, the variable was arranged so that the first term had the largest exponent, the second term the next largest exponent, and so on, with the constant term last. This rearrangement can be done because of the commutative and associative properties of addition of real numbers, and it makes the answer easier to check.

Sometimes it is convenient to arrange the polynomials to be multiplied in vertical order rather than horizontal order, as shown in the following example.

EXAMPLE 5 Multiply $3x^2 + 2x + 4$ by $4x^2 - x + 1$.

Solution

$$\begin{array}{rrrrr} & & 3x^2 & +2x & +4 \\ & & 4x^2 & -\ x & +1 \\ \hline 12x^4 & +8x^3 & +16x^2 & & \\ & -3x^3 & -\ 2x^2 & -4x & \\ & & +\ 3x^2 & +2x & +4 \\ \hline 12x^4 & +5x^3 & +17x^2 & -2x & +4 \end{array}$$

(Multiply top row by $4x^2$)
(Multiply top row by $-x$)
(Multiply top row by $+1$)
(Combine like terms)

EXERCISES

Multiply in Exercises 1–14.

1. $x(x-4)$
2. $x(x+3)$
3. $x^2(3x-1)$
4. $y^2(2y-3)$
5. $a(3a^2+a+2)$
6. $b(4b^2-3b+1)$
7. $2xy^2(x^2y-2xy+y^2)$
8. $-x^3(x^2-3x+2)$
9. $-y^2(3y^2-xy+2x^2)$
10. $z^3(x^3+xy^2z-y^3z^2)$
11. $-3z^2(2z^3-4z^2+z-3)$
12. $5xy(x^2+2xy-y^2)$
13. $x^2y(3x^3-2x^2y+xy^2-y^3)$
14. $5x^2(x^3+3xy+y^2-1)$

In Exercises 15–48 multiply and arrange in descending powers of x.

15. $(x+3)(x+5)$
16. $(x-3)(x+5)$
17. $(x+3)(x-5)$
18. $(x-3)(x-5)$
19. $(2x+1)(5x+2)$
20. $(2x+1)(5x-2)$
21. $(2x-1)(5x+2)$
22. $(2x-1)(5x-2)$
23. $(4x-1)(5x-3)$
24. $(2x+5)(x-3)$
25. $(x+5)(2x-3)$
26. $(2x+3)(3x-2)$
27. $(x-5)(2x+3)$
28. $(2x-3)(3x+2)$
29. $(x^2+3)(x^2-5)$
30. $(x^2-2)(x^2-4)$
31. $(2x^2-3)(3x^2-2)$
32. $(2x^2+5)(5x^2-2)$
33. $x(x+1)(x+2)$
34. $x(x-1)(x-2)$
35. $x(2x+1)(3x-1)$
36. $x(3x+1)(5x+2)$
37. $(2x^2+3x+1)(x+3)$
38. $(x^2+3x+1)(x+2)$
39. $(3x^2-x+1)(2x-1)$
40. $x^2(x+1)(x-2)$
41. $(x+2)^2$
42. $(x-3)^2$
43. $(x-3)(x+3)$
44. $(x-1)(x+1)$
45. $(5x-7)(5x+7)$
46. $(3x-2)(3x+2)$
47. $(x^2-2)(x^2+2)$
48. $(x^2+3)(x^2-3)$
49. $x(x+3)^2$
50. $x(2x+1)^2$

In Exercises 51–76 multiply and express each answer as a simplified polynomial.

51. $2x(x^2-7)(x^2+7)$
52. $-5y(y+9)(y-9)$
53. $-xy(10x-3y)(10x+3y)$
54. $(x+2)(x+2)^2$
55. $(y-5)^3$
56. $(4x+3y)^3$
57. $(x-6)(x^2+6x+36)$
58. $(2x+5y)(4x^2-10xy+25y^2)$
59. $(x+y)(x-y)(x^2+y^2)$
60. $(2-x^2)(x^2+2)(x^4+4)$
61. $(ab+1)^3$
62. $[(x+1)+y][(x+1)-y]$
63. $(a-b-4)(a-b+4)$
64. $(x+y-5)(5+x-y)$
65. $(x+y+z+3)(x-z+y-3)$
66. $(x+y+z)^2$
67. $(a-b+c)^2$
68. $(x^n+1)(x^n-1)$
69. $(y^{2n}-1)(y^n+1)$
70. $a^n(a^2-2ab-b^2)$
71. $x(x^{2a}+x^a+1)$
72. $x^n(x^{2n+1}-x^n)$
73. $(x^n+1)(x^{2n}-x^n-3)$
74. $(x^n+2)(x^n-2)$
75. $(x^a+3)^2$
76. $(y^b-2)^2$

3.4 SPECIAL PRODUCTS

You may have made some interesting observations concerning certain products in the preceding exercise set. Some of these products occur frequently enough to deserve special attention.

SPECIAL PRODUCTS

1. The Square of a Binomial: $(A+B)^2 = A^2 + 2AB + B^2$
$(A-B)^2 = A^2 - 2AB + B^2$

2. The Cube of a Binomial: $(A+B)^3 = A^3 + 3A^2B + 3AB^2 + B^3$
$(A-B)^3 = A^3 - 3A^2B + 3AB^2 - B^3$

3. The Difference of Squares: $(A-B)(A+B) = A^2 - B^2$

EXAMPLE 1 Find the product $(x+5)^2$.

Solution This fits the form of a square of a binomial where $A = x$ and $B = 5$. Thus

$$(A+B)^2 = A^2 + 2AB + B^2$$
$$(x+5)^2 = x^2 + 2(x)(5) + 5^2$$
$$= x^2 + 10x + 25$$

EXAMPLE 2 Expand $(3x-1)^2$.

Solution To "expand" means to multiply. Consider

$$(A-B)^2 = A^2 - 2AB + B^2$$

The expanded result is a trinomial. The first term, A^2, is the square of the first term of the binomial $A - B$. The middle term of the trinomial, $2AB$, is equal to twice the product of the first and second terms of the binomial $A - B$. The third term, B^2, is the square of the last term of the binomial $A - B$. Thus

$$(3x-1)^2 = (3x)^2 - 2(3x)(1) + (1)^2$$
$$= 9x^2 - 6x + 1$$

This result can be checked by multiplying

$$(3x-1)(3x-1) = 3x(3x-1) - 1(3x-1)$$
$$= 9x^2 - 3x - 3x + 1$$
$$= 9x^2 - 6x + 1$$

EXAMPLE 3 Expand $(y-2)^3$.

Solution Using the form of a cube of a binomial where $A = y$ and $B = 2$,

$$(A-B)^3 = A^3 - 3A^2B + 3AB^2 - B^3$$
$$(y-2)^3 = y^3 - 3y^2(2) + 3(2)^2y = (2)^3$$
$$= y^3 - 6y^2 + 12y - 8$$

EXAMPLE 4 Expand $(2b + 1)^3$.

Solution This time the form of a cube of a binomial is used with $A = 2b$ and $B = 1$:

$$\begin{aligned}(2b + 1)^3 &= (2b)^3 + 3(2b)^2(1) + 3(2b)(1)^2 + (1)^3\\ &= 8b^3 + 12b^2 + 6b + 1\end{aligned}$$

EXAMPLE 5 Expand $(x - 3)(x + 3)$.

Solution The binomials to be multiplied are identical except for the middle sign. The form to recognize is the difference of squares form, $A^2 - B^2$, with $A = x$, $B = 3$. Thus

$$\begin{aligned}(A - B)(A + B) &= A^2 - B^2\\ (x - 3)(x + 3) &= x^2 - (3)^2\\ &= x^2 - 9\end{aligned}$$

EXAMPLE 6 Expand $(2y - 5)(2y + 5)$.

Solution Again the difference of squares form may be recognized, with $A = 2y$ and $B = 5$.
Thus

$$\begin{aligned}(2y - 5)(2y + 5) &= (2y)^2 - (5)^2\\ &= 4y^2 - 25\end{aligned}$$

By learning these forms and applying them, special products can be obtained more rapidly than by the longer multiplication method used previously.

A resulting product can be quickly checked by assigning a value to each variable.

EXAMPLE 7 Check that $(2x + 5)^2 = 4x^2 + 20x + 25$ by letting $x = 3$.

Solution For $x = 3$.

$$\begin{aligned}(2x + 5)^2 &= (2[3] + 5)^2 = (6 + 5)^2\\ &= (11)^2 = 121\end{aligned}$$

Check

$$\begin{aligned}4x^2 + 20x + 25 &= 4(3)^2 + 20(3) + 25\\ &= 36 + 60 + 25 = 121\end{aligned}$$

EXERCISES

Expand the products in Exercises 1–50 by using one of the special product forms.

1. $(x + 2)^2$ **2.** $(x + 3)^2$
3. $(x - 2)^2$ **4.** $(x - 3)^2$
5. $(x + 4)^2$ **6.** $(x - 4)^2$
7. $(3x + 1)^2$ **8.** $(3x - 1)^2$
9. $(2x - 3)^2$ **10.** $(2x + 3)^2$

11. $(4x + 5)^2$
12. $(4x - 5)^2$
13. $(3 - x)^2$
14. $(5 - 2x)^2$
15. $(2 + 7x)^2$
16. $(8 - b)^2$
17. $(4 + 3a)^2$
18. $(3 - 2y)^2$
19. $(x + y)^2$
20. $(x - y)^2$
21. $(2x + 5y)^2$
22. $(5x + 2y)^2$
23. $(2x - 5y)^2$
24. $(3a - 2b)^2$
25. $(x + 3)^3$
26. $(y + 8)^3$
27. $(x - 3)^3$
28. $(y - 8)^3$
29. $(2a + 5)^3$
30. $(2a - 5)^3$
31. $(9 + 2y)^3$
32. $(1 - 3b)^3$
33. $(y + 1)(y - 1)$
34. $(2z + 5)(2z - 5)$
35. $(3x + 2)(3x - 2)$
36. $(x + 2y)(x - 2y)$
37. $(4a + 5b)(4a - 5b)$
38. $(x^2 + 1)(x^2 - 1)$
39. $(2x^2 + 3)(2x^2 - 3)$
40. $(3a^2 + 2)(3a^2 - 2)$
41. $(x^2 + 1)^2$
42. $(x^2 - 1)^2$
43. $(x^2 + 1)^3$
44. $(x^2 - 1)^3$
45. $(x + 2y)^3$
46. $(x - 2y)^3$
47. $(x^2 - y^2)(x^2 + y^2)$
48. $(x^2 - y^2)^2$
49. $(x^2 + y^2)^3$
50. $(x^2 - y^2)^3$

3.5 MONOMIAL FACTORS

Since the sides of an equation may be exchanged without changing the truth (or falsity) of the equation, the distributive axiom may also be written in the following form:

$$AB + AC = A(B + C)$$

The product $A(B + C)$ is the factored form of $AB + AC$. *To factor an expression means to write it as a product of factors.*

EXAMPLE 1 Factor $7x + 7y$.

Solution Using the form $AB + AC = A(B + C)$ with $A = 7$, $B = x$, and $C = y$, then

$$7x + 7y = 7(x + y)$$

EXAMPLE 2 Factor $2x^2 + 5x$.

Solution Note that each term has x as a factor.

$$2x^2 + 5x = x(2x) + x(5) = x(2x + 5)$$

It is customary to write the common monomial factor, such as x in Example 2, at the left in the factored form.

It is desirable to express a polynomial as a product of the *greatest* common monomial factor and another polynomial. Thus, although

$$6x^4 + 12x^2 = 2x(3x^3 + 6x)$$

$2x$ is not the greatest common factor. The greatest common factor is $6x^2$, so the desired factored form is

$$6x^4 + 12x^2 = 6x^2(x^2 + 2)$$

Factoring polynomials can be thought of as the inverse or opposite process of multiplying polynomials. For example, the instructions "simplify," "multiply," "express as a single polynomial," or "expand"

$$x(2x + 1)(3x - 1)$$

means the following:
First multiply $(2x + 1)(3x - 1)$ and then multiply the product by x:

$$\begin{aligned} &x[(2x + 1)(3x - 1)] \\ &= x[6x^2 + x - 1] \\ &= 6x^3 + x^2 - x \end{aligned}$$

To factor the polynomial $6x^3 + x^2 - x$, reverse the steps, observing that x is the greatest common factor:

$$6x^3 + x^2 - x = x(6x^2 + x - 1)$$

It is evident from the problem that $6x^2 + x - 1$ is the product of two linear binomials, $2x + 1$ and $3x - 1$, but it is rather difficult to tell by just looking at it. This problem will be explored in greater detail in the next sections. It is presented at this time to develop an awareness of the inverse relationship involved in multiplying and factoring polynomials.

The following example illustrates the procedure for finding the greatest common monomial factor of a polynomial.

EXAMPLE 3 Factor $abx^2 - ab^2x^2 - a^2bx^2$.

Solution

Writing each term of the polynomial in factored form, it reads

$$abxx - abbxx - aabxx$$

Now it is easy to identify the greatest common factor:

$$\begin{aligned} abx^2 - ab^2x^2 - a^2bx^2 &= abxx - abbxx - aabxx \\ &= abxx(1 - b - a) \\ &= abx^2(1 - b - a) \end{aligned}$$

Note the necessity for writing 1 as the first term of the second factor. If this term had been omitted, the product of these two expressions would not have yielded the original polynomial.

EXAMPLE 4 Express $16ax^2 + 40a^2x - 8ax$ as a product of polynomials.

Solution Again, it is helpful to express each term in factored form:

$$(2^4ax^2) + (5 \cdot 2^3a^2x) - (2^3ax)$$

The common factors are 2^3, a, and x; thus the greatest common factor is $8ax$, and

$$16ax^2 + 40a^2x - 8ax = 8ax(2x + 5a - 1)$$

When the leftmost term of a polynomial written in descending powers of a variable begins with a minus sign, it is customary to include -1 as one of the factors of the greatest common monomial factor. The next example demonstrates this convention.

EXAMPLE 5 Find the greatest common monomial factor of $-x^3 - x^2 + x$.

Solution

$$\begin{aligned} -x^3 - x^2 + x &= (-1)x^3 + (-1)x^2 + (-1)(-x) \\ &= (-x)x^2 + (-x)x + (-x)(-1) \\ &= (-x)(x^2 + x - 1) \\ &= -x(x^2 + x - 1) \end{aligned}$$

A factoring problem can be checked by multiplication.

EXAMPLE 6 Check that $-x^3 - x^2 + x = -x(x^2 + x - 1)$ by multiplication.

Solution

$$\begin{aligned} -x(x^2 + x - 1) &= (-x)(x^2) + (-x)(x) + (-x)(-1) \\ &= -x^3 - x^2 + x \end{aligned}$$

A factoring problem can also be checked by assigning a value to each variable and showing that the value of the expanded form is equal to the value of the factored form.

EXAMPLE 7 Factor $8ax^3 - 6ax^2 + 12ax$ and check by letting $a = 5$ and $x = 2$.

Solution $8ax^3 - 6ax^2 + 12ax$

$$\begin{aligned} &= 2ax(4x^2) - 2ax(3x) + 2ax(6) \\ &= 2ax(4x^2 - 3x + 6) \end{aligned}$$

Check For $a = 5$ and $x = 2$,

$$\begin{aligned} 8ax^3 - 6ax^2 + 12ax &= 8(5)(2^3) - 6(5)(2^2) + 12(5)(2) \\ &= 40(8) - 30(4) + 12(10) \\ &= 320 - 120 + 120 = 320 \\ 2ax(4x^2 - 3x + 6) &= 2(5)(2)(4 \cdot 2^2 - 3 \cdot 2 + 6) \\ &= 2(10)(16 - 6 + 6) \\ &= 20(16) = 320 \end{aligned}$$

It is so easy to make a mistake in algebraic work that good algebraic techniques must involve some type of checking.

EXERCISES

In Exercises 1–46 factor by finding the largest common monomial factor.

1. $4x + 12$
2. $5x - 20$
3. $6x - 3$
4. $14x + 7$
5. $3x^2 + 6x + 9$
6. $5x^2 + 15xy + 5y^2$
7. $8ab - 12a + 4$
8. $6x + 3y - 3$
9. $4y^3 - 100y^2$
10. $4x^2 + 2x$
11. $ay - a$
12. $by + by^2$
13. $x^4 - x^3$
14. $x^3 - x^4$
15. $x^4 - x^5$
16. $x^5 - x^4$
17. $24x^3 - 30x^2 + x^2y$
18. $a^2n^2 - 3an^2 + 3a^2n$
19. $c^2n^2 + cn^3$
20. $x^2y^2 - 3xy^2$
21. $ax + ay - az$
22. $x^3 - x^2 + x$
23. $a^2x - ax^2$
24. $ax^3 + a^2x^2 - a^3x$
25. $24x^2 + 12x + 6$
26. $ay^2 + aby + ab$
27. $c^4 - c^3 + c^2 - 2c$
28. $x^2 - x + xy$
29. $-25x^3 - 15x$
30. $a^3b^3 + a^2b^4 - a^2b^3$
31. $-xy^3 - xy^2 - xy$
32. $-xyz - xy - yz$
33. $r^2s - rs^2 - 4rs$
34. $6ax^2y - 12axy^2 + 6axy$
35. $18ab + 27a^2b^2 - 63$
36. $-ab - ac$
37. $-6x^2 + 2x^3 - x^4$
38. $-56mn + 72m^2n^2$
39. $3p^2q + 9p^2q^2 - 12p^2q^3$
40. $15x^2 - 10x^3 - 15x^4$
41. $x^{50} + x^{51}$
42. $x(x + 3) - x^2$
43. $3xy + x(x - 3)$
44. $a(c + d) - ac$
45. $c^2 - c(x - y)$
46. $b^2t - bt(b + c)$

In Exercises 47–55 factor by first replacing the binomial in parentheses by a single letter as follows:

$$\begin{aligned} x(x-3) - y(x-3) &= xN - yN \text{ where } N = x - 3 \\ &= N(x - y) \\ &= (x - 3)(x - y) \end{aligned}$$

47. $a(x + y) + 3(x + y)$
48. $x^2(x - 4) - 5(x - 4)$
49. $x^2(x + 5) - 2y^2(x + 5)$
50. $y(y^2 - 3) + (y^2 - 3)$
51. $5a^2(t^2 + 4) - (t^2 + 4)$
52. $y^2(y + 1) + 4(y + 1)$
53. $t(t^3 + 1) - (t^3 + 1)$
54. $u^2(u - v) + (u - v)$
55. $4(a + b)x^2 + 2(a + b)x + (a + b)$

In Exercises 56–60 factor by finding the largest common monomial. Assume n is a positive integer.

56. $x^n + x^{n+1}$
57. $x^{2n} - x^n$
58. $x^{3n} + x^n$
59. $y^{4n} - y^nz$
60. $x^{n+2} + x^{n+1} + x^n$

OMAR KHAYYAM
POET, ASTRONOMER, MATHEMATICIAN

Ah, but my Computations, People say,
Have squared the Year to human Compass, eh?
'Twas only striking from the Calendar
Unborn Tomorrow, and dead Yesterday.

from the *Rubaiyat*

Omar Khayyam (ca. 1100), probably best known as the Persian poet who wrote the *Rubaiyat,* was also a noted astronomer and mathematician. As royal astronomer, he produced a very accurate reform of the Moslem calendar.

Omar's greatest accomplishment, however, was in algebra, with his work on the geometric solution of cubic equations. He was also the first to give a systematic classification of equations (although it is not the one we use today).

3.6 FACTORING SIMPLE TRINOMIALS

Examining the product of the two binomials

$$(x + 2)(x + 3) \tag{1}$$

the distributive axiom permits writing this product as

$$(x + 2)x + (x + 2)3 \tag{2}$$

Applying the distributive axiom again,

$$x^2 + 2x + 3x + 2 \cdot 3 \qquad (3)$$
$$= x^2 + (2+3)x + 6 \qquad (4)$$
$$= x^2 + 5x + 6 \qquad (5)$$

The first term of the trinomial (5) is the product of the first terms of the two binomials in (1), and the third term of (5) is the product of the second terms of the binomials in (1):

$$\overbrace{(x + 2)(x}^{x^2} + 3) \quad \text{with} \quad (x + \underbrace{2)(x + 3}_{+6})$$

The middle term of the trinomial (5), 5x, is the algebraic sum of the outer product and inner product of the binomials:

$$\overbrace{(x + 2)(x + 3)}^{\text{Outer product}} \quad (x + \underbrace{2)(x}_{\text{Inner product}} + 3)$$

Outer product $= 3x$; inner product $= 2x$; algebraic sum of outer and inner products $= 3x + 2x = 5x$. Thus

$$x^2 + 5x + 6 = x^2 + (2+3)x + (2 \cdot 3) = (x+2)(x+3)$$

In general, the product of two binomials of the form $X + A$ and $X + B$ is

$$(X + A)(X + B) = X^2 + (A + B)X + A \cdot B$$

EXAMPLE 1 Express $x^2 + 3x + 2$ in factored form.

Solution If $x^2 + 3x + 2$ is factorable over the integers—that is, if it can be factored into binomials whose coefficients are integers—then the product of the first terms of the binomials must be x^2:

$$(x \quad)(x \quad)$$

and the factors will be in the form

$$(x + A)(x + B)$$

where $A + B = 3$ and $A \cdot B = 2$. Since the only factors of 2 are 2 and 1, and -2 and -1, and the sum $A + B$ is a positive number, $A = 2$ and $B = 1$. (The same result would have been obtained for $A = 1$ and $B = 2$, since addition and multiplication are each commutative.) Thus

$$x^2 + 3x + 2 = (x + 2)(x + 1)$$

Also

$$x^2 + 3x + 2 = (x + 1)(x + 2)$$

The answer to Example 1 can be checked by multiplication or by substitution of a numerical value for x.

EXAMPLE 2 Factor $x^2 + 3x - 4$ and check by (a) multiplication and (b) substituting 5 for x.

Solution

Again, the factors will be in the form $(X + A)(X + B)$ with $A + B = 3$ and $A \cdot B = -4$. The factors of -4 are $(-1)(4)$, $1(-4)$, and $2(-2)$. If $A = -1$ and $B = 4$, then $A + B = -1 + 4 = 3$.

Thus

$$x^2 + 3x - 4 = (x - 1)(x + 4)$$

Check

a. Multiplying,

$$\begin{aligned}(x - 1)(x + 4) &= x(x + 4) + (-1)(x + 4)\\ &= x^2 + 4x - x - 4\\ &= x^2 + 3x - 4\end{aligned}$$

b. For $x = 5$,

$$\begin{aligned}x^2 + 3x - 4 &= 5^2 + 3(5) - 4\\ &= 25 + 15 - 4\\ &= 36\\ (x - 1)(x + 4) &= (5 - 1)(5 + 4)\\ &= (4)(9)\\ &= 36\end{aligned}$$

If all the numerical coefficients and constants of a factored expression are integers, the polynomial is said to be **factored over the integers.** All the examples worked thus far have been factored over the integers.

EXAMPLE 3 Factor $x^2 - 10x - 24$ over the integers and check.

Solution

The integral factors of -24 are $-1(24)$, $1(-24)$, $-2(12)$, $2(-12)$, $-3(8)$, $3(-8)$, $-4(6)$, $4(-6)$. The only pair of factors whose sum is -10 is 2 and -12. Therefore

$$x^2 - 10x - 24 = (x + 2)(x - 12)$$

Also

$$x^2 - 10x - 24 = (x - 12)(x + 2)$$

Check

Let $x = 7$.

$$\begin{aligned}x^2 - 10x - 24 &= 7^2 - 10(7) - 24\\ &= 49 - 70 - 24\\ &= -21 - 24\\ &= -45\end{aligned}$$

Then

$$\begin{aligned}(x + 2)(x - 12) &= (7 + 2)(7 - 12)\\ &= (9)(-5)\\ &= -45\end{aligned}$$

EXAMPLE 4 Factor $x^2 + 3xy - 10y^2$ over the integers and check.

Solution

1. Comparing the forms:
$$X^2 + (A + B)X + AB = (X + A)(X + B)$$
$$x^2 + 3xy - 10y^2 = (x\ ?\ y)(x\ ?\ y)$$
It is seen that A and B must have the forms py and qy where $p + q = 3$ and $pq = -10$.
2. The pairs of factors of -10 are $(-1)(10)$, $(10)(-1)$, $(-2)(5)$, and $(2)(-5)$. Since $(-2) + (5) = 3$, select $p = -2$ and $q = 5$.
3. Then $x^2 + 3xy - 10y^2 = (x - 2y)(x + 5y)$.
Also, by the commutative axiom for multiplication,
$$x^2 + 3xy - 10y^2 = (x + 5y)(x - 2y)$$

Check Let $x = 3$ and $y = 2$. Then
$$x^2 + 3xy - 10y^2 = 3^2 + 3(3)(2) - 10(2^2)$$
$$= 9 + 18 - 40 = 27 - 40 = -13$$
$$(x - 2y)(x + 5y) = (3 - 2 \cdot 2)(3 + 5 \cdot 2)$$
$$= (3 - 4)(3 + 10) = (-1)(13) = -13$$

EXAMPLE 5 Factor $x^2 + x + 1$ over the integers, if possible.

Solution Comparing the forms:
$$X^2 + (A + B)X + AB = (X + A)(X + B)$$
it is seen that $A + B = 1$ and $AB = 1$. The only pairs of factors of 1 which are integers are $(1)(1)$ and $(-1)(-1)$; in other words, $A = 1$ and $B = 1$ or $A = -1$ and $B = -1$. But
$$A + B = 1 + 1 = 2 \qquad \text{or} \qquad A + B = -1 + (-1) = -2$$
and according to the problem, $A + B = 1$. Therefore, $x^2 + x + 1$ cannot be factored over the integers.

A polynomial that cannot be factored over the integers is said to be **prime** over the integers.

EXERCISES

Supply the missing factor in Exercises 1–10.

1. $x^2 + 9x + 14 = (x + 7)(\quad)$
2. $x^2 - 14x + 24 = (x - 2)(\quad)$
3. $x^2 - 11x - 26 = (x + 2)(\quad)$
4. $x^2 + 4x + 3 = (x + 1)(\quad)$
5. $x^2 + 2x - 8 = (x - 2)(\quad)$
6. $x^2 + 9x + 8 = (x + 8)(\quad)$
7. $x^2 - 7x - 8 = (x - 8)(\quad)$
8. $x^2 + 5x + 6 = (x + 2)(\quad)$
9. $x^2 + 11xy + 10y^2 = (x + 10y)(\quad)$
10. $x^2 - xy - 2y^2 = (x + y)(\quad)$

Factor over the integers, if possible, in Exercises 11–50.

11. $x^2 - 6x + 8$
12. $x^2 - 2x - 8$
13. $x^2 - x - 6$
14. $x^2 - 5x + 6$
15. $y^2 + 9y + 8$
16. $x^2 - 8x + 12$
17. $z^2 + 3z + 4$
18. $a^2 + 8a - 20$
19. $x^2 - 9x + 20$
20. $x^2 - 10x + 21$
21. $r^2 + 4r - 32$
22. $p^2 - 6p - 40$
23. $x^2 + 5x + 6$
24. $p^2 - 5p + 6$
25. $y^2 - 7y + 12$
26. $x^2 - 2x - 3$
27. $x^2 - 2x - 4$
28. $y^2 - y - 2$
29. $x^2 + 2xy + y^2$
30. $x^2 - 2xy - 15y^2$
31. $r^2 + rs - 2s^2$
32. $x^2 + 3xz - 70z^2$
33. $a^2 + 7ab + 10b^2$
34. $a^2 - 2ab - 10b^2$
35. $x^2 + 3ax - 10a^2$
36. $64 - 16x + x^2$
37. $-10 - 3x + x^2$
38. $24 - 10y - y^2$
39. $x^2 + xy - 20y^2$
40. $x^2 + 21xy + 20y^2$
41. $x^2 - 19xt - 20t^2$
42. $x^2 + 19xz - 20z^2$
43. $p^2 + 10pq + 25q^2$
44. $r^2 + 6rs + 9s^2$
45. $x^2 + 11xy + 10y^2$
46. $45 + 14y + y^2$
47. $x^4 + 3x^2 + 2$
48. $x^4 + 11x^2 - 26$
49. $y^4 - y^2 - 6$
50. $a^4 - 7a^2 + 12$

In Exercises 51–70, factor over the integers by first removing the greatest common monomial factor and then factoring the general trinomial factor, if possible.

51. $3x^2 - 9x + 6$
52. $10x^2 - 20x - 350$
53. $150x^4 - 1050x^3 + 1500x^2$
54. $4a^3y + 4a^2y - 48ay$
55. $20y^2 + 140y - 120$
56. $35b^2 - 30b - 5b^3$
57. $4x^2 + 32x + 60$
58. $5x^2 + 30x - 35$
59. $100x^3 - 200x^2 - 800x$
60. $6y^4 - 24y^3 - 72y^2$
61. $15y^2 + 30y + 45$
62. $84 + 7a - 7a^2$
63. $20cd - cd^2 - cd^3$
64. $30u^2 + 150u - 120$
65. $2x^3 + 8x^2y - 120xy^2$
66. $5uv - uv^3 - u^3v$
67. $28nk^2 - 3nk^3 - nk^4$
68. $x^3y - 2x^2y^2 - 35xy^3$
69. $u^4 + 2u^3v - 3u^2v^2$
70. $18d^2 + 18dx + 36x^2$

3.7 FACTORING GENERAL TRINOMIALS

In the trinomials that were factored in the preceding section, the coefficient of the x^2 term was 1. What happens if this coefficient is not 1? Let's begin by examining the product of two binomials.

$$\begin{aligned}(2x+1)(5x+3) &= 2x(5x)+2x(3)+1(5x)+1(3)\\ &= 10x^2+(6+5)x+3\\ &= 10x^2+11x+3\end{aligned}$$

Note that the x^2 term is the product of the x terms of the factors, the constant term 3 is the product of the constant terms of the factors, and the x term, in this case $11x$, is the sum of two products, the outer product (the product of the two terms on the extreme left and right) and the inner product (the product of the two terms next to each other in the factored form).

To factor $10x^2+11x+3$, it is necessary to retrace these steps. This principle is illustrated in the following example.

EXAMPLE 1 Factor $10x^2+11x+3$.

Solution If this trinomial has two binomial factors, the product of their first terms must be $10x^2$. Because we prefer that the leading terms be positive, the possibilities are $2x$ and $5x$ or $10x$ and x.

$$(2x\qquad)(5x\qquad)$$

or

$$(10x\qquad)(x\qquad)$$

Since the product of the second terms must be 3, this produces the following possibilities:

$$(2x+1)(5x+3)\qquad(10x+1)(x+3)$$
$$(2x+3)(5x+1)\qquad(10x+3)(x+1)$$

Each of these yields the correct first and third terms of the given trinomial, but only one of them produces the correct middle term.

$$(2x+1)(5x+3)$$

$5x$	(Inner product)
$6x$	(Outer product)
$11x$	(Sum of inner and outer products)

Therefore, $10x^2+11x+3=(2x+1)(5x+3)$.

EXAMPLE 2 Factor $6x^2 + x - 15$.

Solution If this trinomial has two binomial factors, the product of the first terms must be $6x^2$. The possibilities are $2x$ and $3x$ or $6x$ and x.

$$(2x \quad)(3x \quad) \text{ or } (6x \quad)(x \quad)$$

The product of the second terms must be -15. The possible factors of -15 are 5 and -3, 3 and -5, 15 and -1, and 1 and -15:

$$\begin{array}{ll}
(2x + 5)(3x - 3) & (6x + 5)(x - 3) \\
(2x - 5)(3x + 3) & (6x - 5)(x + 3) \\
(2x + 3)(3x - 5) & (6x + 3)(x - 5) \\
(2x - 3)(3x + 5) & (6x - 3)(x + 5) \\
(2x + 15)(3x - 1) & (6x + 15)(x - 1) \\
(2x - 15)(3x + 1) & (6x - 15)(x + 1) \\
(2x + 1)(3x - 15) & (6x + 1)(x - 15) \\
(2x - 1)(3x + 15) & (6x - 1)(x + 15)
\end{array}$$

There are sixteen possibilities, and it is necessary to select the correct one, because **complete factorization is unique and results in one and only one correct set of factors (except for the order in which they are written).** All the above pairs of binomials yield the correct first and third terms of the original trinomial, but only one will produce the correct middle term:

$$\overbrace{(2x \underbrace{- 3)(3x}_{-9x} + 5)}^{10x}$$

$$(2 \cdot 5 - 3 \cdot 3)x = 10x - 9x = x$$

Therefore

$$6x^2 + x - 15 = (2x - 3)(3x + 5)$$

Also

$$6x^2 + x - 15 = (3x + 5)(2x - 3)$$

EXAMPLE 3 Check the answer to Example 2 by (a) multiplication and (b) substituting 2 for x.

Solution

a. $$\begin{aligned}(2x - 3)(3x + 5) &= 2x(3x + 5) - 3(3x + 5) \\ &= 6x^2 + 10x - 9x - 15 \\ &= 6x^2 + x - 15\end{aligned}$$

b. For $x = 2$,

$$\begin{aligned}6x^2 + x - 15 &= 6 \cdot 2^2 + 2 - 15 \\ &= 24 - 13 = 11 \\ (2x - 3)(3x + 5) &= (2 \cdot 2 - 3)(3 \cdot 2 + 5) \\ &= (4 - 3)(6 + 5) = 11\end{aligned}$$

EXAMPLE 4 Factor $8y^2 - 10y - 7$ over the integers, if possible, and check the result.

Solution The factors of 8 are (1)(8) and (2)(4). Therefore, $8y^2 - 10y - 7$ has the form $(y+b)(8y+d)$ *or* $(2y+b)(4y+d)$. Since $bd = -7$, the possibilities for bd are $(-1)(7)$, $(7)(-1)$, $(1)(-7)$, and $(-7)(1)$.

The possibilities to be tried are:

$$\begin{array}{ll} (y-1)(8y+7) & (2y-1)(4y+7) \\ (y+7)(8y-1) & (2y+7)(4y-1) \\ (y+1)(8y-7) & (2y+1)(4y-7) \\ (y-7)(8y+1) & (2y-7)(4y+1) \end{array}$$

After several trials,

$$(2y+1)(4y-7)$$

$$\begin{array}{ll} 4y & \text{(Inner product)} \\ \underline{-14y} & \text{(Outer product)} \\ -10y & \text{(Sum of inner and outer products)} \end{array}$$

Thus

$$8y^2 - 10y - 7 = (2y+1)(4y-7)$$

Check Let $y = 5$.

$$\begin{aligned} 8y^2 - 10y - 7 &= 8(5^2) - 10(5) - 7 \\ &= 2 \cdot 4(25) - 50 - 7 \\ &= 200 - 57 \\ &= 143 \\ (2y+1)(4y-7) &= (2 \cdot 5 + 1)(4 \cdot 5 - 7) \\ &= (11)(13) \\ &= 143 \end{aligned}$$

EXAMPLE 5 Factor $5x^2 + 6x - 1$ over the integers, if possible.

Solution If the trinomial can be factored, the possibilities are

$$(x+1)(5x-1) \text{ and } (x-1)(5x+1)$$

Trying these,

$$\begin{aligned} (x+1)(5x-1) &= x(5x-1) + (1)(5x-1) \\ &= 5x^2 - x + 5x - 1 \\ &= 5x^2 + 4x - 1 \\ (x-1)(5x+1) &= x(5x+1) + (-1)(5x+1) \\ &= 5x^2 + x - 5x - 1 \\ &= 5x^2 - 4x - 1 \end{aligned}$$

Since none of these possibilities works and since they are the only possibilities, $5x^2 + 6x - 1$ *cannot* be factored over the integers; it is prime.

EXERCISES

Supply the missing factor in Exercises 1–20.

1. $2x^2 - 9x - 110 = (x - 10)(\quad)$
2. $6x^2 - 7x - 20 = (3x + 4)(\quad)$
3. $6x^2 - x - 2 = (2x + 1)(\quad)$
4. $3y^2 + 25y - 50 = (y + 10)(\quad)$
5. $12y^2 - 17y - 5 = (4y + 1)(\quad)$
6. $8a^2 - 26a + 21 = (2a - 3)(\quad)$
7. $10x^2 + 23x - 5 = (2x + 5)(\quad)$
8. $10x^2 + 27x + 5 = (2x + 5)(\quad)$
9. $10x^2 - 23x - 5 = (2x - 5)(\quad)$
10. $10x^2 - 27x + 5 = (2x - 5)(\quad)$
11. $6x^2 + 7x - 20 = (2x + 5)(\quad)$
12. $8a^2 - 10a - 3 = (2a - 3)(\quad)$
13. $3y^2 + 10y - 88 = (3y + 22)(\quad)$
14. $6x^2 + x - 2 = (2x - 1)(\quad)$
15. $10p^2 + 21p - 10 = (2p + 5)(\quad)$
16. $6x^2 + x - 40 = (3x + 8)(\quad)$
17. $4x^2 - 21x - 18 = (4x + 3)(\quad)$
18. $4x^2 + 27x + 18 = (4x + 3)(\quad)$
19. $4x^2 + 21x - 18 = (4x - 3)(\quad)$
20. $4x^2 - 27x + 18 = (4x - 3)(\quad)$

Factor over the integers, if possible, in Exercises 21–80. Always look for common monomial factors first.

21. $3x^2 - 2x - 1$
22. $3x^2 + 3x - 6$
23. $3x^2 - 17x - 6$
24. $9x^2 + 3x + 2$
25. $6x^2 - 11x - 150$
26. $12x^2 - 11x + 2$
27. $6y^2 + 63y - 150$
28. $8a^2 - 34a + 33$
29. $8a^2 - 35a + 33$
30. $8a^2 - 91a + 33$
31. $8a^2 - 50a + 33$
32. $8a^2 + 38a - 33$
33. $4x^2 + 12x + 9$
34. $9b^2 - 30b + 25$
35. $8p^2 + 2p - 21$
36. $8p^2 + 22p - 21$
37. $2x^2 - 3x + 1$
38. $4x^2 - 20x + 25$
39. $12x^2 - 23x + 5$
40. $12x^2 - 17x - 5$
41. $12x^2 - 16x + 5$
42. $3a^2 - 4a - 7$
43. $3a^2 + 4a - 7$
44. $3a^2 + 21a + 7$
45. $3a^2 - 20a - 7$
46. $3a^2 + 20a - 7$
47. $5x^2 + 5x - 2$
48. $15x^2 - 7x - 2$
49. $9y^2 + 24y + 16$
50. $25x^2 - 30x + 9$
51. $10x^2 + 33x - 7$
52. $10x^2 - 9x - 7$
53. $3x + 2x^2 + 1$
54. $-4a + 1 + 4a^2$
55. $15 + 16x + 4x^2$
56. $8 - 21a - 9a^2$
57. $5x + 4x^2 + 1$
58. $-3y - 1 + 4y^2$
59. $6 - 11x + 4x^2$
60. $-5 - 11x + 16x^2$

61. $6a^2 + 8a + 2$
62. $12y^2 - 12y + 3$
63. $16y^2 - 2y - 5$
64. $16y^2 - 16y - 5$
65. $9ax^2 - 21ax - 8a$
66. $4a^2x + ax - 5x$
67. $3a^2 - 7ab + 2b^2$
68. $8x^3 - 20x^2 - 12x$
69. $2m^2 + 5mn - 3n^2$
70. $4p^2 + 5pq + q^2$
71. $15x^2 - 2xy - y^2$
72. $6x^2 + 17xy - 14y^2$
73. $6a^2x + 12ax - 21x$
74. $4x^2y + 2xy - 6y$
75. $3x^5 + 20x^4 - 7x^3$
76. $6x^4 - 10x^3 - 4x^2$
77. $2x^4y^2 + 6x^3y^2 - 20x^2y^2$
78. $x^2 + 4x^3 + 3x^4$
79. $30x^2 - 78x - 36$
80. $2xy + 2x^2y - 60x^3y$
81. For what integers k is $x^2 + kx + 4$ factorable over the integers?
82. For what integers k is $x^2 + kx - 12$ factorable over the integers?
83. For what integers p is $2x^2 + px + 34$ factorable over the integers?
84. For what integers p is $5x^2 + px - 9$ factorable over the integers?

3.8 FACTORING PERFECT SQUARE TRINOMIALS

Some polynomials have factors that are readily recognizable. You should familiarize yourself with these.

The polynomial $x^2 + 2ax + a^2$ is called a **perfect square trinomial** because it is the result of the square of a binomial. Note that

$$(x + a)^2 = (x + a)(x + a) = (x + a)x + (x + a)a$$
$$= x^2 + ax + ax + a^2 = x^2 + 2ax + a^2$$

When a perfect square trinomial is written in descending powers of the variable x, the first term and the last term are positive and perfect squares, such as x^2, 25, 16, a^2, and so on. The middle term is equal to *twice* the product of the first and second terms of the binomial factor, because the outer product and the inner product are the same.

PERFECT SQUARE TRINOMIAL FORM

$$x^2 + 2ax + a^2 = (x + a)^2$$

3.8 FACTORING PERFECT SQUARE TRINOMIALS

EXAMPLE 1 Find the term which when added to $x^2 + 8x$ will make it a perfect square trinomial.

Solution The factors of this perfect square trinomial must be of the form $(x + a)(x + a)$ and their product is $x^2 + 2ax + a^2$. The middle term of this perfect square trinomial is $2ax$, and the middle term of the trinomial we wish to form is $8x$; therefore, let $2a = 8$ and $a = 4$. Since $a = 4$, $a^2 = 16$. The missing term is a^2, so we must add 16 to $x^2 + 8x$ to make it a perfect square trinomial:

$$x^2 + 8x + 16 = (x + 4)^2$$

Note: You should recognize that the solution to Example 1 could have been found very simply and mechanically by taking half of the coefficient of x, $\frac{1}{2}(8) = 4$, and squaring this number, $4^2 = 16$.

EXAMPLE 2 Find the term which when added to $x^2 + 20x$ will make it a perfect square trinomial and thus complete the square.

Solution The middle term of the desired trinomial is $20x$. The coefficient of x is 20; $\frac{1}{2}(20) = 10$; $10^2 = 100$. Therefore, the missing term is 100 and

$$x^2 + 20x + 100 = (x + 10)^2$$

EXAMPLE 3 Express $x^2 + 10x + 25$ as the square of a binomial.

Solution Using the form

$$x^2 + 2ax + a^2 = (x + a)^2$$
$$x^2 + 10x + 25 = x^2 + 2(5x) + 5^2 = (x + 5)^2$$

EXAMPLE 4 Express $4y^2 - 12y + 9$ as the square of a binomial.

Solution

$$\begin{aligned} & x^2 + 2ax \qquad + a^2 = (x + a)^2 \\ 4y^2 - 12y + 9 &= (2y)^2 + 2(-6y) \quad + 3^2 \\ &= (2y)^2 + 2(-3)(2y) + (-3)^2 = (2y + [-3])^2 \\ &= (2y - 3)^2 \end{aligned}$$

EXAMPLE 5 Is $x^2 + 14x - 49$ a perfect square?

Solution No, because the third term is *not* positive.

EXAMPLE 6 Is $y^2 + 3y + 9$ a perfect square?

Solution The only possibility is $(y + 3)^2$. But

$$(y + 3)^2 = y^2 + 2(3)y + 9 = y^2 + 6y + 9$$

Thus $y^2 + 3y + 9$ is not a perfect square.

EXAMPLE 7 Is $x^2 + 16 - 8x$ a perfect square?

Solution First rearranging the polynomial in descending powers of x,

$$x^2 - 8x + 16 = x^2 - 8x + 4^2 = (x - 4)^2$$

The answer is yes.

EXAMPLE 8 Fill in the missing term so that $x^2 + (\qquad) + 9y^2$ is a perfect square trinomial.

Solution Using the form

$$x^2 + 2ax + a^2 = (x + a)^2$$

$$x^2 + (\qquad) + 9y^2 = x^2 + (\qquad) + (3y)^2 = (x + 3y)^2$$

$a = 3y$, $2a = 6y$, and $2ax = 6xy$.

The missing term is $6xy$ and

$$x^2 + 6xy + 9y^2 = (x + 3y)^2$$

EXERCISES

Fill in the missing terms so that the result is a perfect square trinomial in Exercises 1–24.

1. $x^2 - 6x + (\qquad)$

2. $x^2 + 20x + (\qquad)$

3. $x^2 - 14x + (\qquad)$

4. $x^2 + 40x + (\qquad)$

5. $x^2 - 2x + (\qquad)$

6. $a^2 + 12a + (\qquad)$

7. $a^2 - 12a + (\qquad)$

8. $p^2 - 36p + (\qquad)$

9. $x^2 + 18x + (\qquad)$

10. $m^2 + 100m + (\qquad)$

11. $x^2 + 6xy + (\qquad)$

12. $x^2 + 12xy + (\qquad)$

13. $y^2 - 10yz + (\qquad)$

14. $a^2 - 14ab + (\qquad)$

15. $y^2 + (\qquad) + 81$

16. $x^2 + (\qquad) + 25$

17. $a^2 - (\qquad) + 36$

18. $t^2 - (\qquad) + 49$

19. $x^2 + (\qquad) + 16y^2$

20. $a^2 + (\qquad) + 121b^2$

21. $x^2 - (\qquad) + 4y^2$

22. $u^2 - (\qquad) + 9v^2$

23. $(\qquad) - 6xy + y^2$

24. $(\qquad) - 10ab + b^2$

In Exercises 25–30, factor out the common monomial, complete the square, and subtract the constant term that was added so that the resulting expression is equivalent to the original expression.

Example

$$\begin{aligned} 4x^2 + 8x &= 4(x^2 + 2x \qquad) \\ &= 4(x^2 + 2x + 1) - 4(1) \\ &= 4(x + 1)^2 - 4 \end{aligned}$$

25. $4x^2 + 16x$

26. $3x^2 + 12x$

27. $10a^2 - 20a$

28. $5b^2 - 40b$

29. $8y^2 + 16y$

30. $12x^2 - 144x$

Determine which of Exercises 31–40 are perfect square trinomials.

31. $x^2 + 8x + 16$
32. $y^2 + 2y + 1$
33. $a^2 + 2ab - b^2$
34. $9y^2 - 18y + 36$
35. $x^2 + 49y^2 - 14xy$
36. $x^2 + 36 - 12x$
37. $n^2 + 4ny + 16y^2$
38. $x^2 + 4$
39. $u^2 + 81 + 9u$
40. $a^2 - b^2$

In Exercises 41–70, factor over the integers, if possible. Check the answers.

41. $x^2 + 4x + 4$
42. $x^2 - 2x + 1$
43. $x^2 + 18x + 81$
44. $x^2 - 10x + 25$
45. $y^2 + 16y + 64$
46. $9a^2 + 6a + 1$
47. $16p^2 - 8p + 1$
48. $36 - 12x + x^2$
49. $64y^2 - 48y + 9$
50. $x^2 + 14x + 49$
51. $4x^2 - 12x + 9$
52. $25m^2 + 10m + 1$
53. $121n^2 - 22n + 1$
54. $16 - 8x + x^2$
55. $16x^2 - 24x + 9$
56. $x^2 + 40x + 400$
57. $9x^2 + 36x + 36$
58. $4y^2 + 28y + 49$
59. $-24x + 16 + 9x^2$
60. $r^2 + 12rs + 36s^2$
61. $4x^2 - 28x + 49$
62. $9p^2 - 30p + 25$
63. $12a + 36 + a^2$
64. $4x^2 + 4xy + y^2$
65. $9s^2 + 6st + 4t^2$
66. $x^4 + 20x^2 + 100$
67. $121u^2 + 22u + 1$
68. $x^4 + 60x^2 + 900$
69. $4x^2 + 9y^2$
70. $u^2 + 441 - 42u$

3.9 FACTORING SPECIAL BINOMIALS

The product of the two binomials $x + a$ and $x - a$ is not a trinomial, but another binomial.

$$\begin{aligned}(x + a)(x - a) &= (x + a)x - (x + a)a \\ &= x^2 + ax - ax - a^2 \\ &= x^2 - a^2\end{aligned}$$

Notice that the outer and inner products are alike except for sign, which makes them additive inverses whose sum is always zero. Since the resulting binomial is the difference of the squares of a and x, this special product is called the difference of squares.

DIFFERENCE OF SQUARES FORM

$A^2 - B^2 = (A + B)(A - B)$

EXAMPLE 1 Factor $x^2 - 25$.

Solution Since x^2 and 25 are both perfect squares and the binomial is of the form $A^2 - B^2$, it factors as $(A + B)(A - B)$, where $A^2 = x^2$ and $B^2 = 25 = 5^2$.

$$A^2 - B^2 = (A + B)(A - B)$$
$$x^2 - 25 = x^2 - 5^2 = (x + 5)(x - 5)$$

EXAMPLE 2 Write $9x^2 - 4$ in factored form.

Solution $9x^2$ is the square of $3x$, since $(3x)(3x) = 9x^2$. 4 is the square of 2. Therefore

$$9x^2 - 4 = (3x)^2 - (2)^2$$
$$= (3x + 2)(3x - 2)$$

EXAMPLE 3 Factor $2x^2 - 50$.

Solution The two terms have a common factor, 2, so extract this common factor first:

$$2x^2 - 50 = 2(x^2 - 25)$$
$$= 2(x - 5)(x + 5)$$

EXAMPLE 4 Factor $4x^2 - 25y^2$.

Solution $4x^2$ is the square of $2x$. $25y^2$ is the square of $5y$. Therefore

$$4x^2 - 25y^2 = (2x)^2 - (5y)^2$$
$$= (2x + 5y)(2x - 5y)$$

EXAMPLE 5 Factor $x^2 + 1$, if possible.

Solution x^2 is the square of x. 1 is the square of 1. However, these squares are *not* separated by a minus sign, and they are therefore *not the difference* of two squares but their sum. Note that *none* of the following possibilities work:

$$(x + 1)(x + 1) = x^2 + 2x + 1$$
$$(x - 1)(x - 1) = x^2 - 2x + 1$$
$$(x + 1)(x - 1) = x^2 - 1$$

Therefore, $x^2 + 1$ is prime and cannot be factored.

In general, a binomial of the form $x^2 + a^2$ cannot be expressed as the product of two linear factors.

Two other factorable binomials are useful to know.

DIFFERENCE OF CUBES

$A^3 - B^3 = (A - B)(A^2 + AB + B^2)$

3.9 FACTORING SPECIAL BINOMIALS

SUM OF CUBES

$$A^3 + B^3 = (A + B)(A^2 - AB + B^2)$$

These two factorable binomials can be verified by direct multiplication.

EXAMPLE 6 Factor $x^3 - 8$.

Solution $x^3 - 8$ fits the difference of cubes form, with $A^3 = x^3$ and $B^3 = 8 = 2^3$.

$$A^3 - B^3 = (A - B)(A^2 + AB + B^2)$$
$$x^3 - 8 = x^3 - 2^3 = (x - 2)(x^2 + 2x + 4)$$

EXAMPLE 7 Factor $27x^3 + 125y^3$.

Solution Since $27x^3 = (3x)^3$ and $125y^3 = (5y)^3$, and since

$$\begin{aligned} A^3 + B^3 &= (A + B)(A^2 - AB + B^2) \\ 27x^3 + 125y^3 &= (3x)^3 + (5y)^3 \\ &= (3x + 5y)([3x]^2 - [3x][5y] + [5y]^2) \\ &= (3x + 5y)(9x^2 - 15xy + 25y^2) \end{aligned}$$

EXAMPLE 8 Check by multiplication that

$$x^3 - 8 = (x - 2)(x^2 + 2x + 4)$$

Solution

$$\begin{array}{rrrr} x^2 & +\,2x & +\,4 & \\ x & -\,2 & & \\ \hline x^3 + 2x^2 & +\,4x & & \\ & -\,2x^2 & -\,4x & -\,8 \\ \hline x^3 & & & -\,8 \end{array}$$

EXAMPLE 9 Check by multiplication that

$$27x^3 + 125y^3 = (3x + 5y)(9x^2 - 15xy + 25y^2)$$

Solution

$$\begin{array}{llll} 9x^2 - 15xy & +\,25y^2 & & \\ 3x \;+\; 5y & & & \\ \hline 27x^3 - 45x^2y & +\,75xy^2 & & \\ & +\,45x^2y & -\,75xy^2 & +\,125y^3 \\ \hline 27x^3 & & & +\,125y^3 \end{array}$$

EXERCISES

In Exercises 1–46, factor the polynomials over the integers if possible. Remove all common monomials first. Check by multiplication.

1. $x^2 - 81$
2. $9x^2 - 1$
3. $4x^2 - 49$
4. $x^2 + 9$
5. $36x^2 - 25y^2$
6. $y^2 - x^2$
7. $16 - 9a^2$
8. $9y^2 - 100z^2$
9. $x^2 - 2$
10. $x^2 + 1$

11. $x^3 + 1$
12. $x^3 - 1$
13. $x^3 - a^3$
14. $x^2 - a^2$
15. $x^3 + a^3$
16. $x^2 + a^2$
17. $8p^3 + 27$
18. $8p^3 - 27$
19. $x^4 - 9$
20. $25y^4 - 121$
21. $y^4 - 4y^2$
22. $y^5 - 8y^2$
23. $64x^3 + 125y^6$
24. $4a^3 - 121a$
25. $64x^3 - 9x$
26. $y^2 - 144$
27. $y^2 + 144$
28. $16y^2 - 4y^4$
29. $8y^4 - 16y^2$
30. $a^3 - 16a$
31. $x^4 + 216x$
32. $x^4 - 343x$
33. $2y^4z - 54yz^4$
34. $3ax^4 + 81a^4x$
35. $(a + b)^2 - c^2$
36. $c^2 - (a + b)^2$
37. $9(x + y)^2 - 16$
38. $16 - 9(x + y)^2$
39. $36 - (n + 2)^2$
40. $49a^2 - (x + y)^2$
41. $(a + b)^2 - (a - b)^2$
42. $(a - b)^2 - (a + b)^2$
43. $(a + b)^3 + c^3$
44. $(a + b)^3 - c^3$
45. $27x^3 - (y + z)^3$
46. $27x^3 + (y + z)^3$

Factor over the integers in Exercises 47–50. Assume n to be a positive integer.

47. $x^{2n} - y^{2n}$
48. $x^{3n} - y^{3n}$
49. $x^{3n} + y^{3n}$
50. $x^{4n} - y^{4n}$

In Exercises 51–52, using the data

$$x^2 - 1 = (x - 1)(x + 1)$$
$$x^3 - 1 = (x - 1)(x^2 + x + 1)$$
$$x^4 - 1 = (x - 1)(x^3 + x^2 + x + 1)$$

factor each similarly and check by multiplication.

51. $x^5 - 1$
52. $x^7 - 1$

3.10 COMPLETE FACTORING

A polynomial is said to be **completely factored over the integers** when all common factors have been removed and when no further factoring over the integers is possible. For example, $2x^2 - 8 = 2(x^2 - 4)$. However, $x^2 - 4$ can be factored, since it is the difference of squares. Therefore, in completely factored form,

$$2x^2 - 8 = 2(x + 2)(x - 2)$$

3.10 COMPLETE FACTORING

It is often necessary to perform several factoring processes before a polynomial is completely factored. (The instruction *completely factor* means *completely factor over the integers.*

EXAMPLE 1 Factor completely $3ax^4 - 3ay^4$.

Solution $3ax^4 - 3ay^4$

$$3a(x^4 - y^4)$$

$$3a(x^2 + y^2)(x^2 - y^2)$$

$$3a(x^2 + y^2)(x + y)(x - y)$$

Summarizing these steps:

1. Remove the greatest common monomial factor by the distributive axiom:
$$3ax^4 - 3ay^4 = 3a(x^4 - y^4)$$
2. Factor the difference of two squares:
$$= 3a(x^2 + y^2)(x^2 - y^2)$$
3. Factor the difference of two squares:
$$= 3a(x^2 + y^2)(x + y)(x - y)$$

Since the factors of a product can be written in any order, it also follows that
$$3ax^4 - 3ay^4 = 3a(x + y)(x - y)(x^2 + y^2)$$

It is desirable to arrange the factors in such an order that monomials are written first, then linear factors, followed by quadratic factors, and so on. (A **linear** factor is a factor that contains only a simple variable, x, or variables, $x + y$. A **quadratic** factor is one that contains one or more squared variables, x^2, $x^2 + y^2$, etc.; a **cubic** factor is one that contains one or more cubed variables, $x^3 - 2x^2$, and so on.)

PROCEDURE FOR COMPLETE FACTORIZATION

1. Remove the greatest common monomial factor.
2. Factor any binomial, if present, using one of the following forms.
3. Factor any trinomial, if present, using one of the following forms.

FACTORING FORMS

1. Common Monomial Factor	$AB + AC = A(B + C)$ $AB + AC + AD = A(B + C + D)$
2. Difference of Squares	$A^2 - B^2 = (A - B)(A + B)$
3. Difference of Cubes	$A^3 - B^3 = (A - B)(A^2 + AB + B^2)$
4. Sum of Cubes	$A^3 + B^3 = (A + B)(A^2 - AB + B^2)$
5. Perfect Square Trinomial	$A^2 + 2AB + B^2 = (A + B)^2$ $A^2 - 2AB + B^2 = (A - B)^2$
6. Simple Trinomial	$X^2 + (a + b)X + ab = (X + a)(X + b)$
7. General Trinomial	$aX^2 + bX + c = (rX + s)(kX + n)$ where $rk = a$, $sn = c$, and $rn + sk = b$

EXAMPLE 2 Completely factor $6x^2 + 30x - 84$.

Solution
$$\begin{aligned} 6x^2 + 30x - 84 &= 6(x^2 + 5x - 14) \\ &= 6(x + 7)(x - 2) \end{aligned}$$

EXAMPLE 3 Factor completely over the integers $x^4 - 5x^2 - 36$.

Solution
$$\begin{aligned} x^4 - 5x^2 - 36 &= (x^2 - 9)(x^2 + 4) \\ &= (x + 3)(x - 3)(x^2 + 4) \end{aligned}$$

As before, a factorization can be checked by multiplication or by substitution of a value for each variable.

EXAMPLE 4 Check Example 2 by multiplication.

Solution
$$\begin{aligned} 6(x + 7)(x - 2) &= 6(x^2 + 5x - 14) \\ &= 6x^2 + 30x - 84 \end{aligned}$$

EXAMPLE 5 Check Example 3 by letting $x = 2$.

Solution For $x = 2$,
$$\begin{aligned} x^4 - 5x^2 - 36 &= 2^4 - 5 \cdot 2^2 - 36 \\ &= 16 - 20 - 36 \\ &= 16 - 56 = -40 \\ (x + 3)(x - 3)(x^2 + 4) &= (2 + 3)(2 - 3)(2^2 + 4) \\ &= (5)(-1)(8) = -40 \end{aligned}$$

EXERCISES

In Exercises 1–60, factor completely over the integers, if possible, and identify by number which factoring forms were used.

1. $3y^2 - 12$
2. $p^3 - 36p$
3. $18 - 8x^2$
4. $m^3 - m$
5. $9x^2 - 9x - 18$
6. $4k + 2kx - 2kx^2$
7. $4x^2 - 6x - 10$
8. $4x^2 - 6x + 2$
9. $12x^3 + 14x^2 - 10x$
10. $6a^3 + a^2 - 12a$

11. $36a^2 - 36a + 9$
12. $27t^3 + 36t^2 + 12t$
13. $5x^2 - 15x - 50$
14. $4y^2 - 28y + 49$
15. $x^4 - 16$
16. $y^4 - z^4$
17. $81a^4 - 256$
18. $a^5 - a$
19. $x^4 + 4x^2$
20. $x^4 - 3x^2 - 4$
21. $x^4 - 13x^2 + 36$
22. $6x^4 - 54x^2 + 84$
23. $5x^3 - 625$
24. $y^4 - y$
25. $a^7 - a^4$
26. $x^6 - y^6$
27. $x^6 + y^6$
28. $n^6 - 64$
29. $n^6 + 64n^3$
30. $m^5 - m$
31. $64x^3 - x$
32. $2a^3x + 16x$
33. $-x^4 + 4x^3 + 5x^2$
34. $-8x^4 - 8x^3 - 2x^2$
35. $3x^3 + 3x^2 - 126x$
36. $4x^4 + 16x^3 + 64x^2$
37. $4x^4 - 48x^3 + 144x^2$
38. $t^6 + 5t^4 - 36t^2$
39. $5a^5 + 60a^3 - 320a$
40. $36x^3 - 69x^2 + 15x$
41. $2c^2 - 20c^3 + 50c^4$
42. $252a + 32ax - 60ax^2$
43. $t^4 - 48t^2 - 49$
44. $x^4 - 35x^2 - 36$
45. $3x^4 + 81x$
46. $-3x^3 - 27x$
47. $x^8 - y^8$
48. $x^8 + y^8$
49. $2x^4y^4 - 32$
50. $4a^4 - 16b^4$
51. $(a + b)^2 - 4a^2$
52. $25x^2 - (x + y)^2$
53. $a^2(b + c)^2 - a^2d^2$
54. $x^2(y - 1)^2 - 100(y - 1)^2$
55. $(x + 2y) - a(x + 2y)$
56. $a^2(u - v)^2 - a^2(u + v)^2$
57. $5x^{2n} - 5$
58. $x^{3n} - x^n$
59. $y^{n+2} + 2y^{n+1} - 15y^n$
60. $x^{6n+1} - x$

3.11 APPLICATIONS

SOLUTIONS OF EQUATIONS BY FACTORING

If the trinomial $ax^2 + bx + c$ can be factored over the set of integers, then there is an easy way to solve the equation $ax^2 + bx + c = 0$. The method depends on the following theorem.

THE ZERO-PRODUCT THEOREM

A product of two real numbers is zero if and only if one or both of the two numbers is zero.
In symbols, $rs = 0$ if and only if $r = 0$ or $s = 0$.

EXAMPLE 1 Given $3x = 0$. Then by the zero-product theorem $3 = 0$ or $x = 0$. Since $3 \neq 0$, x must $= 0$.

EXAMPLE 2 Solve $(x-4)(x-7)=0$.

Solution

Since the product $(x-4)(x-7)$ is zero, the left factor, $x-4$, is zero, or the right factor, $x-7$, is zero.

$$x-4=0 \quad \text{or} \quad x-7=0$$
$$x=4 \quad \text{or} \quad x=7$$

The solution set is $\{4,7\}$, since each of these numbers makes the original statement true.

Check

For $x=4$, $(4-4)(4-7)=(0)(-3)=0$
For $x=7$, $(7-4)(7-7)=(3)(0)=0$

EXAMPLE 3 Solve the equation $x^2+15x+54=0$.

Solution

In factored form,

$$x^2+15x+54=(x+6)(x+9)$$

and the given equation is equivalent to

$$(x+6)(x+9)=0$$

By the zero-product theorem,

$$x+6=0 \quad \text{or} \quad x+9=0$$
$$x=-6 \quad \text{or} \quad x=-9$$

Check

$$\begin{aligned} x^2+15x+54&=0 \\ (-6)^2+(15)(-6)+54&=0 \\ 36-90+54&=0 \\ 0&=0 \end{aligned} \qquad \begin{aligned} x^2+15x+54&=0 \\ (-9)^2+(15)(-9)+54&=0 \\ 81-135+54&=0 \\ 0&=0 \end{aligned}$$

Therefore, the solution set is $\{-6, -9\}$.

EXAMPLE 4 Solve for x: $x^2+3x=0$.

Solution

The quadratic polynomial x^2+3x has a common factor, x. An equivalent equation is

$$x(x+3)=0$$

By the zero-product theorem:

$$x=0 \quad \text{or} \quad x+3=0$$
$$x=0 \quad \text{or} \quad x=-3$$

and the solution set is $\{0, -3\}$.

EXAMPLE 5 Solve for x: $2x^2 + 4x = x^2 + 5$.

Solution Before attempting a solution, express the given equation as an equivalent equation whose right side is zero:

$$2x^2 + 4x = x^2 + 5$$
$$x^2 + 4x - 5 = 0$$

Now factor:

$$(x + 5)(x - 1) = 0$$

By the zero-product theorem:

$$x + 5 = 0 \quad \text{or} \quad x - 1 = 0$$
$$x = -5 \quad \text{or} \quad x = 1$$

Check For $x = -5$,

$$2x^2 + 4x = x^2 + 5$$
$$(2)(-5)^2 + (4)(-5) = (-5)^2 + 5$$
$$50 + (-20) = 25 + 5$$
$$30 = 30$$

For $x = 1$,

$$2x^2 + 4x = x^2 + 5$$
$$(2)(1)^2 + (4)(1) = (1)^2 + 5$$
$$2 + 4 = 1 + 5$$
$$6 = 6$$

Since both answers check, the solution set is $\{-5, 1\}$.

RAPID CALCULATIONS (OPTIONAL)

A very useful application of factoring is to obtain shortcuts in arithmetic. The following examples illustrate the use of several factoring forms.

Sum and Difference Form: $(a + b)(a - b) = a^2 - b^2$

EXAMPLE 6

$$(29)(31) = (30 + 1)(30 - 1) = (30)^2 - 1 = 900 - 1 = 899$$

EXAMPLE 7

$$(52)(48) = (50 + 2)(50 - 2) = 2500 - 4 = 2496$$

Difference of Squares Form: $a^2 - b^2 = (a - b)(a + b)$

EXAMPLE 8

$$(35)^2 - (34)^2 = (35 - 34)(35 + 34) = (1)(69) = 69$$

EXAMPLE 9

$$(17)^2 - (15)^2 = (17 - 15)(17 + 15) = (2)(32) = 64$$

Perfect Square Form: $(a+b)^2 = a^2 + 2ab + b^2$

EXAMPLE 10

$$(32)^2 = (30+2)^2 = 900 + 2(60) + 4 = 1024$$

EXAMPLE 11

$$(21)^2 = (20+1)^2 = 400 + 40 + 1 = 441$$

First and Ten Form:

$$(10a+b)(10a+[10-b]) = a(a+1) \oplus b(10-b)$$

where $\oplus$ means *tack on,* as shown in the following examples.

The First and Ten form is used for numbers that are two-digit numbers having the same tens digit and with the sum of the units digits equal to 10.

EXAMPLE 12

$$(32)(38) = (3)(4) \oplus (2)(8) = 12 \oplus 16 = 1216$$

EXAMPLE 13

$$(65)(65) = (6)(7) \oplus (5)(5) = 42 \oplus 25 = 4225$$

EXAMPLE 14

$$(26)(24) = (2)(3) \oplus (6)(4) = 6 \oplus 24 = 624$$

EXERCISES

By factoring, determine the solution set of the equations in Exercises 1–50. Check all answers.

1. $(x+2)(x-3) = 0$

2. $(x-1)(x+4) = 0$

3. $(2y-3)(y+2) = 0$

4. $(3a+1)(5a-2) = 0$

5. $(x+5)(x+2) = 0$

6. $(t-3)(t-9) = 0$

7. $(4s-1)(2s+3) = 0$

8. $(3x-4)(6x-1) = 0$

9. $2y^2 + 7y + 6 = 0$

10. $x^2 + 6x = 0$

11. $x^2 - 3x + 2 = 0$

12. $2p^2 - 3p = 0$

13. $z^2 - 5z = 0$

14. $2n^2 - 32 = 0$

15. $x(x+2) = 0$

16. $x^2 - 8x + 12 = 0$

17. $x^2 + 6x = 27$

18. $8k - k^2 = 0$

19. $24x + 99 = 3x^2$

20. $15z + 3z^2 = z - 8$

21. $a^2 + 4a + 12 = 8a + a^2$

22. $x^2 - 2x = 0$

23. $x^2 - 2x = 3$

24. $(y+2)^2 = 3y^2 - 2y + 4$

25. $(x+1)(x-2)=4$
26. $(x-1)^2=x^2-9$
27. $y^2+7y=-10$
28. $x^2=6+x$
29. $a^2-12a-30=15$
30. $x^2+8x-20=4-2x$
31. $(m+3)(m+4)=0$
32. $(m+3)(m+4)=6$
33. $(x+3)(x-3)=8x$
34. $(x+2)(x-1)=x^2+1$
35. $x(x+2)(x-3)=0$
36. $x(x-1)(x+4)=0$
37. $x^2=9$
38. $15-2x=x^2$
39. $u^2=100$
40. $u^2=64$
41. $x^2=16$
42. $x^2=25$
43. $y^2=36$
44. $y^2=49$
45. $(x-5)^2=(x+5)^2$ ✓
46. $(x+1)(x^2-2x)=(x^2+x)(x-2)$
47. $(y+1)^3-y^3=1$
48. $(y+1)(y-1)=2y^2-5$
49. $x^3=8+x^3-2x^2$
50. $(x+3)(x+4)(x+5)(x+6)=0$
51. The square of a number is 91 more than 6 times the number. Find the number.
52. The sum of a number and its reciprocal is 2. Find the number.
53. The product of two consecutive odd integers is 255. Find the integers.
54. The product of two consecutive even integers is 528. Find the integers. $x(x+2)=528$ = x 7
55. If 18 is subtracted from 10 times a number, the result is one half the square of the number. Find the number.
56. $A=\pi R^2-\pi r^2$ is the formula for the area between two concentric circles.
    a. Express the right side of the formula in factored form.
    b. Using the factored form, calculate the area between two circles, where $R=43$ and $r=41$. Use $\pi=\frac{22}{7}$.
57. $M=\frac{4wx^2-5wLx+wL^2}{8}$ is the formula for the bending moment of a uniformly loaded beam having length L and load w pounds per unit length where x is the distance from one end.
    a. Express the numerator on the right side of the formula in factored form.
    b. Using the factored form, calculate M for $L=12$, $w=50$, and $x=4$.
58. $-16t^2+2000t-18{,}400=0$ is used to find the time a certain projectile is in flight. Find t.
59. $s^2=8rh-4h^2$ gives the span s of a circular arch whose height is h and whose radius is r.
    a. Express the right side of the formula in factored form.
    b. Solve for s if $r=50$ and $h=20$.
60. $P=EI-RI^2$ is a formula for electric power. Find the amperage I if $P=360$ watts, $E=110$ volts, $R=5$ ohms.

$360=110x-5x^2$

$5x^2-110x+360$

$I=4$

In Exercises 61–80, find the products by using the rapid calculation methods of this section.

61. (37)(43)
62. (84)(86)
63. (18)(22)
64. $(22)^2$
65. $(34)^2$
66. (31)(39)
67. $(41)^2 - (40)^2$
68. $(85)^2$
69. (27)(23)
70. $(44)^2 - (42)^2$
71. (38)(42)
72. (55)(45)
73. (35)(45)
74. (87)(93)
75. (87)(83)
76. $(61)^2 - (60)^2$
77. $(42)^2$
78. $(65)^2 - (63)^2$
79. (46)(44)
80. $(51)^2$

REVIEW EXERCISES

Simplify the products in Exercises 1–30.

1. $x^2 \cdot x^3$
2. $r^4 \cdot r^9$
3. $x^3 \cdot x$
4. $p^2 \cdot p^3 \cdot p^4$
5. $(-3x)(4x^3)$
6. $-a^3(2a^5)$
7. $(5n^3x)(-2x^3)$
8. $3(a^2)^3$
9. $3x(-2x)^2$
10. $x^{n+1} \cdot x^{n-1}$
11. $x(x^2 + 3x + 2)$
12. $x(x^3 + 2x - 1)$
13. $2x(3x^2 - 4x - 1)$
14. $4x(ax^2 - bx + c)$
15. $(x - 2)(x - 3)$
16. $(y + 1)(y - 4)$
17. $(2a + 3)(3a - 1)$
18. $(a + 5)^2$
19. $(5x + 1)(5x - 1)$
20. $(2y - 3)^2$
21. $x(x + 2)(2x - 7)$
22. $x^3(2x^2 + x - 2)$
23. $-x^4(3x^3 + 2x - 4)$
24. $(2x + y)(3x - 16y)$
25. $x(x + 4)(2x - 5)$
26. $2x(3x + 2)^2$
27. $(x + 2)(x + 3)^2$
28. $(x^2 + 3x + 2)(x - 4)$
29. $(2x^2 - x + 3)(3x + 1)$
30. $(x^2 + 5x + 6)(x^2 - 3x + 1)$

In Exercises 31–55, factor completely.

31. $3x^2 - 6x + 24xy$
32. $t^2 + 11t + 24$
33. $x^2 + 10x + 25$
34. $49y^4 - 1$
35. $x^3 - 1$
36. $a^3 + 1$
37. $-3x^3 + 27x$
38. $6a^2 - 7a - 3$
39. $36x + 3x^3 - 3x^5$
40. $100p^2 - 25q^2$
41. $64y^3 - 36y$
42. $x^6 - y^6$
43. $12x^2y - 22xy - 20y$
44. $8a^2 + 5ab - 3b^2$
45. $2y^5 - 162y$
46. $15ax^6 + 42ax^5 - 9ax^4$
47. $25r^2 + 10r + 1$
48. $36x^2 - 12x + 1$
49. $4p^2 - 20pq + 25q^2$
50. $x(y + 2) + 3(y + 2)$
51. $5(x - 3) + p(x - 3)$
52. $3x - x^2(x + 4)$
53. $y^2z(a - 1) + yz$
54. $x(a + 2)^2 + y(a + 2)$
55. $3(x + y) - 2(x + y)^2$

REVIEW EXERCISES

In Exercises 56–60, fill in the missing term so that the result is a perfect square trinomial.

56. $x^2 - 6x + (\quad\quad)$
57. $x^2 + 16x + (\quad\quad)$
58. $y^2 - 8y + (\quad\quad)$
59. $a^2 - (\quad\quad) + 36b^2$
60. $y^2 + (\quad\quad) + 49z^2$

Solve the equations in Exercises 61–70.

61. $2x^2 - 3x - 14 = 0$
62. $x^2 + 7x = 0$
63. $x^2 + 7x = 60$
64. $45y - 15y^2 = 0$
65. $t(t - 11) = -18$
66. $12z^2 + 24z + 12 = 0$
67. $2x - (x + 2) = 3x$
68. $x^2 + 6 = 7x$
69. $x^2 = 3x$
70. $x^2 = 64$

71. The product of two consecutive even integers is 18 more than 15 times the larger number. Find the two integers.

72. Five times the square of a number added to 10 times the number equals 315. Find the number.

73. $b^2 = c^2 - a^2$ is a formula for finding side b of a right triangle when the hypotenuse c and side a are given.
a. Rewrite the formula, expressing the right side in factored form.
b. Using the result of (a), calculate b for
1. $c = 85$ and $a = 84$
2. $c = 37$ and $a = 35$

74. $A = 2\pi rh + 2\pi r^2$ is a formula for the total area A of a right circular cylinder having radius r and height h.
a. Rewrite the formula, expressing the right side in factored form.
b. Using the result of (a), calculate A for $r = 15$ and $h = 20$. Use $\pi = \frac{22}{7}$.

75. $D = ckwL^2 - 4c^2kwL + 4c^3kw$ is a formula that gives the maximum deflection for a certain beam of length L.
a. Rewrite the formula, expressing the right side in factored form.
b. Using the result of (a), calculate D for $L = 12$, $c = \frac{1}{4}$, $w = 200$, and $k = \frac{1}{500}$.

76. $1600y = 1200x - x^2$ is an equation of the orbit of a certain projectile initially fired at 200 feet per second.
a. Find x for $y = 0$. (The largest value gives the range.)
b. Find x for $y = 200$. (This gives the horizontal distance the projectile has traveled when its vertical height is 200 feet.)

77. In chemistry, $x^2 = 4(1 - x)^2$ gives the number of moles, x, that react when 1 mole of pure ethyl alcohol is mixed with 1 mole of acetic acid. Find x.

FRACTIONS

In algebra, numbers may be designated by letters or numerals, and polynomials are formed by combining these numbers by means of the operations of addition, subtraction, and multiplication. If the numbers used are elements of the set of integers, then the polynomial represents an integer, because the set of integers is closed with respect to addition, subtraction, and multiplication. Thus a polynomial is considered to be an **integral algebraic expression.** However, it is desirable to consider a polynomial in a broader sense, and the numbers used in forming the polynomial may be elements of the set of rational numbers, the set of real numbers, or the set of complex numbers. Until it is stated otherwise, the numbers will be considered as elements of the set of real numbers.

A **rational algebraic expression** is an expression that is obtained by adding, subtracting, multiplying, or dividing polynomials. For example, the expressions

$$t - \frac{1}{t} + 5,\ \frac{y^2+9}{y+3},\ \text{and}\ \frac{x-2}{x^2-5x+6} + \frac{3x+5}{x^2-9}$$

are rational expressions.

The choice of the word *rational* to describe these expressions was influenced by the fact that these expressions designate rational numbers—numbers that are the "ratio" of two integers, a and b, $b \neq 0$—whenever the polynomials designate integers or rational numbers.

Similar to the polynomial, a rational algebraic expression is given a broader meaning. Until stated otherwise, *the numbers involved in forming a rational expression shall be considered as elements of the set of real numbers.*

A rational algebraic expression is also called an **algebraic fraction** or, for simplicity, a **fraction.**

4.1 SIMPLIFICATION OF FRACTIONS

From experience with the arithmetic of fractions, one learns that a fraction can be named in more than one way.

For example, by examining the geometric models illustrated in Figs. 4.1 and 4.2, it can be seen that $\frac{3}{4}$ and $\frac{9}{12}$ are names for the same number.

Figures 4.1 and 4.2 illustrate that further subdivisions of a basic unit cause a subdivision of the original parts of the unit used to represent the fraction.

Before stating a "fundamental theorem," the following definition is in order.

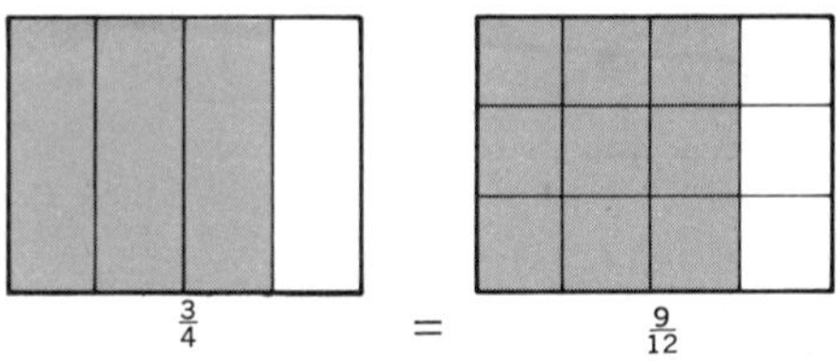

FIG. 4.1

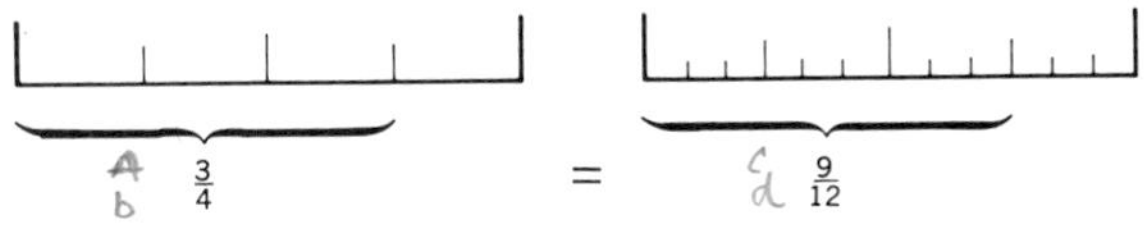

FIG. 4.2

DEFINITION OF EQUAL QUOTIENTS

If a, b, c, and d are real numbers and if $bd \neq 0$, then

$$\frac{a}{b} = \frac{c}{d} \text{ if and only if } ad = bc$$

Thus $\frac{3}{4} = \frac{9}{12}$ because $3(12) = 4(9)$ and $\frac{2}{3} = \frac{4}{x}$ if and only if $2x = 12$ and $x = 6$.

The following theorem is so important in connection with everything pertaining to fractions that it is called the fundamental theorem of fractions.

THE FUNDAMENTAL THEOREM OF FRACTIONS

If n, d, and k are real numbers and $d \neq 0$ and $k \neq 0$, then

$$\frac{nk}{dk} = \frac{n}{d}$$

This theorem is valid since $(nk)d = (dk)n$ by the associative and commutative axioms for multiplication.

The fundamental theorem of fractions is used to simplify a fraction—that is, to reduce a fraction to lowest terms.

The **simplification of a fraction, or the reduction of a fraction to lowest terms, means the renaming of a fraction so that the numerator and denominator do not have a factor in common.**

Since all common factors of the numerator and denominator must be removed, simplification of a fraction requires that the numerator and denominator be completely factored.

EXAMPLE 1 Simplify $\frac{60}{84}$

Solution

$$\frac{60}{84} = \frac{2 \cdot 2 \cdot 3 \cdot 5}{2 \cdot 2 \cdot 3 \cdot 7} = \frac{5 \cdot 12}{7 \cdot 12} = \frac{5}{7}$$

EXAMPLE 2 Reduce $\frac{3x^2}{15x^5}$ to lowest terms.

Solution

$$\frac{3x^2}{15x^5} = \frac{3 \cdot x \cdot x}{3 \cdot 5 \cdot x \cdot x \cdot x \cdot x \cdot x} = \frac{1 \cdot 3x^2}{5x^3 \cdot 3x^2} = \frac{1}{5x^3}$$

EXAMPLE 3 Simplify $\frac{35x^2y^3}{7xy}$

Solution

$$\frac{35x^2y^3}{7xy} = \frac{5 \cdot 7 \cdot xxyyy}{7xy} = \frac{5xy^2 \cdot 7xy}{1 \cdot 7xy} = \frac{5xy^2}{1} = 5xy^2$$

Note in the preceding example that $\frac{5xy^2}{1}$ names the same number as $5xy^2$, just as $\frac{5}{1}$ names the same number as 5. The integral forms $5xy^2$ and 5 are considered to be the simplified forms of $\frac{5xy^2}{1}$ and $\frac{5}{1}$, respectively.

4.1 SIMPLIFICATION OF FRACTIONS

The factoring technique is also used to reduce a fraction with a polynominal numerator or a polynomial denominator.

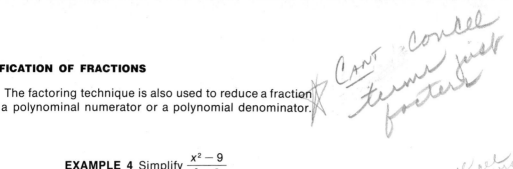

EXAMPLE 4 Simplify $\dfrac{x^2-9}{x^2-3x}$

Solution Factoring numerator and denominator,

$$\frac{x^2-9}{x^2-3x}=\frac{(x+3)(x-3)}{x(x-3)}=\frac{x+3}{x}$$

EXAMPLE 5 Reduce $\dfrac{x^2-1}{x-1}$ to lowest terms.

Solution

$$\frac{x^2-1}{x-1}=\frac{(x+1)(x-1)}{x-1}=\frac{(x+1)(x-1)}{1(x-1)}=\frac{x+1}{1}=x+1$$

EXAMPLE 6 Simplify $\dfrac{3x^2-75y^2}{3x^2-21xy+30y^2}$

Solution

$$\frac{3x^2-75y^2}{3x^2-21xy+30y^2}=\frac{3(x^2-25y^2)}{3(x^2-7xy+10y^2)}$$
$$=\frac{3(x-5y)(x+5y)}{3(x-5y)(x-2y)}$$
$$=\frac{x+5y}{x-2y}$$

Since the number $\dfrac{n}{d}$ can be considered as the quotient obtained when the numerator, n, is divided by the denominator, d, there are three numbers involved in this operation; accordingly, there are three signs associated with the number $\dfrac{n}{d}$:

the sign of the numerator n
the sign of the denominator d

and

the sign of the quotient $\dfrac{n}{d}$

As a result, there are four different ways to name a negative number such as $\dfrac{-3}{7}$:

$$\frac{-3}{7}=-\frac{3}{7}=\frac{3}{-7}=-\frac{-3}{-7}$$

The preferred form is $\dfrac{-3}{7}$, that is, the minus sign is placed in the numerator. It is very easy to "drop" a minus sign in a calculation, and this convention helps to prevent this error.

EXAMPLE 7 Simplify $\frac{21xy}{-14xz}$

Solution

$$\frac{21xy}{-14xz} = \frac{-21xy}{14xz} = \frac{(-3y)(7x)}{2z(7x)} = \frac{-3y}{2z}$$

Special attention is called to the forms $a - b$ and $b - a$, which are additive inverses of each other.

$$-(b - a) = -(b + (-a)) = -1(b) + (-1(-a))$$
$$= -b + a = a + (-b) = a - b$$

Thus

$$-(b - a) = a - b \quad \text{and} \quad a - b = -(b - a).$$

This property is needed sometimes in the process of renaming fractions. Its use is illustrated in the following examples.

EXAMPLE 8 Simplify $\frac{x-1}{1-x}$

Solution Since $1 - x = -(x - 1)$,

$$\frac{x-1}{1-x} = \frac{x-1}{-(x-1)} = \frac{1(x-1)}{(-1)(x-1)} = \frac{1}{-1} = -1$$

EXAMPLE 9 Simplify $\frac{15-5y}{y^2-3y}$

Solution

$$\frac{15-5y}{y^2-3y} = \frac{5(3-y)}{y(y-3)} = \frac{5 \cdot -(y-3)}{y \cdot (y-3)} = \frac{-5 \cdot (y-3)}{y \cdot (y-3)} = \frac{-5}{y}$$

EXERCISES

In Exercises 1–84 reduce each fraction to lowest terms.

1. $\frac{4}{12}$
2. $\frac{-12}{36}$
3. $\frac{15}{-25}$
4. $\frac{-42}{-105}$
5. $-\frac{150}{200}$
6. $\frac{60x}{90x}$
7. $\frac{6xy}{6xy}$
8. $\frac{7a^2b}{7ab}$
9. $\frac{25x^3}{75x^5}$
10. $\frac{75x^5}{25x^3}$
11. $-\frac{m}{m^3n}$
12. $\frac{3xy}{-6y}$

13. $\dfrac{-300x^3y^2}{-75xy}$

14. $\dfrac{80a^2b^2}{16ab}$

15. $-\dfrac{-a^3b}{-a^3b}$

16. $\dfrac{3x^2y^2}{xy}$

17. $\dfrac{xy}{3x^2y^2}$

18. $\dfrac{xy^2z}{-x^2y^2z^2}$

19. $\dfrac{-ab^2c}{-a^2b^2c^2}$

20. $\dfrac{3x(a+b)}{12x^2}$

21. $\dfrac{7x+21}{7x}$

22. $\dfrac{4y}{4y^2-8y}$

23. $\dfrac{x^2-4x}{x^2-2x}$

24. $\dfrac{x^2-4}{x^2-2x}$

25. $\dfrac{5y-40}{5y}$

26. $\dfrac{6xy}{2x^2y+6xy^2}$

27. $\dfrac{5x-5y}{5x+5y}$

28. $\dfrac{5x-5y}{x^2-xy}$

29. $\dfrac{y^2+5y}{25+5y}$

30. $\dfrac{u^2v+uv^2}{(u+v)^2}$

31. $\dfrac{4cd+2c^2}{4cd+8d^2}$

32. $\dfrac{3a+3b}{9a+9b}$

33. $\dfrac{4r+r^2}{4r+16}$

34. $\dfrac{9t^2-81}{t+3}$

35. $\dfrac{8a+8b}{8a-8b}$

36. $\dfrac{8a-8b}{8b-8a}$

37. $\dfrac{4m^2+4}{4m+4}$

38. $\dfrac{t-3}{2t^2-5t-3}$

39. $\dfrac{8y^2-12y}{4y}$

40. $\dfrac{(r+2s)^2}{(r+2s)^5}$

41. $\dfrac{y+y^2}{3y+3}$

42. $\dfrac{3a^2+3ab}{4b^2+4ab}$

43. $\dfrac{(c-d)^2}{6c-6d}$

44. $\dfrac{2u+2v}{6u+6v}$

45. $\dfrac{3y+y^2}{3y+9}$

46. $\dfrac{75n^2-3}{5n+1}$

47. $\dfrac{7x-7y}{7x+7y}$

48. $\dfrac{7x-7y}{7y-7x}$

49. $\dfrac{3a^2+3}{3a+3}$

50. $\dfrac{3t+1}{4-36t^2}$

51. $\dfrac{3x^2+6x}{3x}$

52. $\dfrac{(a-b)^3}{(a-b)^2}$

53. $\dfrac{x^2-9}{9-x^2}$

54. $\dfrac{3x+15}{x^2+3x-10}$

55. $\dfrac{x^2-1}{x^2+3x-4}$

56. $\dfrac{x^2+2x-8}{x^2-4}$

57. $\dfrac{4t^2-4t-24}{6t^2-36t+54}$

58. $\dfrac{z^2-10z+25}{z^2-z-20}$

59. $\dfrac{m^2n - mn^2 + mn}{m^2n + mn^2 - mn}$

60. $\dfrac{x^2y - xy^2 + xyz}{yz^2 - y^2z + xyz}$

61. $\dfrac{6x^2 - 6}{6x^2 + 36x - 42}$

62. $\dfrac{5 - x}{x^2 - 25}$

63. $\dfrac{5a^2 + 15a - 140}{10a^2 + 110a + 280}$

64. $\dfrac{5n^2 - 17n + 6}{5n^2 - 13n - 6}$

65. $\dfrac{9x^2 - 4y^2}{2y - 3x}$

66. $\dfrac{x^3 - 8}{x^2 + 2x - 8}$

67. $\dfrac{x^2 - 25}{x^3 + 125}$

68. $\dfrac{(r - s)(r - t)}{(t - r)(t - s)}$

69. $\dfrac{2y + 4}{y^2 - 2y - 8}$

70. $\dfrac{r^2 - 2s^2}{2s^2 - r^2}$

71. $\dfrac{a^2 - b^2}{(a - b)^2}$

72. $\dfrac{x^2 - 3x - 10}{x^2 - 2x - 15}$

73. $\dfrac{4a^2 - 4ab}{a^2 - b^2}$

74. $\dfrac{8t^2 - 12t - 20}{8t^2 - 28t + 20}$

75. $\dfrac{2n^3 + 4n^2 + 2n}{n^3 - n^2 - 2n}$

76. $\dfrac{x^4y^2 - 4x^3y^3}{x^3y^5 - 4x^2y^6}$

77. $\dfrac{7 - x}{x^2 - 49}$

78. $\dfrac{75n^2 - 3}{1 + 5n}$

79. $\dfrac{3n^3 - 21n^2 - 24n}{3n^3 - 3n}$

80. $\dfrac{49n^2 - 21n - 10}{49n^2 - 25}$

81. $\dfrac{6y^4 + 15y^3 - 9y^2}{9y^2 + 27y}$

82. $\dfrac{x^3 + 64}{x^2 - 16}$

83. $\dfrac{x^2 + 3x + 9}{x^3 - 27}$

84. $\dfrac{(a - b)(a - c)(b - c)}{(c - a)(c - b)(b - a)}$

4.2 RAISING A FRACTION TO HIGHER TERMS

In order to add or subtract certain fractions, the fractions must be renamed so that they have the same denominator, called a **common denominator.** The process of renaming a fraction by multiplying the numerator and denominator by the same number is called **raising the fraction to higher terms.** This process is justified by the fundamental theorem of fractions used in its symmetric form:

$$\frac{n}{d} = \frac{nk}{dk}$$

4.2 RAISING A FRACTION TO HIGHER TERMS

In practice, it is useful to consider the renaming of a fraction as a multiplication of the original fraction by the number 1, with 1 renamed as $\frac{k}{k}$. Thus

$$\frac{n}{d}=\frac{n}{d}\cdot 1=\frac{n}{d}\cdot\frac{k}{k}=\frac{nk}{dk}$$

EXAMPLE 1 Express the fraction $\frac{3}{5}$ in higher terms with denominator 20.

Solution

$$\frac{3}{5}=\frac{3k}{5k}=\frac{3k}{20}$$

Since $5k=20$, then $k=4$ and $3k=3\cdot 4=12$. Thus

$$\frac{3}{5}=\frac{3\cdot 4}{5\cdot 4}=\frac{12}{20}$$

In other words, the question is: "What number multiplied by 5 equals 20?" Clearly, the answer is 4. Thus 4 is the multiplier of the numerator and the denominator.

EXAMPLE 2 Raise $\frac{7}{9y}$ to higher terms with denominator $18y^3$.

Solution

$$\frac{7}{9y}=\frac{7\cdot k}{9y\cdot k}=\frac{7k}{18y^3}$$

Since $18y^3=9y\cdot 2y^2$, the multiplier k is $2y^2$.

In other words, the multiplier can be found by dividing the new denominator by the original denominator:

$$\frac{18y^3}{9y}=2y^2$$

Therefore

$$\frac{7}{9y}=\frac{7(2y^2)}{9y(2y^2)}=\frac{14y^2}{18y^3}$$

EXAMPLE 3 Raise $\frac{8}{15xy^2}$ to higher terms with denominator $45x^3y^3$.

Solution Find the multiplier:

$$\frac{45x^3y^3}{15xy^2}=3x^2y$$

Multiply the numerator and denominator by $3x^2y$:

$$\frac{8}{15xy^2}=\frac{8(3x^2y)}{15xy^2(3x^2y)}=\frac{24x^2y}{45x^3y^3}$$

Another type of problem uses the property that $x = \frac{x}{1}$ to build up a fraction or to change a polynomial into a rational expression with a designated denominator.

EXAMPLE 4 Rename 6 as a fraction with denominator 5.

Solution

$$6 = \frac{6}{1} = \frac{6(5)}{1(5)} = \frac{30}{5}$$

EXAMPLE 5 Express the polynomial $x - 2$ as a rational expression with denominator $x + 3$.

Solution

$$x - 2 = \frac{x-2}{1} = \frac{(x-2)(x+3)}{1(x+3)} = \frac{x^2+x-6}{x+3}$$

Some problems involve the signs of a fraction and the special property that $b - a = -(a - b)$.

EXAMPLE 6 Express $\frac{3}{7-x}$ with denominator $x - 7$.

Solution Since $7 - x = -(x - 7)$, then

$$\frac{3}{7-x} = \frac{3}{-(x-7)} = \frac{-3}{x-7}$$

EXAMPLE 7 Rename $\frac{x}{x+3}$ as an equal fraction with denominator $x^2 - 9$.

Solution First find the multiplier:

$$\frac{x^2-9}{x+3} = \frac{(x-3)(x+3)}{x+3} = x - 3$$

Thus

$$\frac{x}{x+3} = \frac{x(x-3)}{(x+3)(x-3)} = \frac{x^2-3x}{x^2-9}$$

EXAMPLE 8 Express $\frac{3}{x+2}$ in higher terms having the denominator $x^2 - 5x - 14$.

Solution First find the multiplier:

$$\frac{x^2-5x-14}{x+2} = \frac{(x-7)(x+2)}{x+2} = x - 7$$

Then

$$\frac{3}{x+2} = \frac{3(x-7)}{(x+2)(x-7)} = \frac{3x-21}{x^2-5x-14}$$

EXAMPLE 9 Find n so that $\frac{6}{6-x} = \frac{n}{x^2-36}$

Solution

$$\frac{x^2-36}{6-x} = \frac{(x+6)(x-6)}{(-1)(x-6)} = \frac{x+6}{-1} = (-1)(x+6)$$

$$\frac{6}{6-x} = \frac{6(-1)(x+6)}{(-1)(x-6)(-1)(x+6)} = \frac{-6(x+6)}{x^2-36}$$

Thus $n = -6(x+6)$.

EXERCISES

Express the fractions in Exercises 1–62 in terms of the denominators indicated.

1. $\frac{5}{9} = \frac{}{36}$
2. $\frac{3}{8} = \frac{}{56}$
3. $\frac{4}{7} = \frac{}{21}$
4. $\frac{3}{5} = \frac{}{25}$
5. $\frac{2}{-3} = \frac{}{42}$
6. $-5 = \frac{}{35}$
7. $\frac{4}{9} = \frac{}{36}$
8. $\frac{-2}{5} = \frac{}{20}$
9. $\frac{3}{-7} = \frac{}{42}$
10. $4 = \frac{}{-10}$
11. $\frac{x}{15} = \frac{}{45}$
12. $\frac{3}{4} = \frac{}{16x^2}$
13. $\frac{2}{5} = \frac{}{15xy}$
14. $\frac{3}{-5x} = \frac{}{45x^2}$
15. $\frac{2x}{15} = \frac{}{45x^2}$
16. $-\frac{5x}{7y^2} = \frac{}{21xy^3}$
17. $-\frac{2xy}{3z} = \frac{}{42x^2z^2}$
18. $\frac{a^2}{b^3} = \frac{}{4a^2b^4}$
19. $\frac{3x}{-8} = \frac{}{40x^2}$
20. $-\frac{2x}{5y^2} = \frac{}{30xy^3}$
21. $-\frac{3xy}{7z} = \frac{}{42xyz}$
22. $\frac{a}{b^2} = \frac{}{5ab^3}$
23. $\frac{5}{x+1} = \frac{}{2x+2}$
24. $\frac{x}{2x-5} = \frac{}{6x-15}$
25. $\frac{x-3}{x+4} = \frac{}{5x+20}$
26. $\frac{2x}{x-2} = \frac{}{x^2-2x}$
27. $\frac{x}{x-5} = \frac{}{2x^2-10x}$
28. $\frac{2}{y} = \frac{}{y^2+2y}$
29. $\frac{3y}{y+3} = \frac{}{y^2-9}$
30. $\frac{t+3}{t-2} = \frac{}{t^2+t-6}$

31. $x+2=\frac{\quad}{x+1}$

32. $\frac{1}{4x-3}=\frac{\quad}{3-4x}$

33. $\frac{-x}{7-x}=\frac{\quad}{x-7}$

34. $\frac{1}{5-2x}=\frac{\quad}{2x^2-5x}$

35. $\frac{y}{4-y}=\frac{\quad}{y^2-16}$

36. $\frac{x+3}{x+4}=\frac{\quad}{x^2+6x+8}$

37. $\frac{a+1}{a-3}=\frac{\quad}{a^2-2a-3}$

38. $x=\frac{\quad}{6x^2-6x}$

39. $\frac{t-2}{t+2}=\frac{\quad}{14+9t+t^2}$

40. $\frac{a-b}{a+b}=\frac{\quad}{(a+b)^2}$

41. $\frac{2x}{2x-1}=\frac{\quad}{4x^2-1}$

42. $\frac{1+t}{1+3t}=\frac{\quad}{18t^2+6t}$

43. $\frac{r}{r+4}=\frac{\quad}{r^2+r-12}$

44. $\frac{u-5}{u-6}=\frac{\quad}{u^2-4u-12}$

45. $6x-5=\frac{\quad}{x-2}$

46. $\frac{1}{5-6y}=\frac{\quad}{6y-5}$

47. $\frac{-t}{1-t}=\frac{\quad}{t-1}$

48. $\frac{x}{5-x}=\frac{\quad}{x^2-25}$

49. $\frac{-1}{7-2r}=\frac{\quad}{4r^2-49}$

50. $\frac{x+2}{x+4}=\frac{\quad}{2x^3+5x^2-12x}$

51. $\frac{y-1}{y-2}=\frac{\quad}{12-8y+y^2}$

52. $\frac{6x}{x+6}=\frac{\quad}{2x^2+2x-60}$

53. $x=\frac{\quad}{5x+10}$

54. $\frac{2x+3y}{2x-3y}=\frac{\quad}{(2x-3y)^2}$

55. $\frac{x}{3}=\frac{\quad}{3x^2-75x}$

56. $\frac{3}{3y+1}=\frac{\quad}{1-9y^2}$

57. $\frac{6a^2}{5a-1}=\frac{\quad}{10a^2+13a-3}$

58. $\frac{r+1}{r+2}=\frac{\quad}{7r^4-28r^2}$

59. $\frac{-a}{2}=\frac{\quad}{4a^2-10a}$

60. $\frac{9}{x^2-9}=\frac{\quad}{(x-3)(x+3)^2}$

61. $\frac{5n+5}{n-1}=\frac{\quad}{3n^3-3n}$

62. $\frac{ab}{(a-b)^2}=\frac{\quad}{(b-a)^2}$

4.3 ADDITION AND SUBTRACTION

The procedures for adding and subtracting algebraic fractions are based on the theorems for the addition and subtraction of quotients of real numbers and on the fundamental theorem of fractions.

Let n, m, and d be any real numbers with $d \neq 0$.

★ 2 fractions only:

$\frac{3}{4} + \frac{1}{7}$ $\frac{3}{4} \times \frac{1}{7} = \frac{21+4}{28}$

cross multiply & bottom multiply

THE ADDITION OF QUOTIENTS THEOREM

$$\frac{n}{d} + \frac{m}{d} = \frac{n+m}{d}$$

THE SUBTRACTION OF QUOTIENTS THEOREM

$$\frac{n}{d} - \frac{m}{d} = \frac{n-m}{d}$$

Examination of the addition and subtraction theorems for the quotients of real numbers reveals that fractions cannot be combined into a single fraction by the operations of addition and subtraction unless the denominators of the fractions being combined are the same. The fundamental theorem of fractions provides a technique for renaming fractions so that they will have a common denominator. A common denominator can always be found by multiplying the denominators of the fractions that are to be added or subtracted.

To provide insight into this process, a visual model for the addition of two fractions of arithmetic is provided in Fig. 4.3.

Now consider the addition problem from arithmetic,

$$\frac{5}{12} + \frac{7}{18}$$

By multiplying the denominators, a common denominator can be found: $12 \cdot 18 = 216$:

$$\frac{5}{12} = \frac{5 \cdot 18}{12 \cdot 18} = \frac{90}{216} \quad \text{and} \quad \frac{7}{18} = \frac{7 \cdot 12}{18 \cdot 12} = \frac{84}{216}$$

Thus

$$\frac{5}{12} + \frac{7}{18} = \frac{90}{216} + \frac{84}{216} = \frac{90+84}{216} = \frac{174}{216}$$

However, $\frac{174}{216}$ is not in its lowest terms and so must be simplified:

$$\frac{174}{216} = \frac{2 \cdot 87}{2 \cdot 108} = \frac{2 \cdot 3 \cdot 29}{2 \cdot 3 \cdot 36} = \frac{29}{36}$$

Thus

$$\frac{5}{12} + \frac{7}{18} = \frac{29}{36}$$

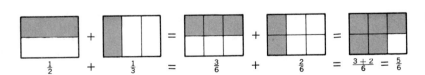

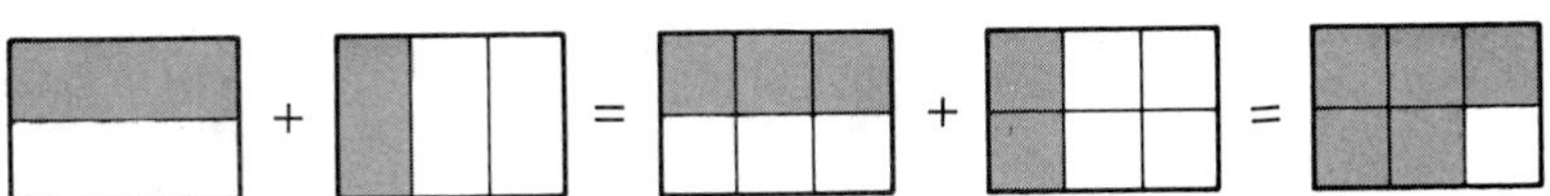

$$\frac{1}{2} + \frac{1}{3} = \frac{3}{6} + \frac{2}{6} = \frac{3+2}{6} = \frac{5}{6}$$

FIG. 4.3

There is another procedure for finding a common denominator that simplifies the arithmetical calculations involved and sometimes, but not always, avoids the final simplification. This procedure is called finding the **least common denominator,** or **L.C.D.** The objective is to find the smallest common denominator—that is, the smallest number that has each of the original denominators for a factor. Thus, to find the least common denominator, the original denominators must be factored into prime factors. The L.C.D. is the product of all the primes that occur in each factorization, with each prime taken the greatest number of times it occurs in any denominator.

For example, to find the L.C.D. of $\frac{5}{12}$ and $\frac{7}{18}$, factor 12 and 18:

$$12 = 2 \cdot 2 \cdot 3 \quad \text{and} \quad 18 = 2 \cdot 3 \cdot 3$$

Then the L.C.D. is $2 \cdot 2 \cdot 3 \cdot 3 = 36$.

Now the sum $\frac{5}{12} + \frac{7}{18}$ is obtained as follows:

$$\frac{5}{12} + \frac{7}{18} = \frac{15}{36} + \frac{14}{36} = \frac{29}{36}$$

This procedure is similar to the one that is used in adding or subtracting algebraic fractions, with the objective of finding the smallest number for the common denominator replaced by the objective of finding the polynomial of smallest degree for the common denominator.

EXAMPLE 1 Express $\frac{3}{16x} + \frac{5}{16x}$ as a single fraction.

Solution The denominators of the two fractions are the same; therefore, the addition of quotients theorem can be applied directly:

$$\frac{3}{16x} + \frac{5}{16x} = \frac{3+5}{16x} = \frac{8}{16x}$$

But

$$\frac{8}{16x} = \frac{8 \cdot 1}{8 \cdot 2x} = \frac{1}{2x}$$

Therefore, in lowest terms,

$$\frac{3}{16x} + \frac{5}{16x} = \frac{1}{2x}$$

EXAMPLE 2 Express $\frac{5}{6x^2} + \frac{1}{9x}$ as a single fraction.

Solution The two fractions have unlike denominators.

1. Find the L.C.D. by factoring $6x^2$ and $9x$:
   $$6x^2 = 2 \cdot 3 \cdot x \cdot x \quad \text{and} \quad 9x = 3 \cdot 3 \cdot x$$
   Thus the L.C.D. is $2 \cdot 3 \cdot 3 \cdot x \cdot x = 18x^2$.
2. Rename the fractions by using the fundamental theorem of fractions:
   $$\frac{5}{6x^2} = \frac{5 \cdot 3}{6x^2 \cdot 3} = \frac{15}{18x^2} \quad \text{and} \quad \frac{1}{9x} = \frac{1 \cdot 2x}{9x \cdot 2x} = \frac{2x}{18x^2}$$
3. Apply the theorem for the addition of quotients:
   $$\frac{5}{6x^2} + \frac{1}{9x} = \frac{15}{18x^2} + \frac{2x}{18x^2} = \frac{15 + 2x}{18x^2}$$
   $$= \frac{2x + 15}{18x^2} \quad \text{(Conventional form)}$$

EXAMPLE 3 Express $\frac{3}{y} + \frac{2}{3} - \frac{y}{y + 3}$ as a single fraction.

Solution

1. The L.C.D. is $3y(y + 3)$.
2. Rename the fractions so that each has the denominator $3y(y + 3)$:
   $$\frac{3}{y} = \frac{3 \cdot 3(y + 3)}{y \cdot 3(y + 3)} = \frac{9y + 27}{3y(y + 3)}$$
   $$\frac{2}{3} = \frac{2 \cdot y(y + 3)}{3 \cdot y(y + 3)} = \frac{2y^2 + 6y}{3y(y + 3)}$$
   $$\frac{y}{y + 3} = \frac{y \cdot 3y}{(y + 3) \cdot 3y} = \frac{3y^2}{3y(y + 3)}$$
3. Apply the theorem for the addition and subtraction of quotients and combine like terms:
   $$\frac{9y + 27}{3y(y + 3)} + \frac{2y^2 + 6y}{3y(y + 3)} - \frac{3y^2}{3y(y + 3)}$$
   $$= \frac{(9y + 27) + (2y^2 + 6y) - (3y^2)}{3y(y + 3)}$$
   $$= \frac{-y^2 + 15y + 27}{3y(y + 3)}$$

In subtracting fractions, it is especially important to remember that the bar, the horizontal line separating the numerator and denominator, is a grouping symbol indicating that the numerator is to be considered as a single number and that the denominator is to be considered as a single number.

In Example 4 the parentheses are used to enclose the numerator of each fraction in order to emphasize this fact.

EXAMPLE 4 Simplify $\dfrac{5}{x^2-6x+9}-\dfrac{4}{x^2-9}$

Solution

1. $x^2-6x+9=(x-3)(x-3)$

   $x^2-9=(x-3)(x+3)$

   Thus the L.C.D. $=(x-3)^2(x+3)$.

2. $\dfrac{5}{(x-3)^2}=\dfrac{5(x+3)}{(x-3)^2(x+3)}=\dfrac{5x+15}{(x-3)^2(x+3)}$

   $\dfrac{4}{x^2-9}=\dfrac{4(x-3)}{(x-3)(x+3)(x-3)}=\dfrac{4x-12}{(x-3)^2(x+3)}$

3. $\dfrac{5}{(x-3)^2}-\dfrac{4}{x^2-9}=\dfrac{(5x+15)}{(x-3)^2(x+3)}-\dfrac{(4x-12)}{(x-3)^2(x+3)}$

   $=\dfrac{(5x+15)-(4x-12)}{(x-3)^2(x+3)}$

   $=\dfrac{x+27}{(x-3)^2(x+3)}$

EXAMPLE 5 Simplify $\dfrac{2}{x^2-4x+4}+\dfrac{3x}{4-x^2}$

Solution

1. $x^2-4x+4=(x-2)(x-2)$

   $4-x^2=-(x^2-4)=-(x-2)(x+2)$

   It is advisable at this time to rewrite the second fraction.

   $\dfrac{3x}{4-x^2}=\dfrac{3x}{-(x^2-4)}=\dfrac{-3x}{x^2-4}$

   Thus the L.C.D. $=(x-2)(x-2)(x+2)$

   $=(x-2)^2(x+2)$

2. $\dfrac{2}{x^2-4x+4}=\dfrac{2(x+2)}{(x-2)(x-2)(x+2)}=\dfrac{2x+4}{(x-2)^2(x+2)}$

   $\dfrac{-3x}{x^2-4}=\dfrac{-3x(x-2)}{(x-2)(x-2)(x+2)}=\dfrac{-3x^2+6x}{(x-2)^2(x+2)}$

3. $\dfrac{2}{x^2-4x+4}+\dfrac{3x}{4-x^2}=\dfrac{2}{x^2-4x+4}+\dfrac{-3x}{x^2-4}$

   $=\dfrac{(2x+4)+(-3x^2+6x)}{(x-2)^2(x+2)}$

   $=\dfrac{-3x^2+8x+4}{(x-2)^2(x+2)}$

EXAMPLE 6 Simplify $\dfrac{3}{x-2} - \dfrac{2}{3x} - \dfrac{18}{3x^2 - 6x}$

Solution

1. $x - 2 = x - 2$ } These expressions are already
   $3x = 3x$ } in factored form.
   $3x^2 - 6x = 3x(x-2)$
   Thus the L.C.D. $= 3x(x-2)$.

2. $$\frac{3}{x-2} = \frac{3 \cdot 3x}{3x(x-2)} = \frac{9x}{3x(x-2)}$$
   $$\frac{2}{3x} = \frac{2(x-2)}{3x(x-2)} = \frac{2x-4}{3x(x-2)}$$
   $$\frac{18}{3x^2-6x} = \frac{18}{3x(x-2)}$$

3. $$\frac{3}{x-2} - \frac{2}{3x} - \frac{18}{3x^2-6x}$$
   $$= \frac{9x}{3x(x-2)} - \frac{2x-4}{3x(x-2)} - \frac{18}{3x(x-2)}$$
   $$= \frac{9x - (2x-4) - 18}{3x(x-2)}$$
   $$= \frac{9x - 2x + 4 - 18}{3x(x-2)}$$
   $$= \frac{7x-14}{3x(x-2)}$$
   $$= \frac{7(x-2)}{3x(x-2)}$$
   $$= \frac{7}{3x}$$

EXERCISES

Rewrite each of Exercises 1–60 as a single fraction in lowest terms.

1. $\dfrac{3}{7} + \dfrac{2}{7}$

2. $\dfrac{1}{5} - \dfrac{4}{5}$

3. $\dfrac{2}{b} + \dfrac{5}{b} - \dfrac{2a}{b}$

4. $\dfrac{x}{x+1} + \dfrac{2x}{x+1} - \dfrac{3x}{x+1}$

5. $\dfrac{3x+2y}{5} - \dfrac{2x+3y}{5}$

6. $\dfrac{1}{6} + \dfrac{2}{15} - \dfrac{1}{3}$

7. $\dfrac{3}{4} - \dfrac{7}{12} + \dfrac{5}{8}$

8. $\dfrac{2}{3} + \dfrac{3}{5} + \dfrac{5}{2}$

9. $\dfrac{1}{2a} + \dfrac{3}{6a} + \dfrac{5}{14a}$

10. $\dfrac{x}{6y} - \dfrac{2}{8y} + \dfrac{5x}{24y}$ $= \dfrac{3x-2y}{8y}$

11. $\frac{2x}{9y^2} - \frac{3x}{8y^2} + \frac{5x}{18y^2}$

12. $\frac{5x-2}{x} - \frac{2x-5}{x}$

13. $\frac{4}{9} + \frac{5}{12} - \frac{2}{15}$

14. $\frac{5}{14} + \frac{3}{28} - \frac{1}{21}$

15. $\frac{1}{3} + \frac{1}{4} + \frac{1}{5} + \frac{1}{6}$

16. $\frac{2}{3y} + \frac{5}{12y} + \frac{1}{18y}$

17. $\frac{1}{2x} + \frac{1}{6x} - \frac{1}{3x}$

18. $\frac{2}{x} + \frac{3}{x^2}$

19. $\frac{1}{2x} + \frac{4}{3x^2} - \frac{1}{6x^3}$

20. $\frac{3}{x} + \frac{2}{x+1}$

21. $\frac{1}{b-1} - \frac{1}{b}$

22. $\frac{x}{x+2} + \frac{1}{x} + \frac{1}{2}$

23. $\frac{4}{y+1} - \frac{3}{y+2}$

24. $\frac{2}{a+3} + \frac{5}{a} - \frac{1}{3}$

25. $\frac{3}{5y} + \frac{2}{15y^2} - \frac{1}{10y^3}$

26. $\frac{1}{a} + \frac{2}{a+1}$

27. $\frac{x}{y+1} - \frac{x}{y}$

28. $\frac{m}{m+4} + \frac{1}{m} + \frac{3}{4}$

29. $\frac{2}{x-1} - \frac{x}{x-2}$

30. $\frac{3}{a} + \frac{2}{a+5} - \frac{1}{5}$

31. $\frac{a}{b} + \frac{b}{a}$

32. $\frac{5x}{(3x-1)^2} + \frac{4}{3x-1}$

33. $\frac{y}{(2y-3)^2} + \frac{5}{2y-3} - \frac{3}{2y+3}$

34. $2x + \frac{3}{x}$

35. $2x - \frac{x^2}{x+1}$

36. $2 - \frac{x-1}{x+1}$

37. $\frac{x}{x^2+5x+4} + \frac{3}{x^2+4x+3}$

38. $\frac{x+2}{3x^2+5x+2} - \frac{x+3}{3x^2-16x-12}$

39. $\frac{2y}{y^2-5y+6} + \frac{3}{2+3y-2y^2}$

40. $\frac{2}{x-2} + \frac{3}{2-x}$

41. $\frac{a-2}{3a+3} + \frac{a-3}{2a+2}$

42. $\frac{x}{5x-5} - \frac{2}{3-3x}$

43. $\frac{x^2+3}{24-2x-x^2} + \frac{2x+1}{2x-8}$

44. $\frac{2}{c-5} + \frac{3}{c+5} - 1$

45. $\frac{3}{y^2-5y} + \frac{2}{y^2+5y} - \frac{4}{y^2-25}$

46. $\frac{1}{x^2-49} + \frac{1}{(x+7)^2} - \frac{1}{(x-7)^2}$

47. $1 + \frac{2}{x} - \frac{x-1}{x^2-x}$

48. $2a - 5 + \frac{25}{2a+5}$

49. $\frac{x}{x+y} + \frac{y}{x-y} - \frac{2xy}{x^2-y^2}$

50. $\frac{7y}{2y^2+5y-3} - \frac{10y}{3y^2+8y-3}$

51. $\frac{a}{b-a} + \frac{b}{a-b}$

52. $\frac{x+7}{4-6x} + \frac{3x^2+14}{9x^2-4}$

53. $\frac{y+9}{4y^2-5y-6} - \frac{y+7}{5y^2-11y+2}$

54. $\frac{5}{2x+8} - \frac{7}{3x-12} + \frac{20}{x^2-16}$

55. $\dfrac{1}{a^2-1} - \dfrac{1}{a^2+2a+1}$

56. $\dfrac{2}{2x+x^2} - \dfrac{3}{2x-x^2} - \dfrac{4}{x^2-4}$

57. $\dfrac{t^2-2t-21}{t^2-4t-5} + \dfrac{t-6}{5-t}$

58. $\dfrac{x^2-2x+4}{x-2} - \dfrac{x^2+2x+4}{x+2} - \dfrac{8x}{x^2-4}$

59. $\dfrac{4a^2}{x^2-a^2} - \dfrac{x-a}{x+a} - \dfrac{x+a}{x-a}$

60. $\dfrac{x+a}{x^3-a^3} - \dfrac{1}{x^2-a^2}$

4.4 MULTIPLICATION AND DIVISION

MULTIPLICATION

THEOREM: PRODUCT OF FRACTIONS

The product of two fractions is obtained by multiplying the numerators to obtain the new numerator and by multiplying the denominators to obtain the new denominator.

In symbols, if n, d, r, and s are any real numbers such that $d \neq 0$ and $s \neq 0$, then

$$\frac{n}{d} \cdot \frac{r}{s} = \frac{nr}{ds}$$

EXAMPLE 1 Express $\dfrac{3}{5} \cdot \dfrac{2}{7}$ as a single fraction.

Solution $\dfrac{3}{5} \cdot \dfrac{2}{7} = \dfrac{3 \cdot 2}{5 \cdot 7} = \dfrac{6}{35}$

EXAMPLE 2 Simplify $\dfrac{5}{8} \cdot \dfrac{4}{15}$

Solution $\dfrac{5}{8} \cdot \dfrac{4}{15} = \dfrac{5 \cdot 4}{8 \cdot 15} = \dfrac{5 \cdot 4}{(5 \cdot 3)(4 \cdot 2)} = \dfrac{1}{6}$

EXAMPLE 3 Simplify $\frac{3}{10} \cdot \frac{5}{12} \cdot \frac{4}{24}$

Solution

First method:

$$\frac{3}{10} \cdot \frac{5}{12} \cdot \frac{4}{24} = \frac{3 \cdot 5 \cdot 4}{10 \cdot 12 \cdot 24} = \frac{60}{2880}$$

$$= \frac{2 \cdot 2 \cdot 3 \cdot 5}{2 \cdot 2 \cdot 2 \cdot 2 \cdot 2 \cdot 2 \cdot 3 \cdot 3 \cdot 5} = \frac{1}{48}$$

Second method:

$$\frac{3}{10} \cdot \frac{5}{12} \cdot \frac{4}{24} = \frac{3}{10} \cdot \frac{5}{12} \cdot \frac{1}{6}$$

$$= \frac{3 \cdot 5}{(2 \cdot 5)(3 \cdot 4) \cdot 6} = \frac{1}{48}$$

Notice how the arithmetic in Example 3 was much simpler when the fractions were reduced as soon as possible rather than multiplying everything first.

EXAMPLE 4 Express $\frac{7x^2}{3y} \cdot \frac{12y^2}{35x^3}$ as a simplified single fraction.

Solution

$$\frac{7x^2}{3y} \cdot \frac{12y^2}{35x^3} = \frac{7 \cdot 12x^2y^2}{3 \cdot 35x^3y}$$

(Using the commutative and associative axioms to rearrange the factors so that the numerals occur first and the letters are arranged in alphabetical order)

$$= \frac{4y(3 \cdot 7x^2y)}{5x(3 \cdot 7x^2y)}$$

(Rearranging the factors to form the pattern $\frac{ak}{bk}$)

$$= \frac{4y}{5x}$$

(Since $(3 \cdot 7x^2y)$ is a common factor, the fraction can be reduced)

EXAMPLE 5 Simplify $\frac{t^2 + 3t}{6t - 2} \cdot \frac{9t^2 - 1}{t^2 - 9}$

Solution

$$\frac{t^2 + 3t}{6t - 2} \cdot \frac{9t^2 - 1}{t^2 - 9} = \frac{t(t + 3)}{2(3t - 1)} \cdot \frac{(3t - 1)(3t + 1)}{(t - 3)(t + 3)}$$

(Factoring)

$$= \frac{t(3t + 1)(t + 3)(3t - 1)}{2(t - 3)(t + 3)(3t - 1)}$$

(Rearranging factors)

$$= \frac{t(3t + 1)}{2(t - 3)}$$

(Eliminating the common factors)

The final simplified fraction in Example 5 is left in factored form.

Note that each fraction was expressed in factored form, and the terms were rearranged to simplify reducing.

$\frac{\frac{3}{4}}{\frac{7}{8}} = \frac{3}{4} \cdot \frac{8}{7}$

EXAMPLE 6 Simplify $\dfrac{x^2+3x+2}{x^2-4x-12} \cdot \dfrac{x-6}{x+1}$

Solution First factor the trinomials, if possible:

$$\frac{x^2+3x+2}{x^2-4x-12} = \frac{(x+2)(x+1)}{(x+2)(x-6)}$$

Thus

$$\begin{aligned}\frac{x^2+3x+2}{x^2-4x-12} \cdot \frac{x-6}{x+1} &= \frac{(x+2)(x+1)}{(x+2)(x-6)} \cdot \frac{(x-6)}{(x+1)} \\ &= \frac{(x+1)}{(x-6)} \cdot \frac{(x-6)}{(x+1)} \\ &= \frac{(x-6)(x+1)}{(x-6)(x+1)} \\ &= 1\end{aligned}$$

Note that the first fraction in Example 6 was simplified before the two fractions were multiplied. It is usually desirable to reduce a fraction as soon as possible to avoid any cumbersome arithmetic or algebra.

DIVISION

By the definition of division, $\frac{10}{2}$ represents the number that must be multiplied by 2 to produce 10. Thus $\frac{10}{2} = 5$ since $2 \cdot 5 = 10$.

Similarly, $\frac{2}{3} \div \frac{5}{7}$ represents the number $\frac{a}{b}$ that must be multiplied by $\frac{5}{7}$ to produce $\frac{2}{3}$.

$$\frac{5}{7} \cdot \frac{a}{b} = \frac{2}{3}$$

Multiplying each side by $\frac{7}{5}$,

$$\frac{7}{5} \cdot \frac{5}{7} \cdot \frac{a}{b} = \frac{2}{3} \cdot \frac{7}{5} \quad \text{and} \quad \frac{a}{b} = \frac{2}{3} \cdot \frac{7}{5}$$

Thus,

$$\frac{2}{3} \div \frac{5}{7} = \frac{2}{3} \cdot \frac{7}{5} = \frac{14}{15}$$

We say that $\frac{7}{5}$ is obtained by *inverting* $\frac{5}{7}$.

Generalizing this result, the following theorem can be stated.

THEOREM: QUOTIENT OF FRACTIONS

The quotient of one fraction divided by another fraction is obtained by inverting the divisor and multiplying the resulting fractions.

In symbols, for n, d, r, and s any real numbers with $d \neq 0$, $s \neq 0$, and $r \neq 0$,

$$\frac{n}{d} \div \frac{r}{s} = \frac{n}{d} \cdot \frac{s}{r} = \frac{ns}{dr}$$

EXAMPLE 7 Express $\frac{3}{5} \div \frac{1}{4}$ as a single fraction.

Solution

$$\frac{3}{5} \div \frac{1}{4} = \frac{3}{5} \cdot \frac{4}{1} = \frac{12}{5}$$

EXAMPLE 8 Simplify $\frac{3a^2}{5b^3} \div \frac{6a}{10b}$

Solution

$$\frac{3a^2}{5b^3} \div \frac{6a}{10b} = \frac{3a^2}{5b^3} \cdot \frac{10b}{6a}$$

$$= \frac{(3a^2)(10b)}{(6a)(5b^3)} = \frac{(a)(2)}{(2)(b^2)} = \frac{a}{b^2}$$

EXAMPLE 9 Simplify $\frac{x+1}{x} \div \frac{x^2+3x+2}{x^2+x}$ by expressing the indicated quotient as a single fraction in lowest terms.

Solution

$$\frac{x+1}{x} \div \frac{x^2+3x+2}{x^2+x} = \frac{x+1}{x} \cdot \frac{x^2+x}{x^2+3x+2}$$

$$= \frac{x+1}{x} \cdot \frac{x(x+1)}{(x+2)(x+1)}$$

$$= \frac{x(x+1)(x+1)}{x(x+2)(x+1)}$$

$$= \frac{x+1}{x+2}$$

EXAMPLE 10 Simplify $\frac{x^2+4x}{x^3+4x^2+4x} \div \frac{5x+20}{x^3-4x^2-12x}$ by expressing the indicated quotient as a single fraction in lowest terms.

Solution

$$\frac{x^2+4x}{x^3+4x^2+4x} \cdot \frac{x^3-4x^2-12x}{5x+20}$$

$$= \frac{x(x+4)(x)(x+2)(x-6)}{x(x+2)(x+2)5(x+4)}$$

$$= \frac{x(x-6)(x)(x+2)(x+4)}{5(x+2)(x)(x+2)(x+4)}$$

$$= \frac{x(x-6)}{5(x+2)}$$

EXERCISES

Simplify Exercises 1–60.

1. $\dfrac{2}{3} \cdot \dfrac{4}{3}$

2. $\dfrac{3}{8} \cdot \dfrac{16}{27}$

3. $\dfrac{5}{8} \cdot \dfrac{2}{3} \cdot \dfrac{3}{5}$

4. $\dfrac{1}{10} \cdot \dfrac{4}{5} \cdot \dfrac{7}{12}$

5. $\dfrac{2}{3} \div \dfrac{4}{3}$

6. $\dfrac{3}{8} \div \dfrac{1}{4}$

7. $\dfrac{1}{3} \div \dfrac{1}{9}$

8. $\left(\dfrac{2}{3} \cdot \dfrac{3}{5}\right) \div \dfrac{5}{12}$

9. $\left(\dfrac{2}{3} \div \dfrac{3}{5}\right) \cdot \dfrac{5}{12}$

10. $\left(\dfrac{1}{4} \div \dfrac{2}{3}\right) \div \dfrac{3}{8}$

11. $\dfrac{3x}{y-2} \cdot \dfrac{2y}{x-3}$

12. $\dfrac{3}{y} \cdot \dfrac{y^2}{6xy}$

13. $\dfrac{2}{5ab^2} \cdot \dfrac{15ab}{22}$

14. $\dfrac{4c-8}{14c} \cdot \dfrac{35c}{6c-12}$

15. $\dfrac{4abc}{-6xy^2} \cdot \dfrac{-8x^2y}{12a^2bc^2}$

16. $\dfrac{(u-v)^2}{2uv} \cdot \dfrac{8u^3v^3}{(v-u)^3}$

17. $\dfrac{x+y}{4} \cdot \dfrac{x-y}{4}$

18. $\dfrac{2}{x} \cdot \dfrac{x^2}{4}$

19. $\dfrac{5}{3x^2y} \cdot \dfrac{21y^2}{7x}$

20. $\dfrac{3a+3}{25a} \cdot \dfrac{5a}{9a+9}$

21. $\dfrac{-6xyz}{4a^2b} \cdot \dfrac{10ab^2}{15xyz^2}$

22. $\dfrac{r+s}{rs} \cdot \dfrac{r^2s^2}{(r+s)^2}$

23. $\dfrac{a^2-25}{5} \cdot \dfrac{10a}{a^2+4a-5}$

24. $\dfrac{x^2-4xy+4y^2}{9x^3} \cdot \dfrac{18x}{4x-8y}$

25. $\dfrac{x^2+6x+9}{3x^2+6x} \cdot \dfrac{x^2-4}{x^2+x-6}$

26. $\dfrac{3x^2+3}{x^2-x-6} \cdot \dfrac{x^2-5x+6}{x^2+1}$

27. $\dfrac{a^2-b^2}{3} \cdot \dfrac{3a-3b}{a^2+ab}$

28. $\dfrac{5y^2-5y}{4y-40} \cdot \dfrac{y^3}{3} \cdot \dfrac{y^2-9y-10}{2-2y}$

29. $\dfrac{2n^2-3n-2}{n^3+2n^2-3n} \cdot \dfrac{6n^2-6n}{6n^2+3n}$

30. $\dfrac{x^2-5x}{x^2-3x+2} \cdot \dfrac{x^2-x}{5x-25}$

31. $\dfrac{a^2-3a+2}{a-1} \cdot \dfrac{a+5}{a^2+3a-10}$

32. $\dfrac{-48a^3bc^2}{18ab^2} \cdot \dfrac{-9c}{24a^2c^3} \cdot 4a$

33. $\dfrac{14x^2}{9y^2} \div \dfrac{35x^2}{36y^2}$

34. $\dfrac{-5a^2b^3}{7cd^2} \div \dfrac{10a^3b^2}{21c^2d}$

35. $\dfrac{7x}{x^2-49} \div \dfrac{x^2-14x+49}{x^2+14x+49}$

36. $\dfrac{-10ab^2}{4x^2yz} \div \dfrac{-15a^2b^3}{12xy}$

37. $\dfrac{y^2-y-12}{y^2-16} \div \dfrac{y^2-9}{12y^2-36y}$

38. $\dfrac{(x-2)(x^2-6)}{8x^3+24x^2} \div \dfrac{x^4-36}{2x^9+6x^8}$

39. $\dfrac{25x^2-1}{25} \cdot \dfrac{75x}{5x^2+6x+1}$

40. $\dfrac{4a^2-a-3}{12a^2-7a-12} \div \dfrac{2a^2-a-1}{6a^2-5a-4}$

41. $\dfrac{x^2+6x+9}{x^2+4x+3} \cdot \dfrac{2x^2+2x}{x^2-9}$

42. $\dfrac{7a+14}{a^2+4a+4} \cdot \dfrac{a^2-4}{5a-10}$

43. $\frac{3x^2-3x}{x^2-81} \cdot \frac{x^2+4x-45}{3x-15}$

44. $\frac{10y-21}{y^2-4y+4} \cdot \frac{y^2+y-6}{10y^2+9y-63}$

45. $\frac{2x^2+13x+15}{2x^2-x-6} \cdot \frac{x^2-x-2}{x^2+6x+5}$

46. $\frac{3x^2-3x}{5x-40} \cdot \frac{x^2}{3} \cdot \frac{x^2-7x-8}{4-4x}$

47. $3xy^2 \cdot \frac{5x-15}{15xy-45x^2y^2}$

48. $\frac{10y^2-11y-6}{3y^2-6y} \cdot \frac{y^2-y-2}{6y^2-13y+6}$

49. $\frac{y^2+5y}{y^2-5y-6} \cdot \frac{y^2-7y+6}{y^2+4y-5} \cdot \frac{1}{y+1}$

50. $\frac{x^2+12x+36}{x^2-12x+36} \div \frac{x^2+5x-6}{x^2-5x-6}$

51. $\frac{x^2+x-2}{x^2-x-12} \div \frac{x^2+3x+2}{x^2-7x+12}$

52. $\frac{a^2+6a-16}{a^2-64} \div (a-2)$

53. $\frac{x^3+27}{x^2+3x} \div \frac{x^2+9x}{x^2+7x-18}$

54. $\frac{1+3x-18x^2}{6x^2-17x-3} \div \frac{x-3}{3x-1}$

55. $\frac{x-y}{z-x} \cdot \frac{x-z}{z-y} \cdot \frac{y-z}{y-x}$

56. $\frac{x^2y^2+xy-42}{x^2y^2-xy-42} \cdot \frac{x^2y^2-49}{x^2y^2-36}$

57. $\frac{y^3+1}{y^2+1} \cdot \frac{y^4-1}{y+1}$

58. $\frac{t^3-64}{t^2+4t+16} \cdot \frac{t}{t^2-16}$

59. $\frac{x^3+y^3}{x^2-xy+y^2} \cdot \frac{x^2-2xy+y^2}{x^2-y^2}$

60. $\left(\frac{a^3-8}{a^2+3a+2} \div \frac{a^2-4}{a+1}\right) \cdot \frac{a+2}{2}$

4.5 COMBINED OPERATIONS

A complex fraction is a fraction that contains a fraction in the numerator or in the denominator or in both numerator and denominator.

A complex fraction is simplified by first expressing the numerator and denominator as single fractions, and then by dividing the resulting fractions.

EXAMPLE 1 Simplify $\dfrac{3+\frac{1}{3}}{2-\frac{3}{5}}$

Solution This problem is the following indicated division:

$$\left(3+\frac{1}{3}\right) \div \left(2-\frac{3}{5}\right)$$

Rewriting the numerator and denominator as single fractions,

$$\left(\frac{9}{3}+\frac{1}{3}\right) \div \left(\frac{10}{5}-\frac{3}{5}\right) = \frac{10}{3} \div \frac{7}{5} = \frac{10}{3} \cdot \frac{5}{7} = \frac{50}{21}$$

EXAMPLE 2 Express $\left(x + \frac{1}{y}\right) \div \left(x^2 - \frac{1}{y^2}\right)$ as a single fraction in lowest terms.

Solution Express the divisor as a single fraction and the dividend as a single fraction:

$$x + \frac{1}{y} = \frac{xy + 1}{y}$$

$$x^2 - \frac{1}{y^2} = \frac{x^2y^2 - 1}{y^2}$$

Now

$$\left(x + \frac{1}{y}\right) \div \left(x^2 - \frac{1}{y^2}\right) = \frac{xy + 1}{y} \div \frac{x^2y^2 - 1}{y^2}$$

$$\begin{aligned} \frac{xy + 1}{y} \div \frac{x^2y^2 - 1}{y^2} &= \frac{xy + 1}{y} \cdot \frac{y^2}{x^2y^2 - 1} \\ &= \frac{xy + 1}{y} \cdot \frac{y^2}{(xy + 1)(xy - 1)} \\ &= \frac{y \cdot y(xy + 1)}{y(xy - 1)(xy + 1)} \\ &= \frac{y}{xy - 1} \end{aligned}$$

EXAMPLE 3 Simplify $\left(\frac{x}{x - y} - \frac{y}{x + y}\right) \div \left(\frac{x}{x + y} + \frac{y}{x - y}\right)$

Solution First express the terms within parentheses as single fractions.

$$\frac{x}{x - y} - \frac{y}{x + y} = \frac{x(x + y) - y(x - y)}{(x - y)(x + y)} = \frac{x^2 + y^2}{x^2 - y^2}$$

and

$$\frac{x}{x + y} + \frac{y}{x - y} = \frac{x(x - y) + y(x + y)}{(x + y)(x - y)} = \frac{x^2 + y^2}{x^2 - y^2}$$

Now the problem becomes

$$\left(\frac{x^2 + y^2}{x^2 - y^2}\right) \div \left(\frac{x^2 + y^2}{x^2 - y^2}\right) = \frac{x^2 + y^2}{x^2 - y^2} \cdot \frac{x^2 - y^2}{x^2 + y^2} = 1$$

EXAMPLE 4 Simplify $\dfrac{\frac{1}{x} + \frac{1}{2}}{\frac{1}{4}}$

Solution Writing this as a division problem,

$$\begin{aligned} \frac{\frac{1}{x} + \frac{1}{2}}{\frac{1}{4}} &= \left(\frac{1}{x} + \frac{1}{2}\right) \div \frac{1}{4} \\ &= \left(\frac{2 + x}{2x}\right) \cdot \frac{4}{1} \\ &= \frac{(2 + x)2}{x} = \frac{2(x + 2)}{x} \end{aligned}$$

EXAMPLE 5 Simplify $\dfrac{1}{1+\dfrac{1}{1+\dfrac{1}{2}}}$

Solution As a division problem this becomes

$$1 \div \left(1 + \frac{1}{1+\frac{1}{2}}\right) = 1 \div \left(1 + \frac{1}{\frac{3}{2}}\right)$$
$$= 1 \div \left(1 + \frac{2}{3}\right)$$
$$= 1 \div \left(\frac{5}{3}\right)$$
$$= 1 \cdot \frac{3}{5} = \frac{3}{5}$$

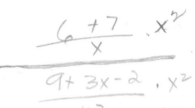

EXERCISES

Simplify and write as single fractions in Exercises 1–30.

1. $\left(2+\frac{3}{4}\right) \div \left(3+\frac{7}{8}\right)$
2. $\left(2-\frac{3}{4}\right) \div \left(3-\frac{7}{8}\right)$
3. $\left(1+\frac{1}{3}\right) \div \left(1+\frac{1}{9}\right)$
4. $\left(3-\frac{5}{7}\right) \div \left(5+\frac{3}{14}\right)$
5. $\left(\frac{2}{3}+\frac{1}{4}\right) \div \left(\frac{5}{3}\right)$
6. $\frac{5}{3} \div \left(\frac{2}{3}+\frac{1}{4}\right)$
7. $\left(1+\frac{1}{y}\right) \div \left(1-\frac{1}{y^2}\right)$
8. $\left(1+\frac{3}{2t-3}\right) \div \left(\frac{1}{2t-3}\right)$
9. $\left(1-\frac{x^2}{9}\right) \div \left(1+\frac{x}{3}\right)$
10. $(a-b) \div \left(\frac{a}{b}-\frac{b}{a}\right)$
11. $\left(\frac{t}{2}+\frac{t}{3}\right) \div \left(t^2-\frac{t}{2}\cdot\frac{t}{3}\right)$
12. $\left(6+\frac{7}{x}-\frac{3}{x^2}\right) \div \left(9+\frac{3}{x}-\frac{2}{x^2}\right)$
13. $\left(\frac{x}{y}+\frac{y}{5}\right) \div \frac{xy}{10}$
14. $\left(\frac{x}{a}-\frac{x}{b}\right) \div \frac{x}{ab}$
15. $\left(a+\frac{3}{a}\right) \div \left(a^2-\frac{9}{a^2}\right)$
16. $\left(3-\frac{1}{y}\right) \div \left(9-\frac{1}{y^2}\right)$
17. $\left(x+3-\frac{10}{x}\right) \div \left(x-\frac{25}{x}\right)$
18. $\left(y+2-\frac{8}{y}\right) \div \left(y-\frac{16}{y}\right)$
19. $\left(y-\frac{9}{y}\right) \div \left(y-7+\frac{12}{y}\right)$
20. $\left(\frac{1}{3}+\frac{1}{n}\right) \div \left(1-\frac{1}{3n}\right)$
21. $\dfrac{1}{\frac{1}{x}+\frac{1}{y}}$
22. $\dfrac{1}{\frac{2}{a}+\frac{3}{b}}$

23. $\left(1-\frac{1}{x+1}\right)\div\left(1+\frac{1}{x-1}\right)$

24. $\left(1+\frac{5}{x-5}\right)\div\left(1-\frac{5}{x+5}\right)$

25. $\left(\frac{1}{a}-\frac{2}{a^2}-\frac{3}{a^3}\right)\div\left(1-\frac{9}{a^2}\right)$

26. $\left(3-\frac{2}{\frac{1}{5}+\frac{1}{3}}\right)\div\left(5-\frac{2}{\frac{1}{5}+\frac{1}{3}}\right)$

27. $\left(2+\frac{1}{\frac{1}{4}+\frac{1}{3}}\right)\div\left(4-\frac{1}{\frac{1}{4}+\frac{1}{3}}\right)$

28. $\dfrac{1}{2-\dfrac{1}{1+\dfrac{1}{2}}}$

29. $\dfrac{1}{1-\dfrac{1}{1-\dfrac{1}{x}}}$

30. $\dfrac{1}{y-\dfrac{1}{y+\dfrac{1}{y}}}$

4.6 CHANGING QUOTIENTS INTO SUMS

DIVISION OF A POLYNOMIAL BY A MONOMIAL

Since one-half of a number means the division of the number by 2,

$$\begin{aligned}\frac{6x^2-4x+3}{2}&=\frac{1}{2}(6x^2-4x+3)\\&=\frac{1}{2}(6x^2)-\frac{1}{2}(4x)+\frac{1}{2}(3)\\&=3x^2-2x+\frac{3}{2}\end{aligned}$$

In other words, the distributive axiom applies, and each term of the numerator must be divided by the divisor.

EXAMPLE 1 Rewrite $\dfrac{9x^3-12x^2+6x+2}{3x}$ as a sum.

Solution Since each term of the numerator must be divided by $3x$,

$$\begin{aligned}\frac{9x^3-12x^2+6x+2}{3x}&=\frac{9x^3}{3x}-\frac{12x^2}{3x}+\frac{6x}{3x}+\frac{2}{3x}\\&=3x^2-4x+2+\frac{2}{3x}\end{aligned}$$

WHAT IS A FRACTION?

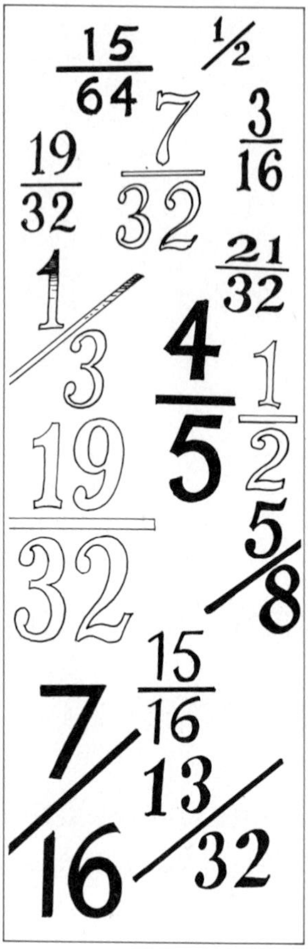

Throughout history people have had difficulty in understanding fractions. The ancient Egyptians limited their fractions by requiring that the numerator be the number 1. They were unable to grasp the concept of a pair of natural numbers representing a single number, such as the fraction $\frac{5}{6}$, which is a single number made from the integers 5 and 6.

Before the time of Archimedes (287–212 B.C.), the Greeks disliked the idea of breaking unity into parts, so they worked with ratios of integers. Thus if Alpha had 50 coins and Beta had 60 coins, the ratio of their amounts would be 5 to 6.

The Romans avoided fractions by the use of subunits; feet were divided into inches and pounds into ounces. A twelfth part of the Roman unit was called *uncia,* from which is derived our modern "ounce" and "inch." Instead of regarding a measurement as $\frac{5}{6}$ of a unit, the Romans considered this measurement as 10 *uncias* $\left(\frac{5}{6} = \frac{5 \cdot 2}{6 \cdot 2} = \frac{10}{12}\right)$.

Now the rational number $\frac{5}{6}$ is interpreted as the quotient obtained when 5 is divided by 6. The number $\frac{5}{6}$ is also interpreted as the ratio of 5 to 6, and this interpretation influenced the choice of the word "rational" to describe numbers that are the quotient of two integers.

DIVISION OF A POLYNOMIAL BY A POLYNOMIAL: LONG DIVISION

It is sometimes desirable to replace a single fraction by a sum or difference of two or more rational expressions. There are several applications (for example, problems in calculus) that require that a quotient of two polynomials be changed into the sum of fractions in which the numerator of each has a degree smaller than the degree of the denominator.

The method used to replace a quotient of two polynomials by a sum or difference is similar to the long-division algorithm used in arithmetic. (An algorithm is a method or pattern of performing a calculation.) For example, the division of 865 by 23 is done as follows:

$$\begin{array}{r} 37 \\ 23\,\overline{)\,865} \\ \underline{69} \\ 175 \\ \underline{161} \\ 14 \end{array}$$

Thus

$$\frac{865}{23} = 37 + \frac{14}{23} = 37\frac{14}{23}$$

Check: $23(37) + 14 = 851 + 14 = 865.$

In arithmetic, the division process is stopped when the remainder is less than the divisor.

In algebra, the division process is stopped when the degree of the remainder polynomial is less than the degree of the divisor polynomial.

EXAMPLE 2 Express $\dfrac{x^3 - 5x^2 + 4x + 7}{x^2 + 2}$ as a sum of rational expressions with the degree of the polynomial in the numerator of any fraction smaller than the degree of the polynomial in its denominator.

Solution

1. Divide x^3 by x^2 to obtain the partial quotient, x:

$$\begin{array}{r} x\phantom{{}-5x^2+4x+7} \\ x^2+2\,\overline{)\,x^3 - 5x^2 + 4x + 7} \end{array}$$

2. Subtract the product of x and $x^2 + 2$ from the dividend:

$$\begin{array}{r} \underline{x^3 \qquad\quad + 2x\phantom{{}+7}} \\ -5x^2 + 2x + 7 \end{array}$$

3. Repeat the process:
   Divide $-5x^2$ by x^2 to obtain -5:

$$\begin{array}{r} x - 5\phantom{{}+4x+7} \\ x^2+2\,\overline{)\,x^3 - 5x^2 + 4x + 7} \end{array}$$

4. Subtract the product of -5 and $x^2 + 2$ from the remainder polynomial, $-5x^2 + 2x + 7$:

$$\begin{array}{r} \underline{x^3 \qquad\quad + 2x\phantom{{}+7}} \\ -5x^2 + 2x + 7 \\ \underline{-5x^2 \qquad\; - 10} \\ 2x + 17 \end{array}$$

5. Since the degree of the remainder, $2x + 17$, is less than the degree of the divisor, $x^2 + 2$, the process is stopped at this point, and the quotient is expressed as the following sum:

$$\frac{x^3 - 5x^2 + 4x + 7}{x^2 + 2} = x - 5 + \frac{2x + 17}{x^2 + 2}$$

Check $(x^2+2)\left(x-5+\dfrac{2x+17}{x^2+2}\right)$

$$= (x^2+2)(x-5) + (x^2+2)\left(\frac{2x+17}{x^2+2}\right)$$
$$= (x^3-5x^2+2x-10) + (2x+17)$$
$$= x^3-5x^2+4x+7$$

A quick check could also be made numerically by assigning a value to x. For instance, let $x=2$. Then

$$x^3-5x^2+4x+7 = 2^3-5(2^2)+4(2)+7=3$$

and

$$x^2+2=2^2+2=6$$

For $x=2$,

$$\frac{x^3-5x^2+4x+7}{x^2+2}=\frac{3}{6}=\frac{1}{2}$$

Also, for $x=2$,

$$x-5+\frac{2x+17}{x^2+2}=2-5+\frac{4+17}{4+2}$$
$$=-3+\frac{21}{6}=\frac{-18+21}{6}=\frac{3}{6}=\frac{1}{2}$$

Since

$$\frac{x^3-5x^2+4x+7}{x^2+2}=x-5+\frac{2x+17}{x^2+2} \quad \text{for} \quad x=2$$

there is assurance that the problem has been worked correctly.

EXAMPLE 3 Divide $\dfrac{x^3+1}{x+1}$ by using the long-division algorithm.

Solution The polynomial x^3+1 can also be considered as

$$x^3+0\cdot x^2+0\cdot x+1$$

so places must be provided for the missing x^2 and x terms:

$$\begin{array}{r|l} & x^2 - x + 1 \\ \hline x+1 & x^3 \qquad\qquad + 1 \\ & \underline{x^3 + x^2 \qquad\quad} \\ & \quad -x^2 \qquad + 1 \\ & \quad \underline{-x^2 - x \quad\;} \\ & \qquad\quad + x + 1 \\ & \qquad\qquad \underline{x + 1} \end{array}$$

Thus $\dfrac{x^3+1}{x+1}=x^2-x+1$

Check $(x+1)(x^2-x+1)$

$$= (x+1)(x^2-x)+(x+1)(1)$$
$$= x^3+x^2-x^2-x+x+1=x^3+1$$

In Example 3, the remainder is zero. Thus $x+1$ is a factor of x^3+1.

Note that

$$\frac{x^3+1}{x+1}=\frac{(x+1)(x^2-x+1)}{(x+1)} \qquad \text{(Factoring the sum of cubes)}$$
$$= x^2-x+1$$

For cases such as this, when the divisor is an exact factor of the dividend, it is much easier to use the method of reducing a fraction presented earlier than to use the long-division algorithm.

It is important when using the long-division algorithm that both dividend and divisor be arranged in the same order—that is, the terms of both must be in descending order or the terms of both must be in ascending order.

EXAMPLE 4 Divide and check $\dfrac{7y + y^4 - 7 + y^3}{3 - y + y^2}$

Solution First arrange the polynomials in descending powers of y:

$$\frac{7y + y^4 - 7 + y^3}{3 - y + y^2} = \frac{y^4 + y^3 + 7y - 7}{y^2 - y + 3}$$

$$\begin{array}{r|l}
 & y^2 + 2y - 1 \\ \hline
y^2 - y + 3 & y^4 + y^3 \qquad + 7y - 7 \\
 & \underline{y^4 - y^3 + 3y^2} \\
 & \qquad 2y^3 - 3y^2 + 7y - 7 \\
 & \qquad \underline{2y^3 - 2y^2 + 6y} \\
 & \qquad\qquad - y^2 + y - 7 \\
 & \qquad\qquad \underline{- y^2 + y - 3} \\
 & \qquad\qquad\qquad\quad -4
\end{array}$$

Therefore

$$\frac{y^4 + y^3 + 7y - 7}{y^2 - y + 3} = y^2 + 2y - 1 + \frac{-4}{y^2 - y + 3}$$

Quick Check Letting $y = 2$,

$$\frac{y^4 + y^3 + 7y - 7}{y^2 - y + 3} = \frac{16 + 8 + 14 - 7}{4 - 2 + 3} = \frac{31}{5}$$

$$y^2 + 2y - 1 + \frac{-4}{y^2 - y + 3} = 4 + 4 - 1 + \frac{-4}{4 - 2 + 3} = 7 - \frac{4}{5} = \frac{31}{5}$$

EXERCISES

Rewrite each quotient in Exercises 1–10 as a sum.

1. $\dfrac{x^3 + 3x^2 - 2x + 4}{x}$
2. $\dfrac{4x^3 - 2x^2 + 5x - 2}{x}$
3. $\dfrac{6y^2 - 4y + 3}{2y}$
4. $\dfrac{15y^3 + 9y^2 - 3y - 1}{3y}$
5. $\dfrac{6x^2 - 4x + 5}{2x}$
6. $\dfrac{12x^5 - 9x^3 - 4}{x^2}$
7. $\dfrac{x^8 - 5x^5 + 3x^3 + 2x}{x^3}$
8. $\dfrac{x^2y + xy^2 - x}{xy}$
9. $\dfrac{9x^3y^2 + 6x^2y - 2xy}{3xy}$
10. $\dfrac{x^3y - 3x^2y^2 + 6xy - 2}{xy}$

In Exercises 11–28, divide by using the long-division algorithm. Check by multiplication.

11. $\dfrac{2x^3 + 5x^2 - 3x + 7}{x + 4}$

12. $\dfrac{5x^4 + x^3 - 4x^2 + 2x - 3}{x + 2}$

13. $\dfrac{2x^3 - 13x^2 + 13x + 10}{x - 5}$

14. $\dfrac{6x^3 - 25x^2 + 3x + 4}{2x - 1}$

15. $\dfrac{4x^3 + 10x^2 - 16x - 14}{2x + 7}$

16. $\dfrac{x^4 - 7x^2 + 9}{x^2 - x - 3}$

17. $\dfrac{5x^4 - 30x^2 + 2x - 1}{x^2 - 6}$

18. $\dfrac{x^3 + 3x^2 + 2x + 7}{x + 3}$

19. $\dfrac{2x^3 - 3x^2 + 5}{x - 1}$

20. $\dfrac{x^4 + 4}{x^2 + 2x + 2}$

21. $\dfrac{a^3 - 729}{a - 9}$

22. $\dfrac{x^3 + 4x^2 + 5x + 12}{x + 4}$

23. $\dfrac{4x^4 - 3x^2 + 7x - 1}{x - 1}$

24. $\dfrac{a^3 + 64}{a + 4}$

25. $\dfrac{y^5 - 3y^4 + 2y^2 - 3y + 2}{y^2 + 3}$

26. $\dfrac{y^3 - 125}{y - 5}$

27. $\dfrac{6x^4 - 32x^2 - 9}{3x^2 - 1}$

28. $\dfrac{2x^4 - 14x^2 - 5}{x^2 - 7}$

In Exercises 29–40, divide and check as indicated.

29. $\dfrac{2x^3 - 10x^2 + 3x - 14}{x - 5}$
Check using $x = 2$.

30. $\dfrac{t^2 - 10t + 8 + t^3}{t + 4}$
Check using $t = 1$.

31. $\dfrac{x^4 - 1}{x - 1}$
Check using $x = 3$.

32. $\dfrac{4x^2 + 7}{2x - 1}$
Check using $x = 1$.

33. $\dfrac{2x^5 + 4x^2 - 6x^3 - 5}{x^2 - 3}$
Check using $x = 2$.

34. $\dfrac{y^4 + 64}{y^2 - 4y + 8}$
Check using $y = 2$.

35. $\dfrac{25a^3 + ab^2 + b^3}{5a + 2b}$
Check using $a = 1$, $b = -2$.

36. $\dfrac{x^6 + x^4 + x^2 + 1}{x^2 + 1}$
Check using $x = 2$.

37. $\dfrac{x^2 - y^2 - 6y - 9}{x - y - 3}$
Check using $x = 4$, $y = 2$.

38. $\dfrac{x^2 - y^2 + 4x - 6y - 5}{x + y + 5}$
Check using $x = 3$, $y = 2$.

39. $\dfrac{a^2 - 4b^2 + 20b - 25}{a + 2b - 5}$
Check using $a = 2$, $b = 2$.

40. $\dfrac{4x^2 - 16y^2 - 4x + 24y - 8}{2x - 4y + 2}$
Check using $x = 3$, $y = 1$.

4.7 FRACTIONAL EQUATIONS

A **fractional equation** is an equation whose terms are rational expressions.

For example, $\frac{1}{x} = 3$ and $\frac{2}{x+2} + \frac{3}{x-3} = 15$ are fractional equations.

To transform a fractional equation into an equivalent equation whose terms are integral expressions, both sides of the equation must be multiplied by the least common denominator of all the fractions involved in the equation. Since this may require multiplication by an expression involving the variable, an equivalent equation is obtained only when the variable is restricted to designate those numbers that do not make the multiplier zero.

For example, to solve $\frac{1}{x} = 3$, both sides of the equation are multiplied by x, and x is restricted so that $x \neq 0$. Then, if $x \neq 0$,

$$\frac{1}{x}(x) = 3(x)$$
$$1 = 3x$$
$$3x = 1$$
$$x = \frac{1}{3}$$

To solve $\frac{x}{x-3} = \frac{3}{x-3}$, both sides are multiplied by $x-3$, and x is restricted, so that $x - 3 \neq 0$; that is, $x \neq 3$.

Thus, if $x \neq 3$,

$$\frac{x}{x-3}(x-3) = \frac{3}{x-3}(x-3) \quad \text{and} \quad x = 3$$

The solution set of

$$\frac{x}{x-3} = \frac{3}{x-3}$$

is the set of real numbers, x, such that $x \neq 3$ and $x = 3$. There is no value for x that makes both of these statements true, so there is no solution. In other words, the solution set is the empty set, $\varnothing$.

The equivalence theorem for multiplication, introduced earlier, is restated below for convenience.

THE EQUIVALENCE THEOREM FOR MULTIPLICATION

If A, B, and C are any real numbers, then

$A = B$ if and only if $AC = BC$ and $C \neq 0$

This theorem is used in solving fractional equations, and care must be taken to exclude any values of a variable that might yield a zero value for C. The values for which $C \neq 0$ are called **restricted values of the variable.**

EXAMPLE 1 State the restricted values of y and solve:

$$\frac{2}{y-5} + \frac{1}{y+5} = \frac{11}{y^2-25}$$

Solution First write all denominators in factored form:

$$\frac{2}{y-5} + \frac{1}{y+5} = \frac{11}{(y-5)(y+5)}$$

The L.C.D. is $(y-5)(y+5)$. Since this product is 0 when $y - 5 = 0$ or $y + 5 = 0$, $y \neq 5$ and $y \neq -5$. Multiplying both sides by the L.C.D. $(y-5)(y+5)$,

$$\left(\frac{2}{y-5} + \frac{1}{y+5}\right)(y-5)(y+5) = \frac{11(y-5)(y+5)}{(y-5)(y+5)}$$

$$2(y+5) + (y-5) = 11$$

$$3y + 5 = 11$$

$$3y = 6$$

$$y = 2$$

Since the common solution to $y \neq 5$, $y \neq -5$, and $y = 2$ is 2, $\{2\}$ is the solution set of the original equation.

Check

$$\frac{2}{y-5} + \frac{1}{y+5} = \frac{2}{2-5} + \frac{1}{2+5} = \frac{-2}{3} + \frac{1}{7} = \frac{-11}{21}$$

$$\frac{11}{y^2-25} = \frac{11}{(2)^2-25} = \frac{11}{4-25} = \frac{-11}{21}$$

EXAMPLE 2 State the restricted values of the variable and solve:

$$\frac{x+1}{x+2} - \frac{x+1}{x-3} = \frac{5}{x^2-x-6}$$

Solution The L.C.D. is $(x+2)(x-3)$.

Since $x + 2 \neq 0$ and $x - 3 \neq 0$, $x \neq -2$ and $x \neq 3$,

$$\left(\frac{x+1}{x+2}\right)(x+2)(x-3) - \left(\frac{x+1}{x-3}\right)(x+2)(x-3) = \frac{5}{(x+2)(x-3)}(x+2)(x-3)$$

$$(x+1)(x-3) - (x+1)(x+2) = 5$$

$$(x^2-2x-3) - (x^2+3x+2) = 5$$

$$-5x - 5 = 5$$

$$-5x = 10$$

$$x = -2$$

Thus $x \neq -2$ and $x \neq 3$ and $x = -2$. Since there is no common solution, the solution set is the empty set, $\emptyset$.

EXAMPLE 3 State the restricted values of the variable and solve:

$$\frac{x}{(x-4)^2}+\frac{2}{x-4}=\frac{3x-8}{(x-4)^2}$$

Solution

$x \neq 4$, because $x-4 \neq 0$.

$$(x-4)^2\frac{x}{(x-4)^2}+(x-4)^2\frac{2}{x-4}=\frac{3x-8}{(x-4)^2}(x-4)^2$$

$$x+2(x-4)=3x-8$$

$$3x-8=3x-8$$

$$3x=3x$$

$$x=x$$

Since $x=x$ is true for all real numbers, the solution set is the set of all real numbers except 4; R, $x \neq 4$.

EXAMPLE 4 State the restricted values and solve:

$$\frac{x-1}{x-3}-\frac{2x}{x-2}=\frac{4}{x^2-5x+6}$$

Solution

$x \neq 3$ and $x \neq 2$, because $x-3 \neq 0$ and $x-2 \neq 0$.

$$\frac{(x-1)(x-2)}{(x-3)(x-2)}-\frac{2x(x-3)}{(x-2)(x-3)}=\frac{4}{(x-2)(x-3)}$$

$$x^2-3x+2-(2x^2-6x)=4$$

$$x^2-3x+2-2x^2+6x=4$$

$$-x^2+3x-2=0$$

$$x^2-3x+2=0$$

$$(x-1)(x-2)=0$$

$$x-1=0 \quad \text{or} \quad x-2=0$$

$$x=1 \quad \text{or} \quad x=2$$

Since $x \neq 2$, 1 is the only possible solution. The solution set is $\{1\}$.

EXAMPLE 5 State the restricted values and solve $\frac{a}{x}-\frac{b}{a}=\frac{1}{3x}$ for x where $a \neq 0$ and $b \neq 0$.

Solution

L.C.D. = $3ax$; $x \neq 0$.

$$\frac{a}{x}-\frac{b}{a}=\frac{1}{3x}$$

$$3ax\left(\frac{a}{x}\right)-3ax\left(\frac{b}{a}\right)=3ax\left(\frac{1}{3x}\right)$$

$$3a^2-3bx=a$$

$$-3bx=a-3a^2$$

$$x=\frac{a-3a^2}{-3b} \qquad \text{since } b \neq 0$$

$$x=\frac{a(3a-1)}{3b}$$

EXERCISES

In Exercises 1–34 state the restricted values of the variable and solve. Check each solution.

1. $\frac{1}{2x} - \frac{2}{3x} = \frac{1}{24}$
2. $\frac{2}{5x} - \frac{1}{2x} = \frac{x+2}{10x}$
3. $\frac{1}{a} + \frac{1}{2a} + \frac{1}{3a} = \frac{1}{a+5}$
4. $\frac{2}{y} + \frac{1}{2y} + \frac{4}{3y} = \frac{3}{y+2}$
5. $\frac{2}{3x-7} = \frac{5}{x+2}$
6. $\frac{6}{y} - \frac{1}{y-2} = \frac{3}{y^2-2y}$
7. $\frac{3}{y} + \frac{5}{1-y} + \frac{2y+3}{y^2-1} = 0$
8. $\frac{x}{5} - \frac{x}{6} = 3$
9. $\frac{5}{x} = 20$
10. $\frac{3}{2x-1} = \frac{7}{3x+1}$
11. $\frac{20+y}{10y+5} = \frac{2}{5}$
12. $\frac{3x+1}{25} - \frac{1}{10} = \frac{3x-1}{30}$
13. $\frac{5}{x} = 0$
14. $\frac{x+1}{x-5} - \frac{x+3}{x+2} = \frac{2}{x^2-3x-10}$
15. $\frac{x-6}{x+6} - \frac{x-2}{x+1} = \frac{15}{x^2+7x+6}$
16. $\frac{4t}{9t+18} + \frac{t+2}{3t-6} = \frac{7}{9}$
17. $\frac{y+12}{y^2-16} + \frac{1}{4-y} = \frac{1}{4+y}$
18. $\frac{8y-1}{5} = \frac{16y+3}{10} - \frac{2y-5}{5y-1}$
19. $\frac{5+x}{x} = 0$
20. $\frac{9y+2}{12} + \frac{17}{9} = \frac{21y-8}{18} - \frac{2y-3}{3}$
21. $\frac{3}{2x-6} + \frac{1}{4x+2} = \frac{2x-3}{2x^2-5x-3}$
22. $\frac{44}{2x^2-9x-5} - \frac{6}{2x+1} = \frac{4}{x-5}$
23. $\frac{5}{t} + \frac{1}{2t} - \frac{2}{3t} = 29$
24. $\frac{2x-29}{x^2+7x-8} = \frac{5}{x+8} - \frac{3}{x-1}$
25. $\frac{5t^2}{t^2-t-20} = \frac{3t+2}{t+4} + \frac{2t+3}{t-5}$
26. $\frac{y-8}{y-3} - \frac{y+8}{y+3} = \frac{y}{9-y^2}$

27. $\dfrac{2}{x+1}+\dfrac{1}{3x+3}=\dfrac{1}{6}$

28. $\dfrac{x}{x+2}-\dfrac{3}{x-2}=\dfrac{x^2-8}{x^2-4}$

29. $\dfrac{5}{5x+3}+\dfrac{2}{1-2x}=\dfrac{4-6x}{10x^2+x-3}$

30. $\dfrac{1}{2x-3}+\dfrac{x}{4x^2-9}=\dfrac{1}{8x+12}$

31. $1+\dfrac{2}{x-1}=\dfrac{2}{x(x-1)}$

32. $2+\dfrac{3}{x-2}-\dfrac{3}{x(x-2)}=0$

33. $\dfrac{x}{x+3}-\dfrac{2}{x+1}=0$

34. $\dfrac{x}{x-2}-\dfrac{30}{(x+4)(x-2)}=\dfrac{5}{x+4}$

35. Solve $\dfrac{a-2x}{b-x}=\dfrac{3}{2}$ for x.

36. Solve $\dfrac{x}{a}-\dfrac{a}{b}=\dfrac{b}{c}$ for x.

37. Solve $\dfrac{3}{x+a}-\dfrac{2}{x-a}=\dfrac{1}{x}$ for x.

38. Solve $\dfrac{a-2}{b}+\dfrac{3}{2b}=\dfrac{2}{x}$ for x.

39. Solve $\dfrac{P}{N}=\dfrac{p}{N+n}$ for N.

40. Solve Exercise 39 for n.

4.8 RATIO AND PROPORTION

At the beginning of this chapter we stated that a fraction, such as $\frac{5}{6}$, is also called the **ratio** of 5 to 6, or the ratio $\frac{5}{6}$. An equation that states that two ratios are equal is called a **proportion.** Thus a proportion has the form

$$\frac{a}{b}=\frac{c}{d}$$

The statement $\frac{a}{b}=\frac{c}{d}$ is expressed sometimes by saying, "a, b, c, and d are in proportion."

A proportion is a simple fractional equation.

If two numbers are in the ratio $\frac{a}{b}$, then the numbers may be represented as ax and bx $(x \neq 0)$ by applying the fundamental theorem of fractions: $\frac{ax}{bx} = \frac{a}{b}$.

EXAMPLE 1 A sum of \$350 is to be divided between two partners in the ratio $\frac{3}{4}$. How much does each partner receive?

Solution Let x = the share of one partner. Then $350 - x$ = the share of the other partner. Then

$$\frac{x}{350 - x} = \frac{3}{4}$$
$$4x = 3(350 - x)$$
$$7x = 3(350)$$
$$x = \$150$$
$$350 - x = \$200$$

EXAMPLE 2 The ratio of women students to men students at a certain college is $\frac{7}{9}$. If there are 2135 women students, how many men students are there?

Solution Let x = the number of men students. Then

$$\frac{7}{9} = \frac{2135}{x}$$
$$7x = 2135 \cdot 9$$
$$x = 305 \cdot 9$$
$$x = 2745$$

The terms a, b, c, and d of the proportion $\frac{a}{b} = \frac{c}{d}$ also have special names. In the order in which they are stated above, a is the first term, b the second, c the third, and d the fourth. The first and fourth terms are called the **extremes** of a proportion, and the second and third terms are called the **means** of the proportion.

THEOREM

In a proportion the product of the means is equal to the product of the extremes. In symbols, if $\frac{a}{b} = \frac{c}{d}$, then $bc = ad$.

EXAMPLE 3 If 3, 4, and 5 are the first three terms, in that order, of a proportion, find the fourth term.

Solution Let $d =$ the fourth term. Then

$$\frac{3}{4} = \frac{5}{d}$$
$$3d = 20$$
$$d = \frac{20}{3} = 6\frac{2}{3}$$

Thus the fourth term is $6\frac{2}{3}$.

EXERCISES

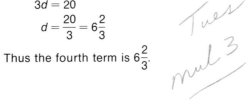

1. The ancient Greeks considered the most beautiful rectangle to be the one whose sides were in the Golden Ratio. Approximating the Golden Ratio by the ratio $\frac{5}{8}$, find the dimensions of the most beautiful rectangle with a perimeter of 182 centimetres.
2. By weight, the ratio of oxygen to hydrogen in pure distilled water is $\frac{8}{1}$. How many grams of each element are in 100 grams of water?
3. Pie crust is made by combining shortening and flour in the ratio $\frac{2}{3}$ by volume. If 2 cups of flour is required per pie, how much shortening is required to make 15 pies? To make one pie?
4. A son and grandson are to divide an inheritance of \$5000 in the ratio $\frac{5}{3}$. How much does each receive if the inheritance tax is \$500 and the lawyer receives \$2700?
5. The batting average of a baseball player is the ratio of the number of hits he makes to the number of times he comes to bat. If a certain player has a batting average of 0.325, how many hits has he made in 40 times at bat?
6. A sampling revealed that on a certain day, for every 1000 tin cans manufactured, 15 were defective. If 250,000 cans were made on that day, how many were defective?
7. The ratio of sodium to chlorine in common table salt is $\frac{35}{23}$. Find the amount of each element in the salt compound weighing 290 pounds.
8. A piece of wire 84 inches long is cut so that the parts are in the ratio $\frac{4}{3}$. How long is each part?

9. One grocer advertises 16 cans of a beverage for $1.00. Another grocer advertises 12 cans for 69 cents. Which is the better buy and why?
10. If 5 pounds of oranges cost 89 cents, what is the cost of 12 pounds of oranges?
11. Two companies contribute a total of $26,400 to a certain charity. If the ratio of their contributions is $\frac{5}{6}$, find the amount that each company contributes.
12. A blueprint has the scale 1 inch = 4 feet. What are the dimensions of a rectangular living room that measures $4\frac{1}{2}$ by 5 inches on the blueprint?
13. The ratio of the size of a medium egg to a large egg is 2 to 3. If medium eggs cost 52 cents per dozen, what should be the equivalent cost for a dozen large eggs?
14. If the first three terms of a proportion are 2, 4, and 6, respectively, find the fourth term.
15. The first term of a proportion is 6 and the second term is 8. The fourth term is the sum of the second and third terms. Find the third and fourth terms.
16. Find the fourth term of a proportion if its first three terms are 7, 14, and 20, in that order.
17. Find the means of a proportion if the product of the extremes is 36 and if the ratio of one mean to the other is 4 to 1.
18. Find the extremes of a proportion if the product of the means is 36 and the ratio of one extreme to the other is 9 to 1.
19. If the ratio of kilometres to miles is 8 to 5, what speed in miles per hour is equivalent to 90 kilometres per hour?
20. Referring to Exercise 19, find the speed in kilometres per hour if the speed in miles per hour is 25.
21. If the exchange ratio of Mexican pesos to United States dollars is $12\frac{1}{2}$ to 1, what is the price in dollars of an article costing 450 pesos?
22. If the exchange rate of Dutch guilders to United States dollars is $2\frac{1}{2}$ to 1, what is the price in dollars of a dozen tulip bulbs costing 18 guilders?
23. For a certain type of concrete mix, the ratio of cement to sand to rock is 1:3:5. Find the number of cubic feet of each component in a 108-cubic-foot mix of this concrete.
24. The profit of an investment is to be divided among the three partners in a business in the ratio of 5:3:2. How much does each receive if the profit is $48,000?
25. A man earns $4200 in thirty weeks. How much could he earn in one year if he worked every week except for two weeks vacation without pay?

4.9 WORK PROBLEMS

Verbal problems that involve work often lead to fractional equations, as illustrated in the following examples.

A formula for a work problem is $w = tr$, where w is the amount of work done, t the time spent working, and r the amount of work done per unit time (the rate). If the work done is a complete job, then $w = 1$.

When several persons work together, it is assumed that the total work done is the sum of the amounts of work done by those persons working.

In summary, $w = tr$ and

$$w \text{ (total)} = w \text{ (worker A)} + w \text{ (worker B)}$$

If the work done is the complete job, then $w = 1$ and $r = \frac{1}{t}$.

EXAMPLE 1 One machine requires 90 minutes to complete a certain job. Another machine completes the same job in 120 minutes. If the machines worked together, how long would it take them to complete the job?

Solution Let x = the number of minutes the machines work together.

	Working Together		
Formula:	t ·	r =	w
First machine	x	$\frac{1}{90}$	$\frac{x}{90}$
Second machine	x	$\frac{1}{120}$	$\frac{x}{120}$

Equation

work done by first + work done by second = total work

$$\frac{x}{90} + \frac{x}{120} = 1$$

$$360\left(\frac{x}{90} + \frac{x}{120}\right) = 360$$

$$4x + 3x = 360$$

$$7x = 360$$

$$x = \frac{360}{7} = 51\frac{3}{7} \text{ minutes}$$

EXAMPLE 2 Working alone, a painter takes twice as much time to paint a job as his father does. If the father works alone for 2 days and then completes the job by working with his son for 3 days, how long would it have taken the father to paint the job alone?

Solution Let $x =$ the time of the father working alone. Then $2x =$ the time of the son working alone.

Working Together

Formula:	t	$\cdot$	r	$=$	w
Father	5		$\frac{1}{x}$		$\frac{5}{x}$
Son	3		$\frac{1}{2x}$		$\frac{3}{2x}$

Equation

father's work + son's work = total work

$$\frac{5}{x} + \frac{3}{2x} = 1$$

$$10 + 3 = 2x$$

$$2x = 13$$

$$x = \frac{13}{2} = 6\frac{1}{2} \text{ days}$$

EXERCISES

1. The denominator of a certain fraction exceeds the numerator by 12. If the numerator is increased by 4 and the denominator is decreased by 3, the value of the resulting fraction is $\frac{3}{4}$. What is the value of the original fraction?
2. The sum of two integers is 168. When the larger is divided by the smaller the quotient is 6 and the remainder is 7. Find these two integers.
3. A mason can lay the same amount of brick in 8 days that his helper can in 12 days. If they worked together, how long would it take them to lay this amount of brick?
4. A roofer requires 10 hours to shingle a roof. His helper can do the same work in 15 hours. How long would it take them if they worked together?

5. Three machines can manufacture a certain article in 12 minutes, 15 minutes, and 20 minutes, respectively. If the three machines worked simultaneously, how long would it take them to manufacture 1000 articles?
6. One pipe can fill a tank in 18 minutes, a second in 30 minutes, and a third in 45 minutes. If all three pipes were opened at the same time, how long would it take to fill the tank?
7. One crew of men can sheetrock a certain building in 15 days. With the help of a second crew, the building can be sheetrocked in 6 days. How long would it take the second crew, working alone, to sheetrock the building?
8. A man can mow his lawn in 40 minutes. His son can mow the lawn in 60 minutes. The man starts to mow the lawn; 10 minutes later his son joins him. How long does it take them to complete the job (assuming they have two lawnmowers)?
9. Three old machines together required 80 minutes to do a certain job. Two new machines were installed, one of which worked 3 times as fast as all the old machines together. The five machines, working together, took 15 minutes to do the same type of job. How long would it take the other new machine working alone to do the work?
10. A new machine can process checks 5 times as fast as an old one. With both machines operating, 1000 checks can be processed in $\frac{1}{2}$ hour. How long would it take each machine alone to process 1000 checks?
11. Two pipes can fill a tank in 9 and 12 hours, respectively. A third pipe can drain the tank in 18 hours. How long would it take to fill the tank if all three pipes were open?
12. An experienced typist can type 3 times as fast as a new one. Working together, they complete a certain job in 9 hours. How long would it have taken each one alone?
13. One number is 4 times another. The sum of their reciprocals is $\frac{3}{4}$. Find the numbers.
14. The sum of a number and its negative reciprocal is $\frac{3}{2}$. Find the number.
15. The focal length F of a concave mirror can be found by using the formula:

$$\frac{1}{F}=\frac{1}{a}+\frac{1}{b}$$

where a is the distance of the object from the mirror and b is the distance of the image from the mirror. A certain concave mirror has a focal length of 5 inches. At what distance from this mirror will an object be if the image distance is $\frac{1}{4}$ the object distance?

16. When two resistors, R_1 and R_2, are connected in parallel, the total resistance R can be found by using the formula

$$\frac{1}{R}=\frac{1}{R_1}+\frac{1}{R_2}$$

If two resistors connected in parallel are such that one has 3 times the resistance of the other, and if the total resistance is 15 ohms, find the number of ohms in each resistor.

REVIEW EXERCISES

Simplify in Exercises 1–10.

1. $\dfrac{10x^3yz^2}{15xy^3z}$

2. $\dfrac{15a^2b}{4ax^2y}\cdot\dfrac{8a^2x^3y^2}{12b^2x}$

3. $\dfrac{a-b}{b-a}$

4. $\dfrac{9x^2-36y^2}{x^2-4xy+4y^2}$

5. $\dfrac{2x^2+5x-150}{2x^2+17x-30}$

6. $\dfrac{x^2-2x+1}{15x^2}\cdot\dfrac{20x^5}{1-x^2}$

7. $\dfrac{x^3+5x^2+6x}{x^2-x}\cdot\dfrac{x^2-3x+2}{(x^2-4)(x+3)}$

8. $\dfrac{5xy+15y}{15y}\div\dfrac{x^2+4x+3}{x^2-1}$

9. $\dfrac{a^3+27}{a^2-3a}\div\dfrac{a^2+3a}{a^2-7a+12}$

10. $\left(\dfrac{x^2-x}{x^2+2x-3}\cdot\dfrac{x^2+2x+1}{x^2+4x}\right)\div\dfrac{x^2-3x-4}{x^2-16}$

In Exercises 11–20 write each as a single fraction reduced to lowest terms.

11. $\dfrac{5}{x+3}-\dfrac{x}{x+3}$

12. $\dfrac{x}{x+3}+\dfrac{5x^2}{x^2-9}$

13. $\dfrac{x}{x^2-6x+5}+\dfrac{3}{x-1}$

14. $\dfrac{2}{x-1}-\dfrac{4}{x}+\dfrac{2}{x+1}$

15. $\dfrac{1}{x}+\dfrac{1}{2}+\dfrac{5}{x+2}$

16. $\dfrac{3}{x^2+5x+4}-\dfrac{2}{x^2+4x+3}$

17. $\dfrac{1}{(x+2)^2}-\dfrac{2}{x^2-4}+\dfrac{1}{(x-2)^2}$

18. $\left(x+\dfrac{3}{y}\right)\div\left(x-\dfrac{3}{y}\right)$

19. $\left(\dfrac{1}{x}-\dfrac{1}{3}\right)\div\left(x-\dfrac{9}{x}\right)$

20. $\left(\dfrac{3x-1}{3x}-\dfrac{3x}{3x+1}\right)\div\left(\dfrac{5x-2}{5x}-\dfrac{5x}{5x+2}\right)$

REVIEW EXERCISES

In Exercises 21–25 divide by using the long-division algorithm. Check by multiplication.

21. $\dfrac{x^3 - 4x^2 + 3x - 1}{x - 3}$ **22.** $\dfrac{x^4 + x^2 - 2}{x^2 + 3}$

23. $\dfrac{39 + 20x^2 + 15x^3}{5x + 10}$ **24.** $\dfrac{a^3 - 1}{a - 1}$

25. $\dfrac{7x^3 - 3x + x^2 + 3x^3 - 5x - 10}{1 + 2x}$

Solve and check Exercises 26–35. State the restricted values of the variable.

26. $\dfrac{5}{x-6} + \dfrac{3}{x+6} = \dfrac{8}{x^2 - 36}$

27. $\dfrac{x+3}{x+2} = \dfrac{3}{2}$

28. $\dfrac{2}{x+3} - \dfrac{2}{x-3} = \dfrac{1}{3-x}$

29. $\dfrac{2x+3}{x-1} = \dfrac{2x-5}{x+3}$

30. $\dfrac{5}{3x+1} - \dfrac{x+2}{4x} + \dfrac{1}{4} = 0$

31. $\dfrac{x}{x+4} - \dfrac{4}{x-4} = \dfrac{x^2+16}{x^2-16}$

32. $\dfrac{1}{1-x} + \dfrac{x}{x-1} = 1$

33. $x + \dfrac{5x}{x-3} = \dfrac{15}{x-3}$

34. Solve $\dfrac{x-a}{x+b} = \dfrac{x+b}{x-a}$ for x.

35. Solve $\dfrac{p-x}{x} = c + \dfrac{1}{x}$ for x.

36. The numerator of a fraction is 3 less than the denominator. If 1 is added to the denominator and 2 is subtracted from the numerator, the value of the new fraction formed is $\frac{1}{4}$. Find the original fraction.

37. The ratio of the numerator of a certain fraction to the denominator is $\frac{3}{5}$. If 20 is subtracted from the numerator and 10 is added to the denominator, the resulting fraction is equal to $\frac{1}{2}$. Find the original fraction.

38. A swimming pool can be filled by a pipe in 10 hours and by a hose in 15 hours. How long does it take to fill the pool using both pipe and hose, assuming there is no loss in water pressure?

39. A mechanic can do a certain repair job in $3\frac{1}{2}$ hours. He and his assistant can complete the job in 2 hours. How long would it take the assistant working alone?

40. For what value of x is the proportion $\frac{x+2}{x+9} = \frac{5}{12}$ true?

41. If a car uses 16 gallons of gasoline on a 720-mile journey, how much gas will be used on a 450-mile trip? (Assume the mileage per gallon to be the same for both trips.)

42. If the ratio of pounds to kilograms is 20 to 9, how many kilograms are equivalent to 120 pounds?

43. If the ratio of gallons to litres is 1 to 3.8, how many litres are there in 5 gallons?

44. If the ratio of feet to centimetres is 30.5 to 1, how tall in centimetres is a person who is 6 feet?

45. Given the algebraic expression $\frac{x-2}{x^2+1} \div \frac{k-3}{x+3}$

a. For what value(s) of x will the expression be undefined?
b. For what value(s) of k will the expression be undefined?
c. For what value(s) of x will the expression equal zero? Why?

5

GRAPHING AND LINEAR SYSTEMS

In geometry, a straight line is thought of as an infinite number of points each of which is said to be on the line. In Chapter 1 we saw how the geometric line can be used to visualize the set of real numbers and their properties.

That discussion focused on linear equations in *one* variable. In this chapter the concept of linear equation will be extended to include the case of *two* variables.

The geometric plane is used to visualize equations in two variables and thereby to provide a better understanding of such equations.

In this chapter you will be introduced to a rectangular coordinate system where a one-to-one correspondence is established between the set of points on a plane and the set of ordered pairs of real numbers. You will then study linear equations in two variables and their graphs. Finally you will be shown how to solve a system of linear equations in two variables and how to use these techniques for solving a variety of practical applications.

5.1 RECTANGULAR COORDINATES

ORDERED PAIRS AND SOLUTIONS

An **ordered pair** is an expression having the form (**a**, **b**) where **a** is called the **first component** (or first member) of the ordered pair and **b** is called the **second component** (or second member) of the ordered pair.

The order in which the components of an ordered pair are written is important. For example, the ordered pair (3, 5) is *not* the same as the ordered pair (5, 3).

DEFINITION

A **solution of an open equation in two variables** x and y is an ordered pair (a, b) such that the equation becomes true when x is replaced by a and y is replaced by b.

EXAMPLE 1 Which of the following is a solution of $3x - y = 10$?
a. (4, 2) b. (2, 4)

Solution

a. For (4, 2), $x = 4$ and $y = 2$. Then
$$3x - y = 3(4) - 2 = 12 - 2 = 10$$
Since $3x - y = 10$ is true for $x = 4$ and $y = 2$, (4, 2) is a solution.

b. For (2, 4), $x = 2$ and $y = 4$. Then
$$3x - y = 3(2) - 4 = 6 - 4 = 2$$
Since $3x - y = 10$ is false for $x = 2$ and $y = 4$, (2, 4) is not a solution.

EXAMPLE 2 Find solutions of $y = 2x + 3$ for:
a. $x = 5$ b. $x = 0$ c. $x = -5$ d. $y = 7$

Solution

a. For $x = 5$, $y = 2(5) + 3 = 10 + 3 = 13$, and (5, 13) is a solution.

b. For $x = 0$, $y = 2(0) + 3 = 3$, and (0, 3) is a solution.

c. For $x = -5$, $y = 2(-5) + 3 = -10 + 3 = -7$, and $(-5, -7)$ is a solution.

d. For $y = 7$, $7 = 2x + 3$, $2x + 3 = 7$, $2x = 4$, $x = 2$. Therefore, (2, 7) is a solution.

In general, most equations in two variables have infinitely many solutions that are ordered pairs of real numbers. As an example of an exception, $x^2 + y^2 = -1$ has no solutions in the set of ordered pairs of real numbers since x^2 and y^2 and $x^2 + y^2$ must be positive or zero.

RECTANGULAR COORDINATES

In Chapter 1 a one-to-one correspondence was established between the set of real numbers and the set of points on a line: Every point on the number line represents a unique real number, and for every real number there exists a corresponding unique point on the number line.

A similar one-to-one correspondence can be established between the set of ordered pairs of real numbers and the set of points on a plane.

A **number plane** is a plane whose points have been placed in one-to-one correspondence with the set of ordered pairs of real numbers.

A **rectangular coordinate system** is obtained by taking two perpendicular number lines, called the **axes,** intersecting at their origins.

The point of intersection of the axes is called the **origin** of the coordinate system.

It is customary to select one axis horizontal, called the **x-axis,** with its positive direction to the right, and the other axis vertical, called the **y-axis,** with its positive direction upward.

Unless it is specified otherwise, the unit segment on the x-axis is selected to be the same length as the unit segment on the y-axis—that is, the same scale is used for both axes.

The axes separate the plane into four regions, called **quadrants,** that are numbered consecutively starting with the upper right quadrant and proceeding counterclockwise (see Fig. 5.1).

To each ordered pair (a, b) of real numbers is associated a unique point P, the point of intersection of a vertical line through point a on the x-axis and a horizontal line through point b on the y-axis.

Conversely, to each point P in the plane is associated a unique ordered pair (a, b) where a is the coordinate of the point of intersection of the vertical line through P and the x-axis and b is the coordinate of the point of intersection of the horizontal line through P and the y-axis.

A point a on the x-axis is assigned the ordered pair $(a, 0)$, and a point b on the y-axis is assigned the ordered pair $(0, b)$. The origin is assigned the ordered pair $(0, 0)$.

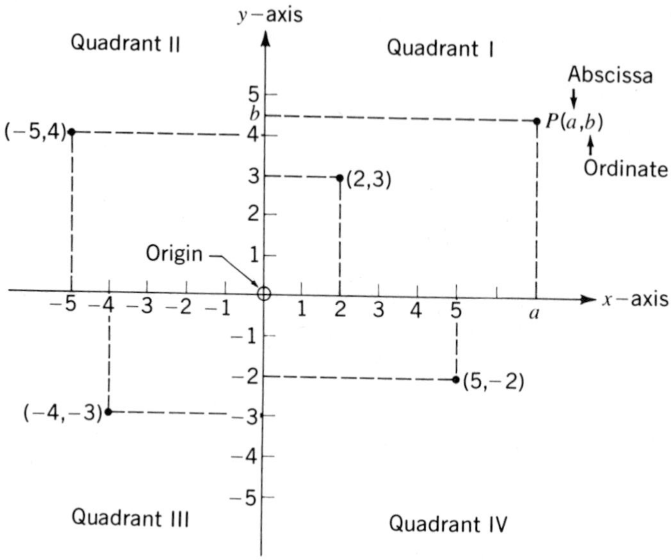

FIG. 5.1

The numbers of the ordered pair (a, b) are called the **coordinates** of P, with the first component, a, called the **abscissa** and the second component, b, called the **ordinate** (see Fig. 5.1). A point will be designated symbolically by P: (a, b).

The association in which two perpendicular coordinate lines are used to establish a one-to-one correspondence between the set of points on a plane and the set of ordered pairs of real numbers is called a **rectangular** (or **Cartesian**) **coordinate system.**

EXAMPLE 3 Graph P: (3, 4).

Solution To locate the point P whose coordinates are (3, 4), draw a vertical line through the point 3 on the x-axis and a horizontal line through the point 4 on the y-axis. The point P is the intersection of these two lines (see Fig. 5.2). This point is located in the first quadrant.

EXAMPLE 4 Graph Q: (−3, 2).

Solution To locate the point Q, whose coordinates are (−3, 2), draw a vertical line through the point −3 on the x-axis and a horizontal line through the point 2 on the y-axis. The intersection of these two lines is point Q. This point is in the second quadrant (see Fig. 5.2).

FIG. 5.2

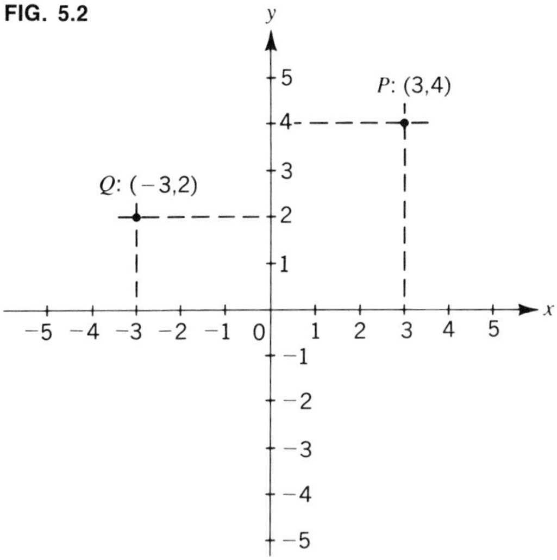

FIG. 5.3

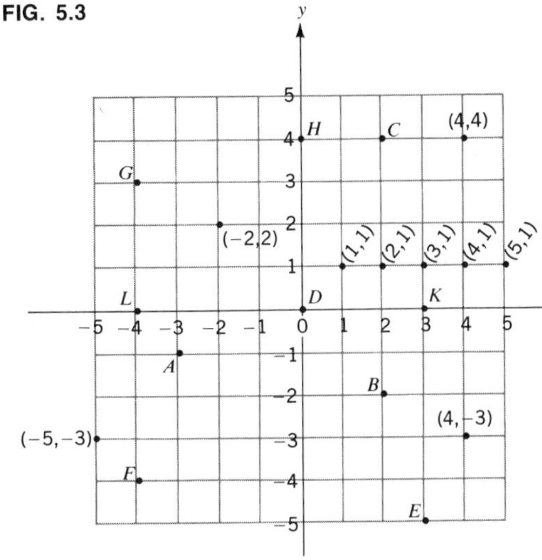

If vertical lines are drawn through every point that corresponds to an integer on the x-axis and horizontal lines are drawn through every point that corresponds to an integer on the y-axis, the intersections of these lines will represent a one-to-one correspondence between the points of intersection of these lines and the set of ordered pairs of integers. The lines form a grid, as shown in Fig. 5.3.

There are many more points on a number plane other than those corresponding to ordered pairs of integers, just as there are many more points on a number line other than those corresponding to integers.

The set of points on a number plane is in one-to-one correspondence with the set of ordered pairs of real numbers.

EXAMPLE 5 Graph the solutions of the equation $2x + y = 6$ for: a. $x = 0$, b. $x = 1$, c. $y = 0$, d. $y = -2$. Join these points in the order a, b, c, d.

Solution

a. For $x = 0$, $2(0) + y = 6$ and $y = 6$. The solution is (0, 6).
b. For $x = 1$, $2(1) + y = 6$ and $y = 4$. The solution is (1, 4).
c. For $y = 0$, $2x + 0 = 6$ and $x = 3$. The solution is (3, 0).
d. For $y = -2$, $2x + (-2) = 6$, $2x = 8$, and $x = 4$. The solution is (4, −2).

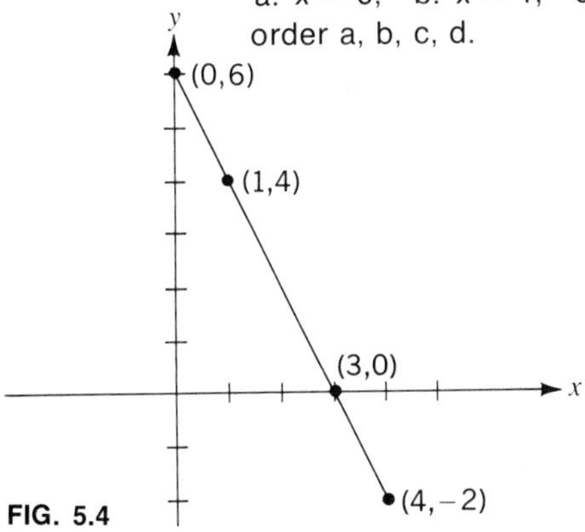

FIG. 5.4

The graph is shown in Fig. 5.4.

EXERCISES

For Exercises 1–10, state the coordinates of each of the points in Fig. 5.3.

1. *A* **2.** *B*
3. *C* **4.** *D*
5. *E* **6.** *F*
7. *G* **8.** *H*
9. *K* **10.** *L*

For Exercises 11–22, locate the points whose coordinates are given on one set of axes. Label each point with its coordinates.

11. (2, 3) **12.** (3, 2)
13. (−1, −4) **14.** (1, −3)
15. (−1, 3) **16.** (0, 4)
17. (4, 0) **18.** (0, 0)
19. (3, −2) **20.** (−2, 1)
21. (0, −2) **22.** (−2, −4)

23. Locate the points (3, 2) and (−1, −2) and connect them with a straight line. Locate the points (2, −2) and (−1, 4) and connect them with a straight line. What are the coordinates of the point of intersection?

24. Locate the points (3, 5) and (6, −4) and connect them with a straight line. Locate the points (7, 1) and (1, −5) and connect them with a straight line. What are the coordinates of the point of intersection?

Which of Exercises 25–30 are solutions of $y = 2x + 3$?

25. (0, 3) **26.** (1, 5)
27. (2, 6) **28.** (3, 0)
29. (5, 13) **30.** (−4, −1)

Which of Exercises 31–36 are solutions of $2x + y = 6$?

31. (3, 0) **32.** (0, 3)
33. (−3, 0) **34.** (−3, 12)
35. (4, −2) **36.** (4, 1)

Which of Exercises 37–42 are solutions of $3x - y = 12$?

37. (0, 12) **38.** (0, −12)
39. (4, 0) **40.** (0, 4)
41. (−1, 15) **42.** (−2, −18)

From the set {(3, 5), (5, 3), (0, 5), (3, 0), (5, −3)} *select one or more solutions for each equation in Exercises 43–48.*

43. $5x + 3y = 15$ **44.** $2y = 3x - 9$

45. $y = 17 - 4x$

46. $5x + 2y = 25$

47. $y = 5$

48. $x = 3$

From the set $\{(2, 6), (-2, 6), (6, -2), (-2, 0), (0, 6)\}$ *select one or more solutions for each equation in Exercises 49–54.*

49. $3x + 2y = 6$

50. $y = 3x + 6$

51. $y = 10 - 2x$

52. $3x + y + 6 = 0$

53. $x = -2$

54. $y = 6$

For Exercises 55–58, copy and complete the table of values, then plot the points on a set of coordinate axes. If the points were connected, what geometric term would describe this graph?

55. $y = 3x - 6$

x	y
0	?
?	0
1	?
−2	?
?	−3

56. $3x + 5y = 15$

x	y
0	?
?	0
−5	?
?	−6
10	?

57. $x - y = 8$

x	y
0	?
?	0
−2	?
?	−4
3	?

58. $3x - 2y = 12$

x	y
0	?
?	0
2	?
−4	?
?	6

5.2 GRAPHS OF LINEAR EQUATIONS

In the previous section we saw that a solution of an equation in two variables is an ordered pair of numbers for which the equation becomes a true statement.

DEFINITION

The **solution set** of an equation in two variables is the set of all solutions of the equation.

For an equation having the form $y = mx + b$ there is exactly one real number y for each real number x. Consequently, an equation in the form $y = mx + b$ has infinitely many solutions.

A **linear function** is the set of ordered pairs (x, y) defined by a rule having the form $y = mx + b$, in other words, the solution set of $y = mx + b$.

The **graph of a linear function** is the graph of the set of ordered pairs belonging to the linear function.

The graph of a linear function is a straight line.

The **set-builder notation** is very useful for describing a set of ordered pairs. In set-builder notation, a linear function is defined as follows.

$\{(x, y) \mid y = mx + b\}$

This is read: "The set of all ordered pairs (x, y) such that $y = mx + b$." Note that the vertical bar is read "such that."

EXAMPLE 1 Graph $\{(x, y) \mid y = 2x + 1\}$.

Solution This means we are to graph all ordered pairs whose y-coordinate is obtained by adding 1 to twice the x-coordinate.

Solutions can be found by arbitrarily assigning values for x and calculating the corresponding values for y. It is convenient to make a table of values:

x	$2x + 1 = y$	(x, y)
1	$2(1) + 1 = 3$	(1, 3)
2	$2(2) + 1 = 5$	(2, 5)
3	$2(3) + 1 = 7$	(3, 7)
0	$2(0) + 1 = 1$	(0, 1)
−2	$2(-2) + 1 = -3$	(−2, −3)

Thus the ordered pairs (1, 3), (2, 5), (3, 7), (0, 1), and (−2, −3) are solutions for the given equation. Figure 5.5 is the graph of these five points. As shown previously, an ordered pair (p, q) is a solution of an equation in two variables, x and y, if the equation is true when $x = p$ and $y = q$.

The plotted points in Fig. 5.6 seem to lie in a straight line, and in fact they do. There are infinitely many solutions to the equation $y = 2x + 1$, and only part of the graph representing the solutions can be shown. The arrows at each end of the line representing the solution set indicate that the line continues indefinitely in both directions.

FIG. 5.5

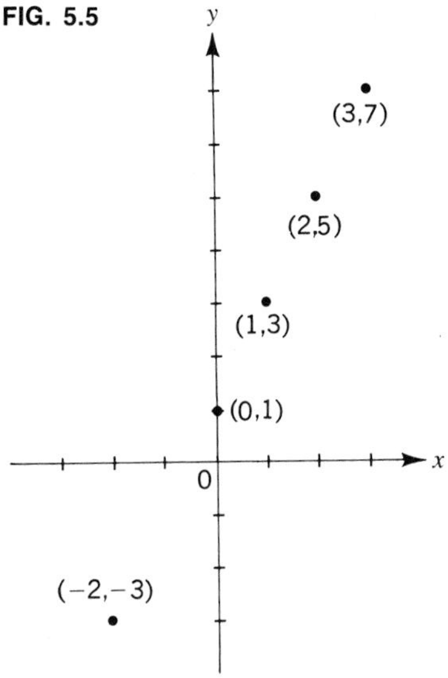

FIG. 5.6

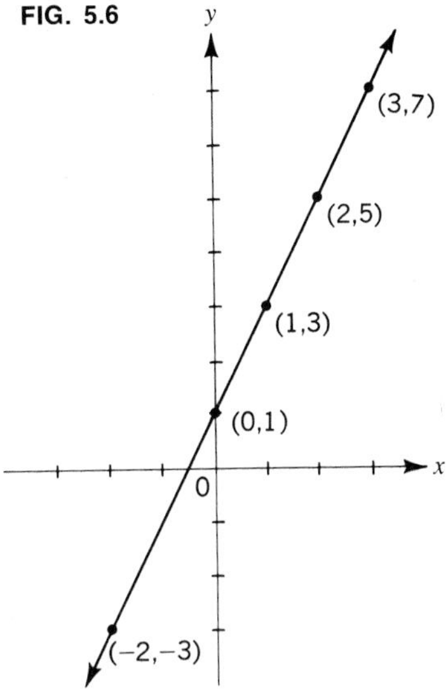

DEFINITION

Any equation in two variables x and y that can be expressed in the form

$$Ax + By + C = 0$$

where A and B are real numbers, not both zero, is called a **linear equation in two variables.**

If $B \neq 0$, then this equation can be solved for y.

$$Ax + By + C = 0$$

$$By = -Ax - C$$

$$y = -\frac{A}{B}x - \frac{C}{B}$$

$$y = mx + b \quad \text{where} \quad m = -\frac{A}{B}$$

$$\text{and} \quad b = -\frac{C}{B}$$

Thus if $B \neq 0$, then $Ax + By + C = 0$ defines a linear function.

If $B = 0$, then $A \neq 0$ and the general equation becomes

$$Ax + C = 0$$

Solving for x,

$$x = -\frac{C}{A}$$

or $x = c$, a real number.

DEFINITION

The **graph of a linear equation** is the graph of its solution set, and for any linear equation in two variables, this graph is a straight line.

To verify that the graph of a linear equation in two variables actually is a straight line, two things must be shown:

1. The set of points whose coordinates satisfy a given linear equation $Ax + By + C = 0$ (A and B real numbers, not both zero) all lie on a straight line.
2. The coordinates (x, y) of any point lying on a straight line satisfy a linear equation in x and y.

Both these statements can be proved, but for now they will be taken for granted, and it will be assumed that in a Cartesian coordinate system the graph of a linear equation in two variables is a line and every line in the plane is the graph of a linear equation in two variables.

Since two points uniquely determine a line, it is only necessary to find two solutions (ordered pairs) that satisfy a given linear equation, plot the points corresponding to the coordinates, and draw a line through these points. This line represents the graph of the given equation. It is a good idea, however, to find a third solution as a check.

EXAMPLE 2 Graph $2x + y = 6$.

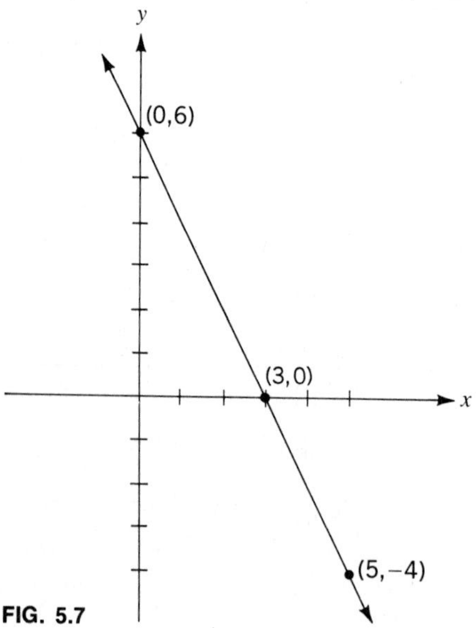

FIG. 5.7

Solution Make a table of solutions. Any value may be selected for x, and then the corresponding y value is computed, using the equation.

Similarly, any value may be selected for y and its x value computed.

It is convenient to select $x = 0$ for one point and $y = 0$ for another point, because the resulting calculations are relatively easy. These resulting points are called the *intercept points.*

Selecting $x = 0$, $y = 0$, and $x = 5$, we make the following table:

x	y	$2x + y = 6$	(x, y)
0		$2(0) + y = 6,\ y = 6$	$(0, 6)$
	0	$2x + 0 = 6,\ x = 3$	$(3, 0)$
5		$2(5) + y = 6,\ y = -4$	$(5, -4)$

The points are plotted and a straight line is drawn through them (see Fig. 5.7).

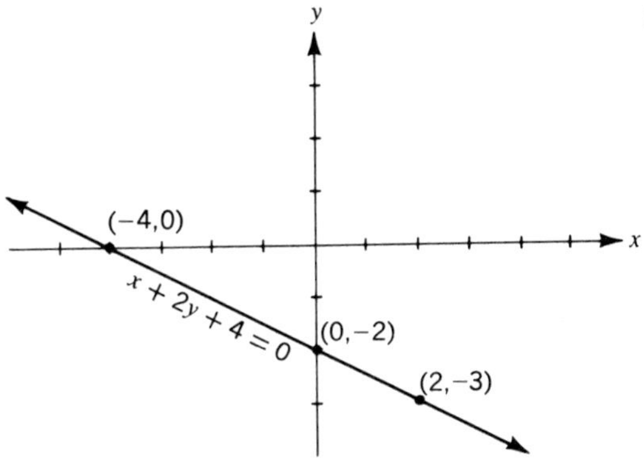

FIG. 5.8

DEFINITION: INTERCEPTS

If a point having coordinates $(a, 0)$ is on a graph, then a is called an x-intercept of the graph. If a point having coordinates $(0, b)$ is on a graph, then b is called a y-intercept of the graph.

EXAMPLE 3 Graph $\{(x, y) \mid x + 2y + 4 = 0\}$.

Solution
Selecting $x = 0$, $y = 0$, and $y = -3$, we make the following table:

x	y	$x + 2y + 4 = 0$	(x, y)
0		$0 + 2y + 4 = 0$, $2y = -4$, $y = -2$	$(0, -2)$
	0	$x + 2(0) + 4 = 0$, $x + 4 = 0$, $x = -4$	$(-4, 0)$
	-3	$x + 2(-3) + 4 = 0$, $x - 6 + 4 = 0$, $x - 2 = 0$, $x = 2$	$(2, -3)$

The plotted points and the line through them are shown in Fig. 5.8.

EXAMPLE 4 Graph $\{(x, y) \mid y = 3\}$.

Solution All ordered pairs whose second component is 3 are solutions of $y = 3$; for example, $(2, 3)$, $(0, 3)$, $(-3, 3)$. The graph is a horizontal line, as shown in Fig. 5.9.

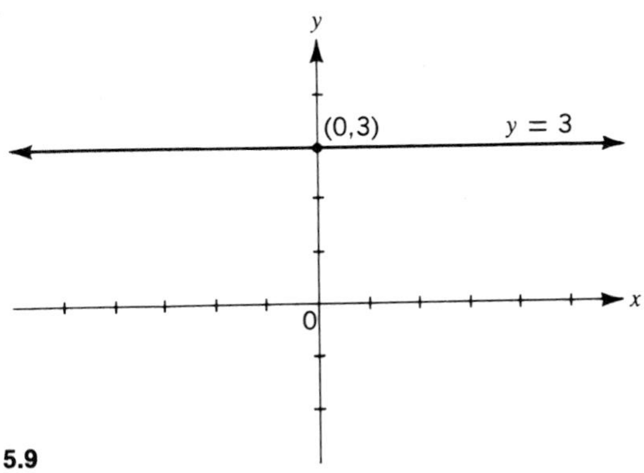

FIG. 5.9

FIG. 5.10

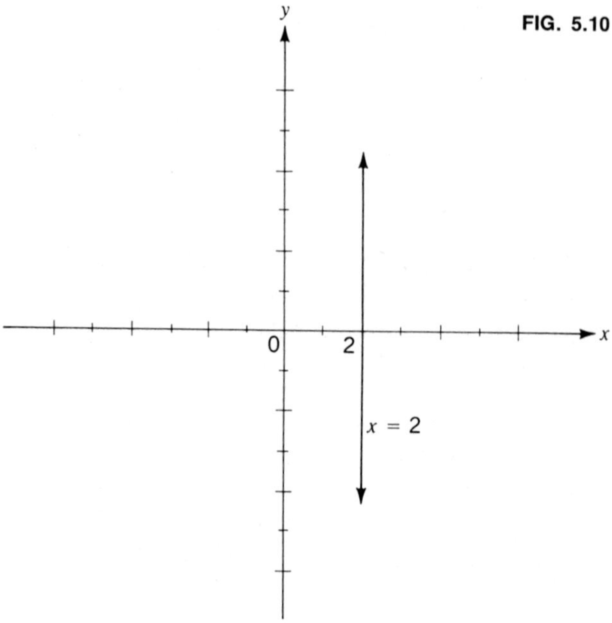

EXAMPLE 5 Graph $\{(x, y) \mid x = 2\}$.

Solution All ordered pairs whose first component is 2 are solutions of $x = 2$; for example, $(2, 4)$, $(2, 0)$, $(2, -3)$. The graph is a vertical line, as shown in Fig. 5.10.

EXERCISES

In Exercises 1–6 determine the x-intercept and the y-intercept and use these values to graph each equation.

1. $y = 2x - 6$
2. $y = 3x - 2$
3. $x + y = 4$
4. $x - y = 4$
5. $3x - 2y = 6$
6. $2x - 3y = 12$

Graph each of Exercises 7–24 on a number plane.

7. $y = 2x + 6$
8. $y = 3x - 9$
9. $y = 4 - x$
10. $y = 8 - 4x$
11. $x + 2y = 0$
12. $3x - 4y = 0$

13. $x - y = 5$
14. $x + 2y = 8$
15. $2x + 3y = 6$
16. $5x - 2y = 10$
17. $x = -3$
18. $y + 1 = 0$
19. $x - 5y = 0$
20. $5x - 2y = 0$
21. $x - 3y = 9$
22. $x + 4y = 12$
23. $3x + 5y = 15$
24. $4x - 5y = 10$

In Exercises 25 and 26, draw the graphs of each of the following equations on one set of coordinate axes. What characteristic do these graphs have in common? How do these graphs differ from one another?

25. a. $y = x + 2$ b. $y = x - 1$ c. $y = x$ d. $y = x + 4$

26. a. $y = 2x + 1$ b. $y = 3x + 1$ c. $y = -5x + 1$ d. $x + y - 1 = 0$

27. a. For what value of k will the point $(k, 3)$ be on the graph of $y = 2x - 7$?
b. For what value of k will the point $(2, k)$ be on the graph of $y = 5x - 1$?

28. The number of hours H that a growing child should sleep may be related to the age A of the child in years by the formula $H = 17 - \frac{A}{2}$.
Represent this relation graphically by selecting the horizontal axis as the A-axis. Graph from $A = 0$ to $A = 18$.

29. The following table shows the changes in temperature in a town on a certain day from 9 a.m. to 3 p.m.

Hour	9	10	11	12	1	2	3
Temperature	62°	66°	71°	74°	70°	69°	67°

a. Draw a graph to show these changes in temperature. Join the points consecutively by straight lines.
b. Mark the points on the graph that indicate the approximate time when the temperature was 68 degrees.
c. Determine from the graph for how long the temperature was above 68 degrees.

30. The formula $A = 100(1 + 0.06t)$ expresses the amount of money A (in dollars) to which a sum of \$100 accumulates if invested at 6 percent simple interest for t years.

a. Graph this equation, finding points for $t = 2, 4, 6, 8$, and 10. Join the points by a straight line.
b. Find out from the graph how much money has accumulated at the end of 5 years.
c. Find out from the graph how long it would take the sum to reach \$142.

31. Using the straight-line depreciation method, a car that costs \$3000 new and that has a probable scrap value of \$500 at the end of 10 years will have a book value B dollars at the end of n years where $B = 3000 - 250n$.

a. Graph this equation for $0 \leq n \leq 10$.
b. From the graph determine the book value at the end of $5\frac{1}{2}$ years.
c. When will the book value be \$1875?
d. On the same set of axes, graph $A = 250n$, the amount in the depreciation fund.
e. When is the amount in the depreciation fund equal to the book value?

5.3 SLOPE AND THE LINEAR EQUATION

SLOPE

If a roof rises 1 foot for every 4 feet of horizontal distance, the steepness or pitch of the roof is $\frac{1}{4}$ (Fig. 5.11). The ratio $\frac{1}{4}$ represents the **slope** of the roof, and it is the ratio of the rise to the run. It is often important to evaluate the slope of a line, and the computation is similar to the roof problem. Consider the graph of the equation $2x - y = 4$ (Fig. 5.12). Choose any two points on the graph, for example, point $P{:}(5, 6)$ and point $Q{:}(1, -2)$:

$$\text{Slope} = \frac{\text{rise}}{\text{run}} = \frac{\text{change in ordinate } (y)}{\text{change in abscissa } (x)}$$

$$= \frac{6 - (-2)}{5 - 1} = \frac{8}{4} = \frac{2}{1}$$

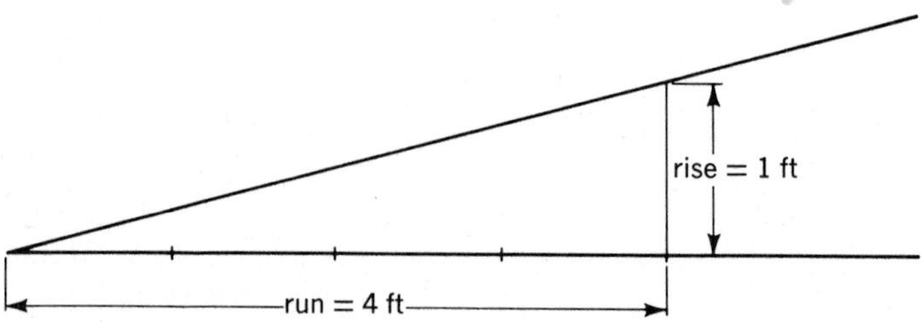

FIG. 5.11

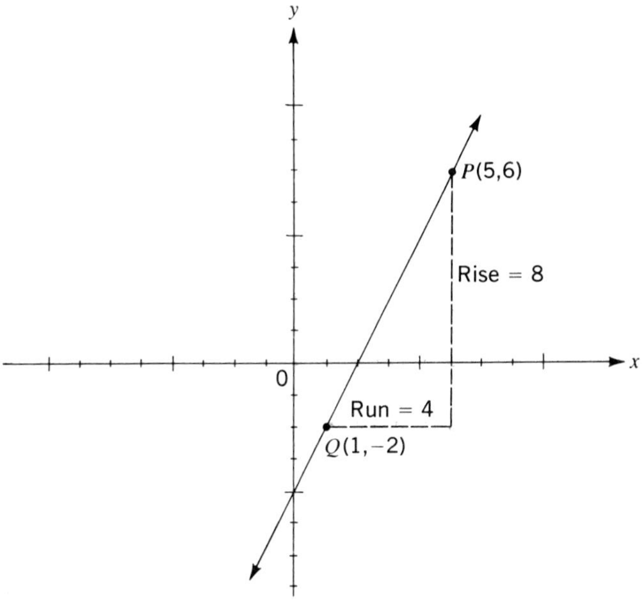

FIG. 5.12

THE ORIGIN OF COORDINATES

The concept of a coordinate system probably originated with the ancient Egyptian surveyors. The hieroglyphic symbol used to designate the districts into which Egypt was divided was a grid symbol.

Records indicate that the Greeks used the ideas of longitude and latitude to locate points in the sky and on the earth. The Romans, who were noted for their surveying techniques, arranged the streets of their cities on a rectangular coordinate system.

The Arab and Persian mathematicians were the first to use geometric figures for algebraic problems. Examples are found in the works of the Arab al-Khowarizmi (ca. 825) and the Persian Omar Khayyam (ca. 1100). This usage is again found in the writings of Fibonacci (1220), Pacioli (1494), and Cardan (1545).

René Descartes (1596–1650) is credited with the invention of analytic geometry, since he used a rectangular coordinate system to establish a relationship between equations and curves. Pierre de Fermat, another great French mathematician, formulated coordinate geometry at the same time and made a considerable contribution in this field. The modern terms *coordinates, abscissa,* and *ordinate* were contributed by the German mathematician Gottfried Wilhelm Leibniz in 1692.

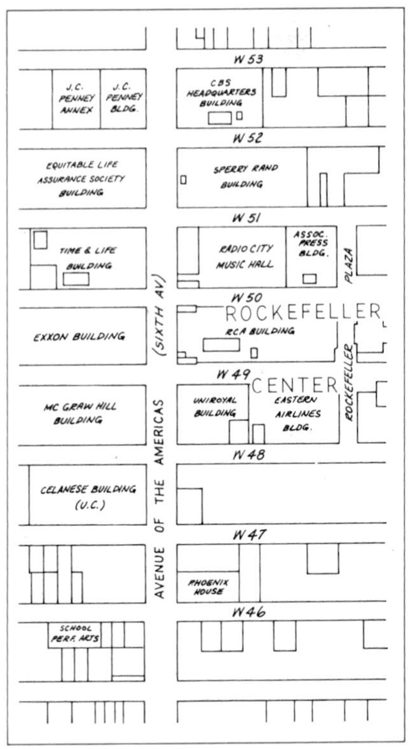

slope = vertical / horizontal

Therefore, the slope is $\frac{2}{1}$, or 2. The slope of a line is the same for all points on the line, not for just the two specific points selected.

A definition for the slope of a general line can be conveniently expressed by using subscripts to indicate two points on the line. For example, P_1, (read "P sub one") and P_2 (read "P sub two") name two points. The numeral 1 at the lower right of P_1 and the numeral 2 at the lower right of P_2 are subscripts used to indicate that P_1 is the first point and P_2 is the second point.

Similarly, the coordinates of P_1 can be expressed as (x_1, y_1) and those of P_2 as (x_2, y_2).

DEFINITION

If P_1: (x_1, y_1) and P_2: (x_2, y_2) are any two points on a line and if $x_1 \neq x_2$, then the **slope** m of the line joining P_1 and P_2 is given by

$$m = \frac{y_2 - y_1}{x_2 - x_1}$$

See Fig. 5.13.

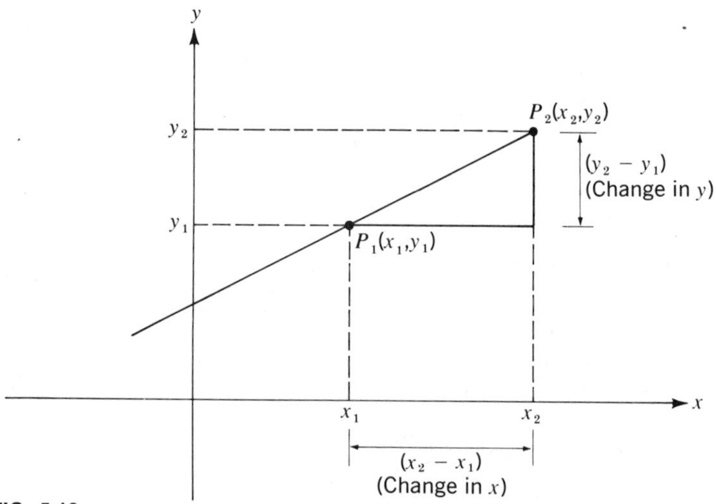

FIG. 5.13

If a line is vertical (parallel to the y-axis), then $x_1 = x_2$ and $x_2 - x_1 = 0$. Since the denominator of the slope ratio is zero, the **slope of a vertical line is undefined** (see Fig. 5.14).

If a line is horizontal (parallel to the x-axis), then $y_1 = y_2$ and $y_2 - y_1 = 0$. In this case, the numerator of the slope ratio is zero, and **the slope of a horizontal line is 0** (see Fig. 5.15).

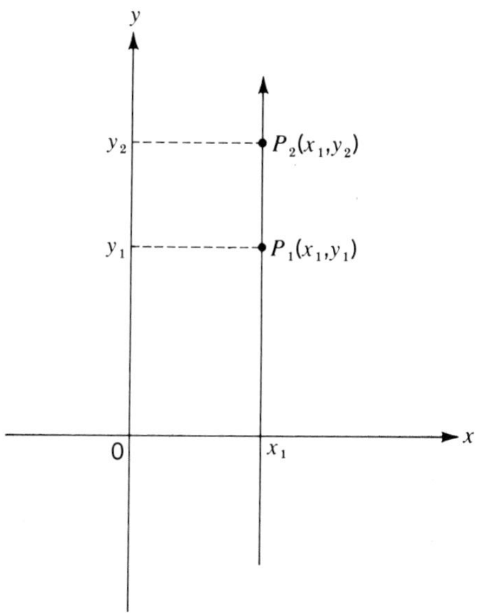

FIG. 5.14

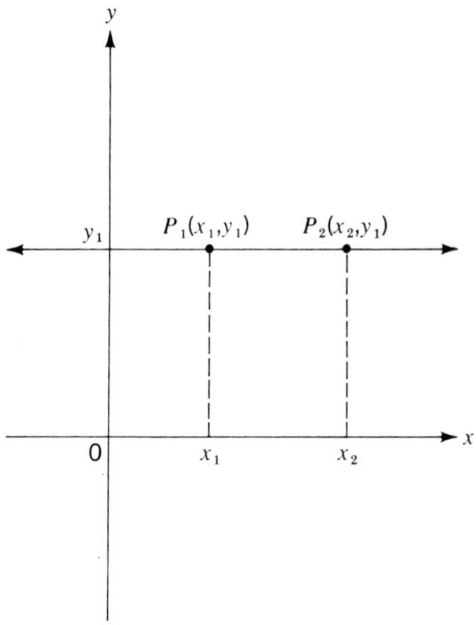

FIG. 5.15

EXAMPLE 1 Find the slope of the line passing through the points whose coordinates are (3, 2) and (5, 1), respectively.

Solution Using

$$m = \frac{y_2 - y_1}{x_2 - x_1} \text{ with } (x_2, y_2) = (5, 1) \text{ and } (x_1, y_1) = (3, 2)$$

$$m = \frac{1 - 2}{5 - 3} = -\frac{1}{2}$$

Alternate Solution Using

$$m = \frac{y_2 - y_1}{x_2 - x_1} \text{ with } (x_2, y_2) = (3, 2) \text{ and } (x_1, y_1) = (5, 1)$$

$$m = \frac{2 - 1}{3 - 5} = -\frac{1}{2}$$

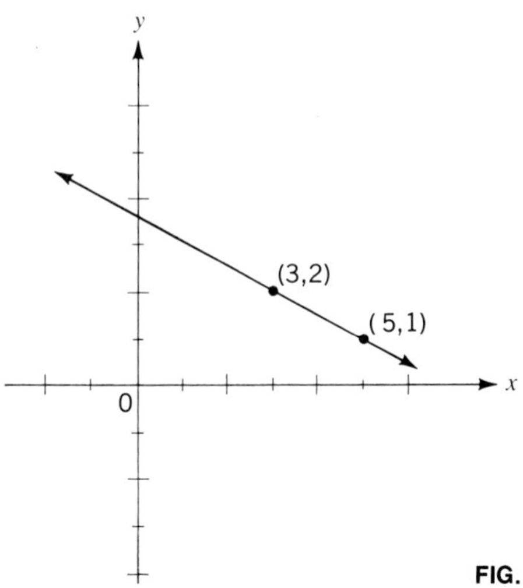

FIG. 5.16

Note in Example 1 that the value of the slope does not depend on which point is called the first point and which the second.

Note also that the slope is negative, which means that the line "falls to the right" (see Fig. 5.16).

EXAMPLE 2 Find the slope of the line passing through (2, 1) and (3, 4).

Solution

$$m = \frac{y_2 - y_1}{x_2 - x_1} = \frac{4-1}{3-2} = 3$$

In this case the slope is positive and the line "rises to the right" (see Fig. 5.17).

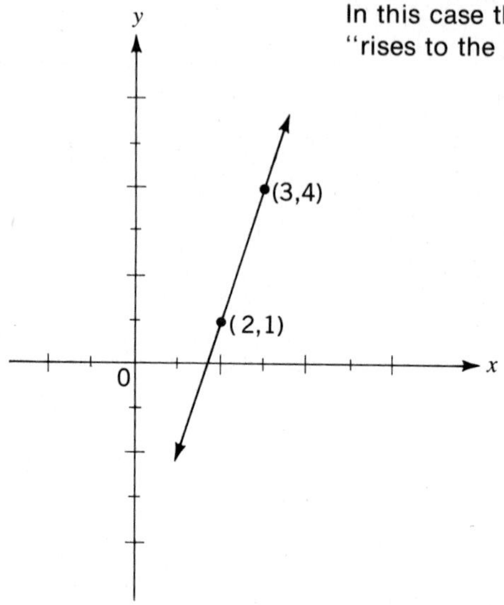

FIG. 5.17

Although the slope of any given nonvertical line is uniquely determined, a given slope does not determine a unique line. Consider the equations

$$y = 2x + 1 \qquad (1)$$

and

$$y = 2x \qquad (2)$$

Select two points on the graph of equation (1) and two points on the graph of equation (2). The coordinates (0, 1) and (1, 3) satisfy equation (1). (See Fig. 5.18.) Slope of line (1) is $\frac{3-1}{1-0} = 2$. The coordinates (0, 0) and (1, 2) satisfy equation (2). Slope of line (2) is $\frac{2-0}{1-0} = 2$. Both lines have the same slope, but from Fig. 5.18 it is clear that the lines are distinct. They are in fact parallel, which leads to the following theorem.

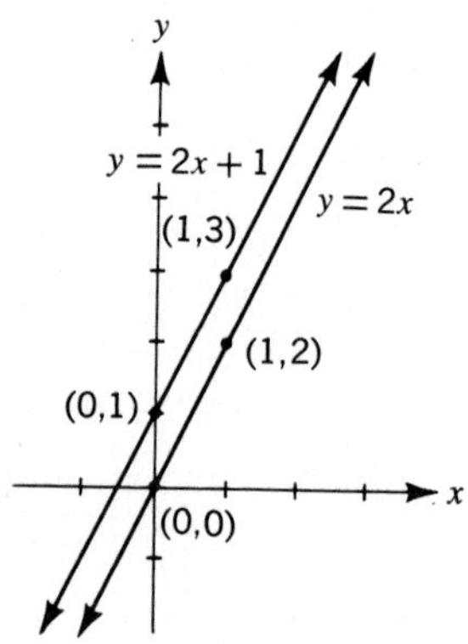

FIG. 5.18

THEOREM

Two distinct nonvertical lines in the same plane are parallel if and only if they have the same slope.

If $2x + 3y = 12$

$y = -2/3x + 4$

$y = mx + b$ slope intercept

THE SLOPE-INTERCEPT FORM OF A LINEAR EQUATION

Every linear equation of the form $Ax + By + C = 0$, where A and B are real numbers not both zero, is equivalent to an equation that is solved explicitly for one variable in terms of the other. For example, the equation

$$2x + 3y + 1 = 0$$

is equivalent to the equation

$$y = -\frac{2}{3}x - \frac{1}{3}$$

To find the slope of the line represented by this equation, two arbitrary points are selected.

For $x = 1$, and $y = -\frac{2}{3}x - \frac{1}{3}$

$$y = -\frac{2}{3}(1) - \frac{1}{3} = -1$$

P_1 is selected as $(1, -1)$.

For $x = -2$, and $y = -\frac{2}{3}x - \frac{1}{3}$

$$y = -\frac{2}{3}(-2) - \frac{1}{3}$$

$$y = \frac{4}{3} - \frac{1}{3} = 1$$

P_2 is selected as $(-2, 1)$.

Calculating the slope,

$$m = \frac{1 - (-1)}{-2 - 1} = \frac{2}{-3} = -\frac{2}{3}$$

Referring to the equation $y = -\frac{2}{3}x - \frac{1}{3}$, it can be seen that the slope $-\frac{2}{3}$ is also the coefficient of x. This is not just a coincidence. In general, if a line is represented by the equation

$$y = mx + b$$

then m, the coefficient of x, represents the slope of the line.

If $x = 0$, then $y = b$, and the ordered pair $(0, b)$ is a solution of $y = mx + b$. The point whose coordinates are $(0, b)$ is located on the y-axis and represents the point where the line crosses the y-axis. This number b in the equation $y = mx + b$ is called the **y-intercept.**

$$y = \underset{\substack{\uparrow \\ \text{slope}}}{mx} + \underset{\substack{\uparrow \\ y\text{-intercept}}}{b}$$

Since the slope and y-intercept can be determined so easily from the form $y = mx + b$, a special name has been given to this form.

DEFINITIONS

$y = mx + b$ is called the **slope-intercept form** of a linear equation.
$Ax + By + C = 0$ is called the **standard form** of a linear equation.

EXAMPLE 3 Find the slope and the y-intercept of the line whose equation is $5x - 4y = 20$.

Solution Solving the equation for y,

$$\begin{aligned} 5x - 4y &= 20 \\ 5x &= 4y + 20 \\ 4y + 20 &= 5x \\ 4y &= 5x - 20 \\ y &= \frac{5}{4}x - 5 \end{aligned}$$

Comparing with $y = mx + b$, the slope of the line is $m = \frac{5}{4}$, and the y-intercept is $b = -5$.

EXAMPLE 4 Check the value of the slope found in Example 3 by selecting any two points on the line and using the slope formula.

Solution

Selecting $y = 5$ and using $5x - 4y = 20$,

$$\begin{aligned} 5x - 4(5) &= 20 \\ 5x &= 40 \text{ and } x = 8 \end{aligned}$$

Let $P_1 = (8, 5)$.

Selecting $y = -10$ and using $5x - 4y = 20$,

$$\begin{aligned} 5x - 4(-10) &= 20 \\ 5x &= -20 \text{ and } x = -4 \end{aligned}$$

Let $P_2 = (-4, -10)$.

$$m = \frac{y_2 - y_1}{x_2 - x_1} = \frac{-10 - 5}{-4 - 8} = \frac{-15}{-12} = \frac{5}{4}$$

EXAMPLE 5 Which of the following lines is parallel to $y = 3x - 5$?

a. $3x - y + 6 = 0$ b. $x + 3y - 5 = 0$

Solution

1. The slope of $y = 3x - 5$ is 3, the coefficient of x, since the equation is in the slope-intercept form.
2. Solving each equation for y to obtain the slope-intercept form,

a. $3x - y + 6 = 0$

$$\begin{aligned} 3x + 6 &= y \\ y &= 3x + 6 \text{ and slope } m = 3 \end{aligned}$$

Since $y = 3x - 5$ and $3x - y + 6 = 0$ have the same slope, these lines are parallel.

b. $x + 3y - 5 = 0$

$$\begin{aligned} 3y &= -x + 5 \\ y &= -\frac{1}{3}x + \frac{5}{3} \text{ and } m = -\frac{1}{3} \end{aligned}$$

Since $-\frac{1}{3} \neq 3$, the lines $y = 3x - 5$ and $x + 3y - 5 = 0$ are not parallel.

EXAMPLE 6 Find the value of k so that the line through $(1, k)$ and $(5, 4k)$ has the property stated:

a. Slope -6 b. Slope 0 c. Parallel to $3x - y = 2$

Solution

a. $m = \dfrac{4k - k}{5 - 1} = \dfrac{3k}{4}$ and $m = -6$

$$\frac{3k}{4} = -6,\ 3k = -24,\ k = -8$$

b. $\dfrac{3k}{4} = 0,\ k = 0$

c. Solving $3x - y = 2$ for y,

$$3x = y + 2$$
$$y = 3x - 2$$

and the slope of this line is 3.

Since parallel lines have the same slope,

$$\frac{3k}{4} = 3,\ 3k = 12,\ k = 4$$

EXERCISES

For Exercises 1-10, find the slope of the line segment joining the two given points.

1. $(4, 2)$ and $(2, 1)$
2. $(0, 1)$ and $(-2, -2)$
3. $(0, 4)$ and $(3, 0)$
4. $(-3, 2)$ and $(2, -3)$
5. $(-1, -2)$ and $(-3, -4)$
6. $(3, 2)$ and $(1, 6)$
7. $(3, 2)$ and $(4, 1)$
8. $(1, 0)$ and $(-4, -3)$
9. $(-2, -1)$ and $(2, 1)$
10. $(-5, -4)$ and $(-2, -3)$

Write each of the equations in Exercises 11–30 in the slope-intercept form, $y = mx + b$, if possible, and determine the slope and the y-intercept of the graph of the equation. Check the value of the slope by selecting any two points on the line and by using the slope formula.

$y = -\frac{2}{1}x + 5$ ← intercept = 5, slope = over one down 2

11. $2x + y = 5$
12. $3x + 2y = 12$
13. $2x - y = 8$
14. $\frac{1}{2}(x + y + 10) = 0$
15. $5x - 2y = 10$
16. $2x - 3y = 9$
17. $5(x - y) + 3 = 0$
18. $2(x - y) - 3(x + y) = 5$
19. $3y - 15 = 0$
20. $3x - 9 = 0$
21. $y - 2x + 4 = 0$
22. $2y - 4x = 5$
23. $3x + 2y = 4$
24. $4x + 16 = 2y$
25. $3(x + 1) = 2y$
26. $x - (y - 1) + 5 = 0$
27. $2x + 8 = 0$
28. $4y + 8 = 0$
29. $y = x$
30. $x + y = 0$

For each pair of lines in Exercises 31–42, state whether the lines are parallel. If they are parallel, give the slope.

31. $2x + 2y = 1$
$3x + 3y = 1$

32. $x = 2y - 6$
$y = 2x - 6$

33. $2x = 3y$
$3x = 2y$

34. $4x = 2y + 1$
$2x - y = 4$

35. $5x + 3y = 15$
$3x + 5y = 30$

36. $x + y = 0$
$x - y = 0$

37. $x = y - 2$
$y = x - 2$

38. $5x - 2y = 3$
$10x - 4y = 5$

39. $2(x + 3y) = 3(x + 2y - 1)$
$5x + 10 = 0$

40. $3x - 4y = 12$
$4x - 3y = 12$

41. $x = 3y + 6$
$2x - 6y = 3$

42. $(x + y) - (x - y) = 6$
$2y - 8 = 0$

In Exercises 43–48, find the value of k so that the line through (2, k) and (5, 3k) has the property stated.

43. Slope 4

44. Slope $\frac{1}{2}$

45. Slope 0

46. Slope -2

47. Parallel to $y = x + 5$

48. Parallel to $2x + y = 4$

49. As an example of a slope, a highway grade expressed as a percentage means the number of feet the road changes in elevation for 100 feet measured horizontally.

a. A certain highway has a $2\frac{1}{2}$ percent grade. How many feet does it rise in a one-mile stretch (horizontal distance)? (*Note:* 1 mile = 5280 feet.)

b. How many feet does a $-3\frac{1}{4}$ percent grade highway drop for a $\frac{1}{2}$-mile horizontal stretch?

50. A certain county specification requires that an inclined water pipe must have a slope greater than or equal to $\frac{1}{4}$. Which of the water pipes whose rises and runs are given below meets this specification?

a. Rise = 20 feet, run = 64 feet
b. Rise = 125 feet, run = 500 feet
c. Rise = 60 feet, run = 250 feet

5.4 DETERMINING THE EQUATION OF A LINE

In the preceding discussion, the emphasis was on graphing the line whose equation was given. Now consider the problem of finding the equation of a line whose geometric conditions are given.

In order to accomplish this task, one of the following conditions must be given:

1. One point on the line and the slope of the line, or
2. Two points on the line

If the coordinates of a point on a line are given and if the slope of the line is known, then the equation of the line can be found by using the definition of the slope. Since (x, y) is to be a general point on the line, then

$$m = \frac{y - y_1}{x - x_1}$$

where (x_1, y_1) and m are the given point and slope, respectively.

Multiplying both sides of this equation by $x - x_1$ yields the point-slope form of a line, $y - y_1 = m(x - x_1)$.

DEFINITION

The **point-slope form** of a line with slope m passing through the point (x_1, y_1) is

$$y - y_1 = m(x - x_1)$$

EXAMPLE 1 Find an equation of a line whose slope is -2 and that passes through the point $(3, 4)$.

Solution $m = -2$ and $(x_1, y_1) = (3, 4)$

Using the point-slope form of a line,

$$y - y_1 = m(x - x_1)$$
$$y - 4 = -2(x - 3)$$
$$y - 4 = -2x + 6$$
$$y = -2x + 10 \qquad \text{(Slope-intercept form)}$$
$$2x + y - 10 = 0 \qquad \text{(Standard form)}$$

It is conventional to express the answer in standard form—that is, the linear equation is written in the form $Ax + By + C = 0$ where $A \geq 0$.

EXAMPLE 2 Find an equation of a line passing through the points (3, 4) and (2, 1).

Solution

1. Find the slope:

$$m = \frac{y_2 - y_1}{x_2 - x_1} = \frac{4 - 1}{3 - 2} = 3$$

2. Selecting (x_1, y_1) as (2, 1), and using the point-slope form,

$$y - y_1 = m(x - x_1)$$
$$y - 1 = 3(x - 2)$$
$$y - 1 = 3x - 6$$
$$y = 3x - 5 \qquad \text{(Slope-intercept form)}$$
$$3x - y - 5 = 0 \qquad \text{(Standard form)}$$

Alternate Solution and Check Selecting (x_1, y_1) as (3, 4) and (x_2, y_2) as (2, 1), the slope,

$$m = \frac{y_2 - y_1}{x^2 - x_1} = \frac{1 - 4}{2 - 3} = \frac{-3}{-1} = 3$$

Using the point-slope form,

$$y - y_1 = m(x - x_1)$$
$$y - 4 = 3(x - 3)$$
$$y - 4 = 3x - 9$$
$$y = 3x - 5 \qquad \text{(Slope-intercept form)}$$
$$3x - y - 5 = 0 \qquad \text{(Standard form)}$$

Note in the preceding example that when two points on the line are given, it makes no difference which is called the first and which is called the second in finding the equation of the line. Since two possibilities are available, one choice can serve as a check for the other choice.

EXERCISES

In Exercises 1–10, write an equation of the line with the given slope and passing through the point whose coordinates are given.

y - 4 = -2(x - 2)

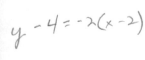

1. $m = -2$; (2, 4)
2. $m = 3$; (1, 5)
3. $m = 6$; (−1, 3)
4. $m = -1$; (2, −1)
5. $m = \frac{1}{2}$; (4, −2)
6. $m = \frac{1}{3}$; (−6, 1)
7. $m = -\frac{3}{4}$; (−3, −4)
8. $m = -\frac{2}{5}$; (−5, −12)
9. $m = 0$; (2, 7)
10. $m = 0$; (5, 0)

In Exercises 11–20, find the slope, if it exists, and write an equation of the line that contains the points whose coordinates are given.

11. (2, 1) and (4, 2)
12. (2, 3) and (−2, −3)
13. (−2, −3) and (4, −1)
14. (−3, −4) and (−4, −3)

15. (5, 2) and (−3, 0)

16. (−2, 5) and (0, −3)

17. (2, 3) and (−5, 3)

18. (4, 6) and $(4, -\frac{1}{2})$

19. (−2, 5) and (−2, −2)

20. (6, −7) and (−5, −7)

For Exercises 21–30, find an equation of the form $Ax + By + C = 0$ for the line satisfying the stated conditions.

21. Parallel to $3x + 2y = 6$ and passing through the point (1, 2)

22. Slope $-\frac{1}{2}$, y-intercept 3

23. Slope $-\frac{1}{2}$, passing through (3, 0)

24. Slope $\frac{3}{4}$, passing through the origin

25. Parallel to the x-axis, passing through (1, 2)

26. Parallel to the y-axis, passing through (1, 2)

27. Parallel to $2x - y + 3 = 0$ and passing through the point (−2, −1)

28. $m = \frac{4}{3}$, y-intercept −2

29. $m = -\frac{4}{3}$, passing through (−2, 0)

30. Passing through the origin and the point (−3, 5)

31. Do the points A: (1, −2), B: (3, 0), and C: (0, 3) lie on a straight line? Why?

32. Do the points P: (0, −1), Q: (2, 0), and R: (4, 1) lie on a straight line? Why?

33. For what value of k will the points (8, 2), (5, 3), (6, k) lie on a straight line?

34. For what value of k will the points (5, 0), (−2, 4), (k, −4) lie on a straight line?

35. The results of a study made by a physiologist for the purpose of trying to predict adult height from height as a child are shown in the following table, where C = the heights of two-year-old children in inches and A = adult heights in inches.

C	30	31	33	34	34	35	37	38
A	60	61	65	67	66	70	73	74

a. Graph the ordered pairs, using the horizontal axis as the C-axis.

b. Draw a straight line that comes closest to passing through all the points plotted. (This is called the *line of best fit.*)

c. Write the equation for this line.

d. Using the equation in (c), predict the adult height of a two-year-old child whose height is

1. 32 inches 2. 36 inches 3. 39 inches

36. The "Bromine number" test is a test used in chemistry to determine the number of double bonds of carbon in a compound. Measurements made at the end of 5 minutes, 10 minutes, and 15 minutes for the chemical reaction yielded the results shown in the following table:

t *Time in Minutes*	B *Bromine Number*
5	35
10	50
15	65

a. Graph the ordered pairs (t, B).
b. Join the ordered pairs with a straight line and extend this line so it intersects the vertical B-axis.
c. From the graph, find the value of B for $t = 0$. (This indicates the number of double bonds of carbon in the compound.)
d. Check the result in (c) by writing the equation of the line in the graph and evaluating B for $t = 0$.

5.5 SYSTEMS OF LINEAR EQUATIONS: GRAPHICAL METHOD

In geometry one learns that two distinct straight lines on a plane either intersect in exactly one point or are parallel. The algebraic counterpart of a set of two straight lines is a set, or system, of two linear equations in two variables. Whether the two linear equations have a common solution corresponds to whether their graphs have a common point of intersection or are parallel lines. *Intersection* is a key concept here, so first the intersection of sets will be explained.

DEFINITION

The **intersection of two sets** A and B is the set consisting of all elements that are in *both* A and B. In symbols,

$A \cap B$ (read "A intersection B")

designates the intersection of A and B.

RENÉ DESCARTES: SOLDIER, PHILOSOPHER, MATHEMATICIAN

René Descartes (1596–1650) was born to a French aristocratic family, from whom he inherited enough money to spend his life studying and traveling. Because of delicate health, when he was in school at the Jesuit college of La Flèche he was allowed to stay in bed in the morning as long as he liked, a habit he retained throughout his life. Descartes said that he formulated his greatest ideas in mathematics and philosophy during these periods.

When he completed his studies at age 16, he was disenchanted with the philosophy he had learned. He wanted first-hand knowledge of the real world, so he went to Paris, where for a time he enjoyed the busy social life. When he tired of this, he became a soldier. For several years he alternated army life, which included fighting in several battles, with a life of travel and meditation. When he was 32, he ended his career as a soldier and spent the next 20 years in Holland, traveling from one small village to another, wanting only peace and quiet for his thoughts and research.

By 1634 Descartes had completed his work *Le Monde,* a philosophical and scientific account of the creation of the universe. He was about to publish it when he learned that in 1633 the Inquisition had forced Galileo to swear on his knees that the earth did not revolve about the sun. Not only had Descartes accepted Galileo's ideas, he had used them in his work. Intimidated and deeply hurt, Descartes stopped publication and vowed he would never publish anything.

Fortunately, however, his friends made him change his mind, and in 1637 his masterpiece was printed. This treatise, called the *Discours de la Méthode* but commonly referred to as *The Method,* contained 3 appendices, the third being the famous "La Géométrie." Almost all of the algebraic symbols that Descartes introduced there are the ones we use today. More than this, "La Géométrie" contains the introduction to modern analytic geometry.

The publication caused a sensation. His name became known throughout Europe. Kings and queens wanted him at their courts. He routinely rejected such offers, preferring only a quiet, peaceful life, but one ruler, Queen Christine of Sweden, was not to be denied. Descartes eventually accepted her offer, but life in Sweden was his downfall. Descartes was accustomed to rising at 11 a.m., but in Sweden the daily instruction began at 5 a.m. in cold, unheated quarters. Four months after his arrival he contracted pneumonia and died.

EXAMPLE 1 If $A = \{1, 2, 3, 4\}$ and $B = \{3, 4, 5\}$, list the elements in $A \cap B$.

Solution $A \cap B = \{3, 4\}$

EXAMPLE 2 List the elements in $A \cap B$ if

$A = \{(2, 5), (3, 8), (4, 7)\}$ and $B = \{(3, 8), (-2, 5), (5, 2)\}$

Solution $A \cap B = \{(3, 8)\}$

EXAMPLE 3 List the elements in $A \cap B$ if

$A = \{(1, -1), (2, -2), (3, -3)\}$ and $B = \{(-1, 1), (-2, 2), (-3, 3)\}$

Solution $A \cap B = \varnothing$, the empty set, and sets A and B are **disjoint.**

EXAMPLE 4 List the elements in $A \cap B$ if

$A = \{(x, y) \mid y = x\}$ and $B = \{(x, y) \mid y = x + 1\}$

Solution If $y = x$ and $y = x + 1$, then

$$x = x + 1$$

and

$$-x + x = -x + x + 1$$
$$0 = 1$$

Since this is impossible, there are no values of x such that $x = x + 1$.

Therefore, the sets do not have an element in common and $A \cap B = \varnothing$, the empty set.

EXAMPLE 5 List the elements in $A \cap B$ if

$A = \{(x, y) \mid y = x + 1\}$ and $B = \{(x, y) \mid y = 9 - x\}$

Solution If $y = x + 1$ and $y = 9 - x$, then

$$x + 1 = 9 - x$$
$$2x = 8 \text{ and } x = 4$$

For $y = x + 1$ and $x = 4$, $y = 5$ and $(4, 5)$ is a solution of $y = x + 1$.

For $y = 9 - x$ and $x = 4$, $y = 9 - 4 = 5$ and $(4, 5)$ is also a solution of $y = 9 - x$.

Therefore, $A \cap B = \{(4, 5)\}$.

It has been seen that the solution set of a linear equation in two variables is an infinite set of ordered pairs. It was also stated that the graph of a linear equation in two variables is a straight line.

When the graphs of two linear equations in two variables are drawn on the same set of axes, then there are three possibilities:

1. The lines intersect in exactly one point.
2. The lines are parallel and there is no point in common.
3. The lines coincide and have all their points in common.

These three possibilities are illustrated by the graphs in Fig. 5.19.

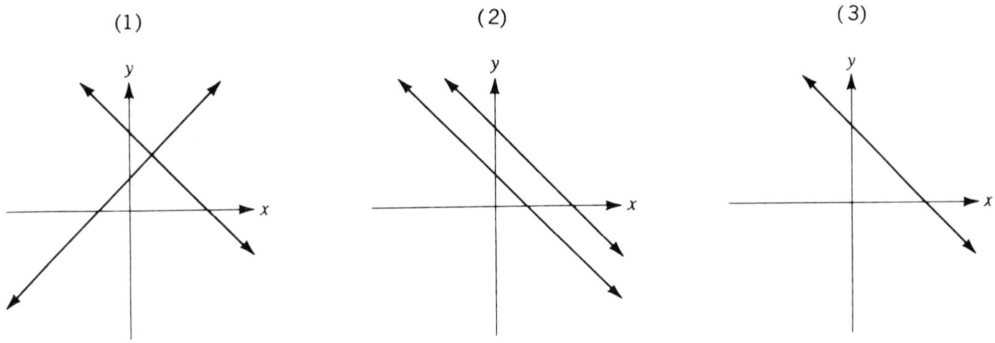

(1)	(2)	(3)
$A = \{(x,y) \mid x + y = 5\}$	$A = \{(x,y) \mid x + y = 5\}$	$A = \{(x,y) \mid x + y = 5\}$
$B = \{(x,y) \mid y = x + 2\}$	$B = \{(x,y) \mid x + y = 2\}$	$B = \{(x,y) \mid 3x + 3y = 15\}$
$A \cap B = \{(\frac{3}{2}, \frac{7}{2})\}$	$A \cap B = \phi$	$A \cap B = \{(x,y) \mid x + y = 5\}$
Intersecting lines	Parallel lines	Coincident lines

FIG. 5.19

DEFINITION

A **system of equations** is a set of equations in two or more variables.

A system of equations is also referred to as a set of **simultaneous equations.**

DEFINITION

The **solution set of a system of equations** in two variables is the set of all ordered pairs that are common solutions to all the equations in the system.

Using the language of set theory, the solution set of a system of two equations in three variables is the intersection of the solution set of one of the equations with the solution set of the other. In symbols, if $A = \{(x, y) \mid ax + by = c\}$ and $B = \{(x, y) \mid dx + ey = f\}$, then $A \cap B$ is the solution of the system.

By examining the graphs in Fig. 5.19, the conclusions shown in Table 5.1 can be made.

TABLE 5.1

THE SYSTEM	*GEOMETRIC MEANING*	*ALGEBRAIC MEANING*
1. $x + y = 5$ $y = x + 2$ $A \cap B = \left\{\left(\frac{3}{2}, \frac{7}{2}\right)\right\}$	The lines have exactly one point in common. The lines intersect. The lines have different slopes.	The equations have exactly one solution in common.
2. $x + y = 5$ $x + y = 2$ $A \cap B = \varnothing$	The lines have no point in common. The lines are parallel. The lines have the same slope and different y-intercepts.	The equations have no common solution—that is, the intersection of their solution sets is the empty set, $\varnothing$.
3. $x + y = 5$ $3x + 3y = 15$ $A \cap B = \{(x, y) \mid x + y = 5\}$	The lines have all their points in common. The lines coincide. The lines have the same slope and the same y-intercept.	The equations have infinitely many solutions in common: the solution set of either equation.

It has been stated that two nonvertical lines are parallel if and only if their slopes are equal. It was also stated that the slope and y-intercept of a line completely determine the line. Thus two nonvertical lines coincide if and only if their slopes and their y-intercepts are equal. Two vertical lines are either parallel or coincide if their x-intercepts are equal. Vertical lines have the form $x = a$, so they can be identified immediately.

Thus it may be concluded that **two nonvertical lines intersect in exactly one point if and only if their slopes are unequal.**

EXAMPLE 6 Determine whether the lines represented by each of the following systems of equations intersect, are parallel, or are coincident:

a. $3x - 5y = 9$
   $3x + 2y = 6$
b. $2x - 2y = 7$
   $3x - 3y = 5$
c. $5x + y = 4$
   $x + 0.2\,y = 0.8$

Solution Solve each equation for y to find the slope of the line. If $y = mx + b$, then $m =$ the slope and $b =$ the y-intercept.

a. $3x - 5y = 9$
$-5y = 9 - 3x$
$y = \frac{3}{5}x - \frac{9}{5}$

Thus the slope is $\frac{3}{5}$.

$3x + 2y = 6$
$2y = 6 - 3x$
$y = -\frac{3}{2}x + 3$

Thus the slope is $-\frac{3}{2}$.

Since the slopes are not equal, the lines intersect in exactly one point.

b. $2x - 2y = 7$
$-2y = -2x + 7$
$y = x - \frac{7}{2}$

Thus the slope is 1, and the y-intercept is $-\frac{7}{2}$.

$3x - 3y = 5$
$-3y = -3x + 5$
$y = x - \frac{5}{3}$

Thus the slope is 1, and the y-intercept is $-\frac{5}{3}$.

Since the slopes are equal and the y-intercepts are not equal, the lines are parallel.

c. $5x + y = 4$
$y = -5x + 4$

Thus the slope is -5, and the y-intercept is 4.

$x + 0.2y = 0.8$
$0.2y = -x + 0.8$
$y = -\frac{1}{0.2}x + 4$
$y = -5 + 4$

Thus the slope is -5, and the y-intercept is 4.

Since the slopes are equal and the y-intercepts are equal, the lines coincide.

Two linear equations in two variables whose graphs intersect are solved by the **graphical method** by the following procedure:

1. Graph both equations on the same set of axes.
2. Determine the point of intersection. (It may be necessary to extend the lines to a considerable length to obtain the point of intersection.) The ordered pair that names the point of intersection is the solution set of the system.
3. Check the solution in both equations. It is necessary to check the solution because the point of intersection cannot always be read accurately from the graph.

EXAMPLE 7 Using the graphical method, solve the system

$$2x + 3y - 5 = 0$$
$$x - 2y + 8 = 0$$

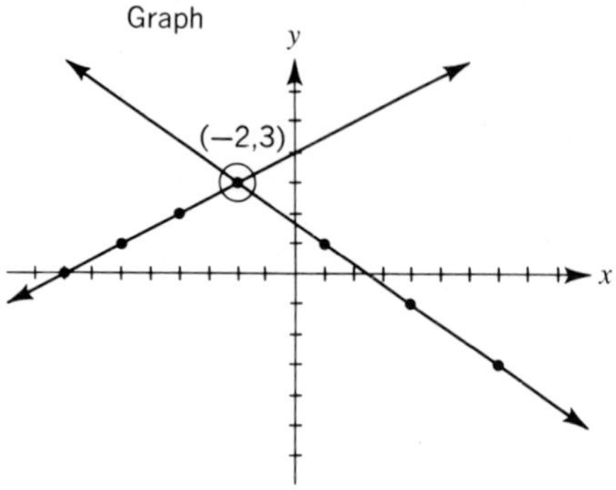

FIG. 5.20

Solution

$2x + 3y - 5 = 0$		$x - 2y + 8 = 0$	
x	y	x	y
1	1	−8	0
4	−1	−6	1
7	−3	−4	2

Solution set: $\{(-2, 3)\}$. See Fig. 5.20.

Check

$$2x + 3y - 5 = 2(-2) + 3(3) - 5$$
$$= -4 + 9 - 5 = 0$$
$$x - 2y + 8 = -2 - 2(3) + 8$$
$$= -2 - 6 + 8 = 0$$

EXERCISES

For each pair of lines represented by the equations in Exercises 1–12,

a. Find the slope of each line.
b. Find the y-intercept of each line.
c. State whether the lines intersect, are parallel, or coincide.
d. State whether each system of equations has exactly one solution, no solution, or a line of solutions.

1. $3x + 3y = 4$
$3x - 3y = 4$

2. $3x + 3y = 4$
$2x + 2y = 5$

3. $3x + 3y = 4$
$6x + 6y = 8$

4. $x + 3 = 0$
$y - 4 = 0$

5. $x + 3 = 0$
$3x + y = 0$

6. $3x - 4y = 12$
$4x - 3y = 12$

7. $3x - 2y = 3$
$5x + 2y = 5$

8. $3x - 2y = 3$
$3x - 2 = 3y$

9. $2x - 1 = 0$
$3y + 4 = 0$

10. $3x - 6y = 3$
$2x - 4y = 2$

11. $x - 2y = 5$
$2y - x = 5$

12. $x = 2y - 6$
$y = 2x - 6$

Solve each system in Exercises 13–22 using the graphical method.

13. $x + y = 7$
$x - y = 1$

14. $4x - 3y = 0$
$2x - 3y = 6$

15. $2x + y = 3$
$x - 2y = 4$

16. $x + 3y = 5$
$2x + y = 5$

17. $x - 4y = 4$
$x + 2y = 10$

18. $x + 2y = 4$
$2x - y = 3$

19. $x - y = 0$
$3x + 2y = 10$

20. $3x + y - 5 = 0$
$4x + y = 4$

21. $3x - 2y = 6$
$x - 2y = 10$

22. $3x + 2y = 7$
$2x + y = 6$

23. A dietitian wants to combine two foods so that the combination will supply 120 units of vitamins and 80 units of minerals. Food *A* supplies 2 units of vitamins and 2 units of minerals per ounce. Food *B* supplies 3 units of vitamins and 1 unit of minerals per ounce. If $x =$ the number of ounces of Food *A* needed and $y =$ the number of ounces of Food *B* needed, then $2x + 3y = 120$ and $2x + y = 80$. Solve this system graphically and state how many ounces of each food should be used.

24. A machine costing \$4800 will have a scrap value of \$800 at the end of 10 years. Using the straight-line method of depreciation, the book value y at the end of the xth year is given by the equation $y = 4800 - 400x$. To offset the depreciation, a contribution is placed in a fund each year. The amount of money y in the fund at the end of the xth year is given by the equation $y = 400x$. Solve this system of equations graphically, thereby finding the year when the amount in the depreciation fund is equal to the book value of the machine.

5.6 SYSTEMS OF LINEAR EQUATIONS: SUBSTITUTION METHOD

While the graphical method affords a valuable visual representation of the solution of a system of equations, it has the disadvantage that the solution cannot always be obtained accurately. Thus it is desirable to investigate other methods of solution.

It should be obvious that the solution of the system

$$x = 2$$
$$y = 3$$

can be recognized immediately. The solution is (2, 3), since this is the only ordered pair that simultaneously satisfies both equations. This special case suggests the possibility of transforming a system whose solution is not obvious into the simpler equivalent form

$$x = p$$
$$y = q$$

DEFINITION

Two systems of equations are equivalent if and only if the systems have the same solution set.

The substitution method is one method for solving a system of two linear equations in two variables. This method is also used to solve systems of equations that are not linear. The procedure is as follows:

1. Solve one of the equations for one variable as a function of the other.
2. Substitute the expression that is obtained into the other equation.
3. Solve the resulting equation in one variable.
4. Substitute the solution obtained in step 3 into the equation obtained in step 1 and simplify.
5. Check the solution obtained in each of the original equations.

EXAMPLE 1 Using the substitution method, solve the system

$2x + y = 8$
$8x - 5y = 5$

Solution

1. Solve $2x + y = 8$ for y:
   $y = 8 - 2x$
2. Substitute $8 - 2x$ for y in $8x - 5y = 5$:
   $8x - 5(8 - 2x) = 5$
3. Solve this equation for x:
   $$8x - 40 + 10x = 5$$
   $$18x - 40 = 5$$
   $$18x = 45$$
   $$x = \frac{45}{18} = \frac{5}{2}$$
4. Substitute $\frac{5}{2}$ for x in $y = 8 - 2x$:
   $$y = 8 - 2\left(\frac{5}{2}\right) = 8 - 5 = 3$$
5. Check the solution $\left(\frac{5}{2}, 3\right)$ in both equations:
   $$2x + y = 2\left(\frac{5}{2}\right) + 3 = 8$$
   $$8x - 5y = 8\left(\frac{5}{2}\right) - 5(3) = 20 - 15 = 5$$

The substitution axiom of the equal relation and the operational theorems of equivalence previously used in the solution of a linear equation in one variable guarantee that the system

$$x = \frac{5}{2}$$
$$y = 3$$

is equivalent to

$$2x + y = 8$$
$$8x - 5y = 5$$

Sometimes it is more convenient to solve for one variable rather than the other. As a general rule, if the coefficient of a variable is 1 in one of the equations, then this variable and this equation are selected for the first step of the solution process.

EXAMPLE 2 Using the substitution method, solve the system

$$4x - 3y = 26$$
$$x - 5y = 15$$

Solution In the second equation, the coefficient of x is 1 and this equation is first solved for x:

1. $x - 5y = 15$ and $x = 5y + 15$
2. $4x - 3y = 26$

$$4(5y + 15) - 3y = 26$$
$$20y + 60 - 3y = 26$$
$$17y = -34$$
$$y = -2$$

3. $x = 5y + 15$

$$x = 5(-2) + 15 = 5$$

The solution is $(5, -2)$.

Check For $4x - 3y = 26$, $4(5) - 3(-2) = 20 + 6 = 26$.
For $x - 5y = 15$, $5 - 5(-2) = 5 + 10 = 15$.

For some equations it may be more convenient to solve for a *multiple* of x or of y instead of x or y. This idea is demonstrated in the following example.

EXAMPLE 3 Using the substitution method, solve the system

$$5x - 2y = 8$$
$$5x - 3y = 2$$

Solution Note that $5x$ occurs in each equation, so either equation can be solved for $5x$ and the resulting expression in y can be substituted in the other equation. Solving $5x - 3y = 2$ for $5x$, then $5x = 3y + 2$. Substituting in $5x - 2y = 8$,

$$(3y + 2) - 2y = 8$$
$$y + 2 = 8$$
$$y = 6$$

Since

$$5x = 3y + 2,$$
$$5x = 3(6) + 2$$
$$5x = 20 \quad \text{and} \quad x = 4$$

The solution is $(4, 6)$

Check For $5x - 2y = 8$, $5(4) - 2(6) = 20 - 12 = 8$.
For $5x - 3y = 2$, $5(4) - 3(6) = 20 - 18 = 2$.

EXERCISES

Solve each system in Exercises 1–30 using the substitution method and check each solution set.

1. $2x + 3y = 16$
   $y = 2x$

2. $3x + 2y = 36$
   $y = 3x$

3. $3y - 5x = 5$
   $y = 2x - 3$

4. $5x + 2y = 25$
   $y = 3x - 4$

5. $3x - 5y = 49$
   $4x - y = 3$

6. $3x - y = 5$
   $x + 2y = 4$

7. $4m - 7n = 9$
   $n = 12 + 5m$

8. $2p - 3q = 1$
   $4p + q = 23$

9. $8a - 5b = 1$
   $2a + b = 7$

10. $8a - 3b = 93$
    $b = 37 - 3a$

11. $2x + 6y = 10$
    $3y = 2 - 4x$

12. $3x + 6y = 12$
    $3x = 4 + 2y$

13. $3x - 5y = 6$
    $x + 7y = -24$

14. $5x - 4y = 22$
    $x - 2y = 5$

15. $3x + 4y = 10$
    $x + 6y = 1$

16. $2r - 3s = 17$
    $2r + 8s = 6$

17. $5r + 5t = 15$
    $r = t - 4$

18. $5x - 2y = 1$
    $5x = y + 7$

19. $3x - 3y = 1$
    $y = x + 5$

20. $2x = -2 - 3y$
    $7y = x - 16$

21. $p = 2q - 3$
    $q = p + 5$

22. $3x + y = 2$
    $6x = 4 - 2y$

23. $r + 2s - 5 = 0$
    $2s + 3r - 1 = 0$

24. $x + y - 2 = 0$
    $2x - y - 4 = 0$

25. $3x - 9y = 3$
    $3y = x - 1$

26. $2x - y = 4$
    $y = 2x + 3$

27. $x + 3y = 0$
    $y = 4x$

28. $x = 3y$
    $y = \frac{1}{2}x$

29. $5 = 3a + 2b$
    $a - b = 3$

30. $3x - 4y = 2$
    $3x = y - 5$

5.7 SYSTEMS OF LINEAR EQUATIONS: ADDITION METHOD

Another method for solving a system of two linear equations in two variables is the addition method. This method is sometimes more convenient to use than the substitution method. Consider the system

$$7x + 3y - 13 = 0$$
$$2x + 3y + 2 = 0$$

If it is assumed that the ordered pair (p, q) is a solution of both equations, then $7p + 3q - 13 = 0$ and $2p + 3q + 2 = 0$. Moreover, by selecting a and b to be two real numbers that are not both zero, then it follows that (p, q) is also a solution of

$$a(7x + 3y - 13) + b(2x + 3y + 2) = 0$$

since

$$a(7p + 3q - 13) + b(2p + 3q + 2) = a(0) + b(0) = 0 + 0 = 0$$

The objective is to obtain an equivalent system having the form

$$x = p$$
$$y = q$$

Either equation of this system can be obtained by choosing a and b in such a manner that the coefficients of one of the variables become additive inverses.

Choosing $a = 1$ and $b = -1$ and writing the system as

$$7x + 3y = 13$$
$$2x + 3y = -2$$

then

$$\left.\begin{aligned} 1(7x + 3y) &= 1(13) \\ -1(2x + 3y) &= -1(-2) \end{aligned}\right\} \rightarrow \begin{aligned} 7x + 3y &= 13 \\ -2x - 3y &= 2 \end{aligned}$$

Adding, $\quad 5x = 15$

$$x = 3$$

If $a = 2$ and $b = -7$, then the coefficients of x become additive inverses, and

$$\left.\begin{aligned} 2(7x + 3y) &= 2(13) \\ -7(2x + 3y) &= -7(-2) \end{aligned}\right\} \rightarrow \begin{aligned} 14x + 6y &= 26 \\ -14x - 21y &= 14 \end{aligned}$$

Adding, $\quad -15y = 40$

$$y = \frac{-8}{3}$$

Thus the system $\begin{aligned} 7x + 3y - 13 &= 0 \\ 2x + 3y + 2 &= 0 \end{aligned}$ is equivalent to $\begin{aligned} x &= 3 \\ y &= \frac{-8}{3} \end{aligned}$

and the solution is $\left(3, \frac{-8}{3}\right)$.

Check

For $7x + 3y - 13 = 0$, $7(3) + 3\left(\frac{-8}{3}\right) - 13 = 21 - 8 - 13 = 0$.

For $2x + 3y + 2 = 0$, $2(3) + 3\left(\frac{-8}{3}\right) + 2 = 6 - 8 + 2 = 0$.

EXAMPLE 1 Using the addition method, solve the system

$$2x - 3y = 18$$
$$7x - 2y = -5$$

Solution

$$\left.\begin{array}{r} 2(2x - 3y = 18) \\ -3(7x - 2y = -5) \end{array}\right\} \rightarrow \begin{array}{r} 4x - 6y = 36 \\ \underline{-21x + 6y = 15} \\ -17x \qquad = 51 \\ x = -3 \end{array}$$

$$\left.\begin{array}{r} 7(2x - 3y = 18) \\ -2(7x - 2y = -5) \end{array}\right\} \rightarrow \begin{array}{r} 14x - 21y = 126 \\ \underline{-14x + \ \ 4y = \ \ 10} \\ -17y = 136 \\ y = -8 \end{array}$$

The solution is $(-3, -8)$.

Check $2x - 3y = 2(-3) - 3(-8)$
$= -6 + 24 = 18$ and $18 = 18$
$7x - 2y = 7(-3) - 2(-8)$
$= -21 + 16 = -5$ and $-5 = -5$

EXAMPLE 2 Using the addition method, solve the system

$$4x - y = 3$$
$$5x + 2y = 20$$

Solution

$$\left.\begin{array}{r} 2(4x - y = 3) \\ 1(5x + 2y = 20) \end{array}\right\} \rightarrow \begin{array}{r} 8x - 2y = \ \ 6 \\ \underline{5x + 2y = 20} \\ 13x \qquad = 26 \\ x = \ \ 2 \end{array}$$

Although this addition process can be used to find the value for y, it is also possible to replace x by 2 in either of the two equations and then solve this equation for y. Selecting the first,

for $x = 2$ and $4x - y = 3$
$4(2) - y = 3$
$8 - y = 3$
$-y = 3 - 8 = -5$
$y = 5$

The solution is $(2, 5)$.

Check For $x = 2$ and $y = 5$,
$4x - y = 4(2) - 5 = 8 - 5 = 3$
$5x + 2y = 5(2) + 2(5) = 10 + 10 = 20$

EXERCISES

Solve each system in Exercises 1–30 using the addition method, and check each solution set.

1. $x + y = 3$
   $x - y = 7$
2. $x + y = 2$
   $x - y = -6$
3. $x - y = -2$
   $x + y = -4$
4. $x - 2y = 11$
   $x - 3y = 18$
5. $2x - 3y = 15$
   $2x - 5y = 25$
6. $4x - 3y = 11$
   $6x - 3y = 12$
7. $2x - y = 3$
   $3x + 2y = 8$
8. $5x + y = 2$
   $4x - 3y = 13$
9. $9m + 4n = -49$
   $9m - 5n = -40$
10. $5m - 3n = 15$
    $m - 5n = -63$
11. $4a - 5b = 48$
    $5a - 4b = 51$
12. $3a - 4b = 17$
    $4a + 3b = 106$
13. $y - 2x = 6$
    $5y - 10x = 1$
14. $8c + d = -3$
    $12c - 5d = 28$
15. $x = 2y$
    $y = 3x + 1$
16. $2x - y = 1$
    $6x - 3y = 5$
17. $p - q = 14$
    $4p = q - 1$
18. $x = 5y - 2$
    $y = 3x - 1$
19. $8 = 2a - 5b$
    $7 = 5a + 7b$
20. $4a - 5b = 3$
    $8a + 10b = 78$
21. $4r - 2s = 10$
    $3s + 5r = 4$
22. $6x = 51 - 7y$
    $5y = 34 - 4x$
23. $x = 2y$
    $3x - y + 1 = 0$
24. $5x - 8y + 2 = 0$
    $10x - 7y + 3 = 0$
25. $2a + 3b - 4 = 0$
    $3a + 2b - 4 = 0$
26. $x - 3y = 14$
    $6y - 2x = -28$
27. $2x - 5y = 0$
    $7x + 11y = 0$
28. $6x - 2y - 9 = 0$
    $9x - 8y - 1 = 0$
29. $8x + 20y = 6$
    $4x + 10y - 3 = 0$
30. $14 - 3a = 8b$
    $22 - 7b = a$

5.8 VERBAL PROBLEMS

Verbal problems that involve two unknown numbers often can be solved more conveniently by using two variables to form two equations.

EXAMPLE 1 Find two numbers whose sum is 135 and whose difference is 61.

Solution Let $x =$ one number and $y =$ the other number.

Then
$$\begin{array}{rl} x + y &= 135 \\ x - y &= \ \ 61 \\ \hline 2x \qquad &= 196 \\ x &= \ \ 98 \end{array} \quad \text{(Solving by using the addition method)}$$

Now if $x = 98$ and $x + y = 135$, then $98 + y = 135$ (by using the substitution axiom).

Thus $y = 135 - 98 = 37$, and the two numbers are 98 and 37.

Check $x + y = 98 + 37 = 135$
$x - y = 98 - 37 = \ \ 61$

EXAMPLE 2 A jet plane traveling with the wind flies 2325 miles in 3 hours. Against the wind, it takes the jet 4 hours to go 2900 miles. Find the speed in still air of the plane and the speed of the wind.

Solution Let $x =$ the speed in still air of the plane and $y =$ the speed of the wind.

Formula	r	$\cdot\ t =$	d
With the wind	$x + y$	3	2325
Against the wind	$x - y$	4	2900

Equations
$$\left.\begin{array}{r} 3(x + y) = 2325 \\ 4(x - y) = 2900 \end{array}\right\} \rightarrow \begin{array}{rl} x + y &= 775 \\ x - y &= 725 \\ \hline 2x \qquad &= 1500 \\ x &= 750 \\ 750 + y &= 775 \\ y &= 25 \end{array}$$

Thus the speed in still air of the jet plane is 750 mph, and the speed of the wind is 25 mph.

EXAMPLE 3 A restaurant bought 3 tablecloths and 5 dozen napkins for \$54. A month later it bought 5 tablecloths and 2 dozen napkins for \$52. Find the cost of one tablecloth and the cost of one dozen napkins if these were the same for both purchases.

Solution Let $x =$ the cost of one tablecloth.
Let $y =$ the cost of one dozen napkins.
Then $3x + 5y = 54$ and $5x + 2y = 52$.

Using the addition method,
$$\left.\begin{array}{r} -2(3x + 5y) = -2(54) \\ 5(5x + 2y) = \ \ 5(52) \end{array}\right\} \rightarrow \begin{array}{rl} -6x - 10y &= -108 \\ 25x + 10y &= \ \ 260 \\ \hline 19x \qquad &= \ \ 152 \\ x &= \ \ \ \ 8 \end{array}$$

Replacing x by 8 in $5x + 2y = 52$,
$$5(8) + 2y = 52$$
$$2y = 12 \text{ and } y = 6$$

Therefore, one tablecloth cost \$8, and one dozen napkins cost \$6.

EXERCISES

Solve Exercises 1–18 by using ***two*** *variables.*

1. The sum of two numbers is 9 and their difference is 19. Find the two numbers.
2. The sum of two numbers is 20 and their difference is 3. Find the numbers.
3. Two numbers are in a ratio of 3 to 2. The sum of the numbers is 115. Find the numbers.
4. Two numbers are in a ratio of 4 to 3. Their difference is 26. Find the numbers.
5. Three loaves of bread and 2 pounds of butter cost $3.86. Five loaves of bread and 3 pounds of butter cost $6.15. Find the price of one loaf of bread and the price of one pound of butter if these were the same for both purchases.
6. In a certain boys' store, 4 sweaters and 3 shirts cost $63, while 3 sweaters and 4 shirts cost $56. If sweaters are one fixed price and shirts are another fixed price, find the price of one sweater and one shirt.
7. A bill for 5 quarts of milk and 2 dozen eggs was $3.84. Another bill for 3 quarts of milk and 3 dozen eggs was $3.69. Find the price of one quart of milk and the price of one dozen eggs if these were the same for both purchases.
8. A sale rack in a department store had the following sign: "All coats on this rack one low price." A second rack advertised all slacks, regardless of original price, for a different single low price. If 4 coats and 5 pairs of slacks could be bought for $138.30, whereas 2 coats and 8 pairs of slacks could be bought for $115.90, find the sale price of one coat, and the sale price of one pair of slacks.
9. A man can walk uphill at 2 mph and downhill at 4 mph on a road no part of which is level. If he walked 24 miles in 9 hours, how much of the road was uphill?
10. During part of its trip, a jet plane traveling 600 mph ran into a storm that reduced its speed by 80 mph. If the total trip of 2380 miles was made in 4 hours, how far did the plane travel during the storm?
11. A crew rows 30 miles downstream in 4 hours. Returning, they cover the same distance in 6 hours 40 minutes. Find the rate of the current and the rate of the boat in still water.
12. A boat travels 120 miles up a river in 6 hours. Its return trip downstream takes 4 hours. Find the speed of the current and the speed of the boat in still water.
13. A plane with a head wind flies 300 miles from city A to city B in 2 hours. On the same day and under the same weather conditions, a plane with the same speed in still air flies from city B to city A in 1 hour 30 minutes. Find the speed of the wind.

14. A plane with a tail wind completes a 2600 mile trip in 5 hours. On the same day and under the same weather condition a second plane flies in the *opposite* direction for 5 hours but completes only 2400 miles. Find the rate of the wind and the still air rate of the planes if both planes fly at the same still air rate.

15. Twenty pounds of ore *A* combined with 30 pounds of ore *B* produce 26.5 pounds of silver. Ten pounds of ore *A* combined with 20 pounds of ore *B* produce 15.5 pounds of silver. Find the percentage of silver in each ore.

16. An alloy containing 74 grams of gold is the combination of two other alloys containing gold: 40 grams of alloy *A* and 70 grams of alloy *B*. If 50 grams of alloy *A* and 90 grams of alloy *B* are combined, the resulting alloy contains 94 grams of gold. Find the percentage of gold in alloy *A* and alloy *B*.

17. A manufacturer must use two different machines for the production of two products. The number of hours required on each machine to produce the two products and the maximum number of hours each machine can be run per week are given in the following table.

Machine	Product *A*	Product *B*	Maximum Hours For Machine
I	3	2	48
II	1	4	46

How many items of each product will be manufactured each week if the machines are used at their maximum capacity?

18. A mail order company charges a fixed fee for shipping and handling the first 10 pounds of merchandise plus an additional fee for each pound over 10 pounds. If the shipping and handling charge for 30 pounds of merchandise is \$2.49 and the charge for 42 pounds is \$3.45, find the fixed fee and the additional fee.

5.9 LINEAR INEQUALITIES IN TWO VARIABLES

Equations and inequalities in one variable can be associated with points on a line, and the solution sets can be shown as line graphs.

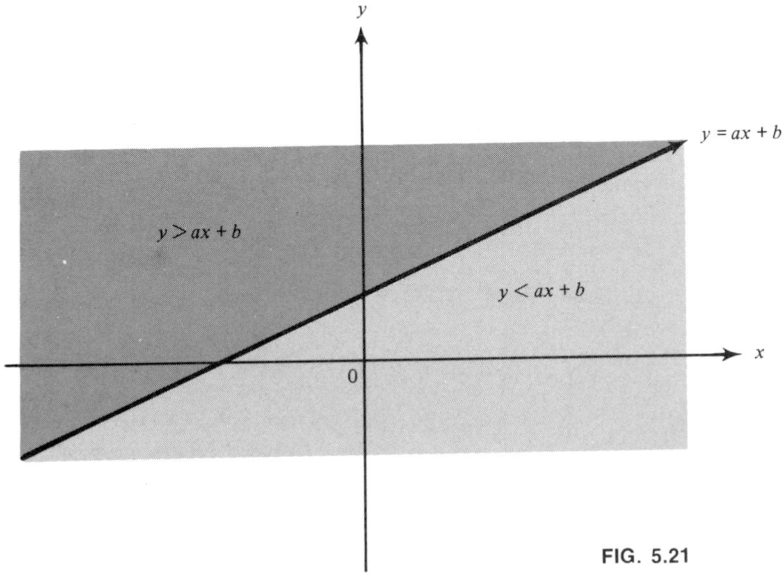

FIG. 5.21

Equations in two variables can be associated with points in a plane, using horizontal and vertical axes as references. Inequalities in two variables can also be graphed in a plane.

The graph of the linear equation $y = ax + b$ divides the plane into three mutually exclusive regions, or three disjoint sets of points:

1. $y = ax + b$
2. $y > ax + b$
3. $y < ax + b$

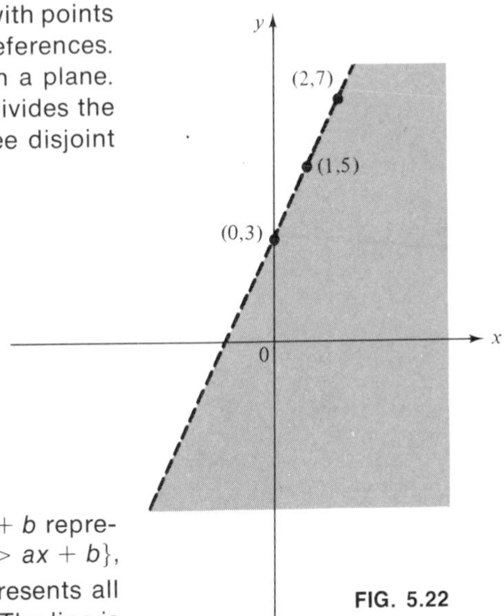

FIG. 5.22

In Fig. 5.21 the region above the line $y = ax + b$ represents all points satisfying the condition $\{(x, y) | y > ax + b\}$, whereas the region below the line $y = ax + b$ represents all points satisfying the condition $\{(x, y) | y < ax + b\}$. The line is the graph of the equation $y = ax + b$.

To graph an inequality of form $y < ax + b$ or $y > ax + b$, first graph the equality, use a broken line to indicate that the graph of the equality is not part of the solution set, and then shade the desired region. See Fig. 5.22.

EXAMPLE 1 Graph the relation $\{(x, y) \mid y < 2x + 3\}$.

Solution First graph the equation $y = 2x + 3$ and use a broken line to indicate that the line is *not* to be included in the solution set.

To graph $y = 2x + 3$, use a table of values such as

x	0	1	2
y	3	5	7

to obtain the ordered pairs (0, 3), (1, 5), (2, 7). Plot these points and draw a dashed line through them.

Since $y < 2x + 3$, shade the region *below* the broken line.

EXAMPLE 2 Graph $3x - 2y > x + y - 1$.

Solution Solve the inequality for y:

$$3x - 2y > x + y - 1$$
$$-3y > -2x - 1$$
$$3y < 2x + 1$$
$$y < \frac{2}{3}x + \frac{1}{3}$$

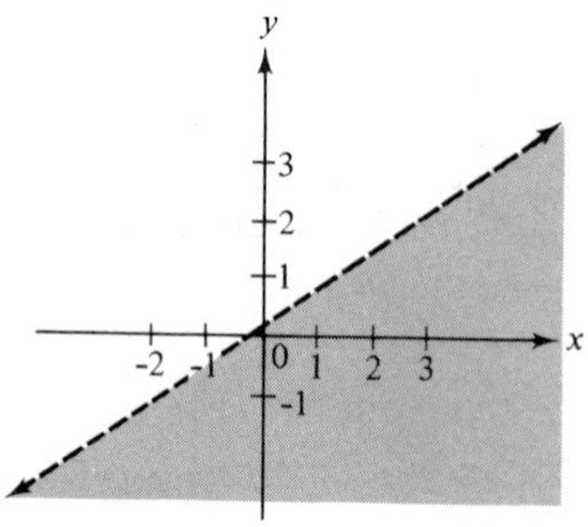

FIG. 5.23

Graph the equality $y = \frac{2}{3}x + \frac{1}{3}$, using a broken line (see Fig. 5.23). All points *below* the broken line are in the solution set

$$\left\{(x, y) \middle| y < \frac{2}{3}x + \frac{1}{3}\right\}$$

Therefore, the shaded region is the graphical solution. (*Note:* The inequality does not define a function, but it does define a relation.)

EXAMPLE 3 Find the graphical solution for the inequality

$y \geq -2x + 4$

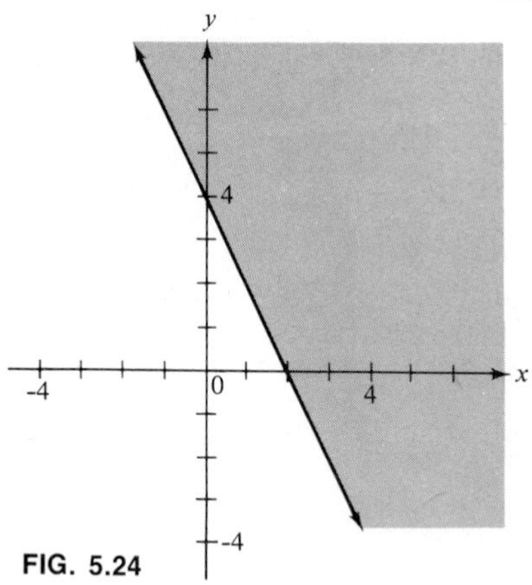

FIG. 5.24

Solution Graph the equation $y = -2x + 4$. Use a solid line, since the line is part of the solution set. Shade the region *above* the line for the points

$$\{(x, y) \mid y > -2x + 4\}$$

The line and the shaded region in Fig. 5.24 represent the solution set

$$\{(x, y) \mid y \geq -2x + 4\}$$

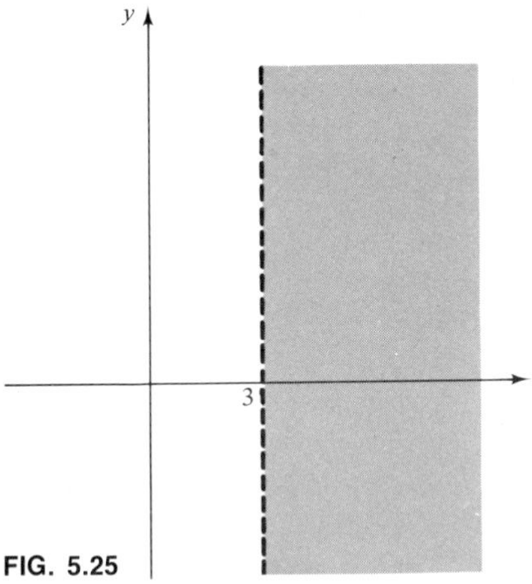

FIG. 5.25

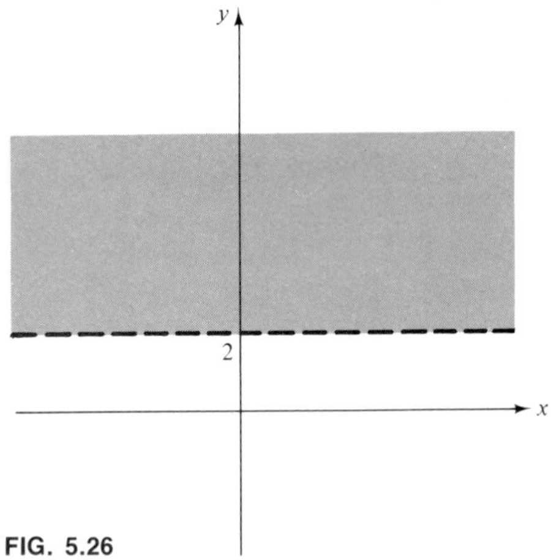

FIG. 5.26

EXAMPLE 4 Graph the relation $\{(x, y) \mid x > 3\}$.

Solution The graph of the equation $x = 3$ is a vertical line through the point (3, 0). All points (x, y) such that $x > 3$ lie to the *right* of this line (Fig. 5.25).

EXAMPLE 5 Graph the relation $\{(x, y) \mid y > 2\}$.

Solution The graph of the constant function $y = 2$ is a horizontal line through the point (0, 2). Since $y > 2$, the shaded region in Fig. 5.26 includes all points *above* this horizontal line.

EXAMPLE 6 Find the graphical solution for the inequality $\{(x, y) \mid 2 \le x < 3\}$.

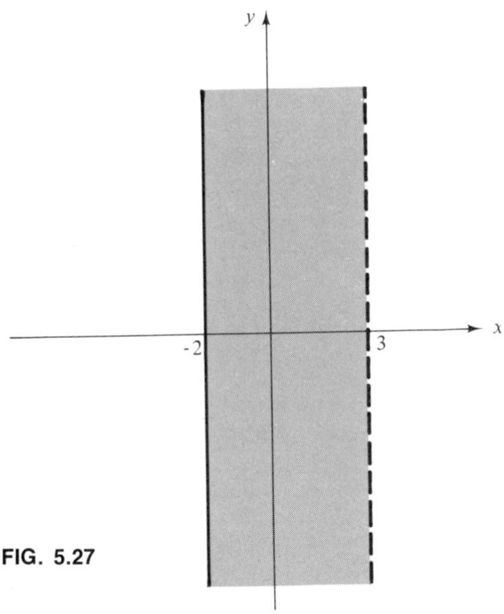

Solution First graph the vertical lines $x = -2$ and $x = 3$. Use a solid line to indicate the inclusion of $x = -2$ and a broken line to show that $x \neq 3$. Then shade the region *between* these lines, since $-2 \le x < 3$ for *all* values of y. See Fig. 5.27.

FIG. 5.27

EXERCISES

Show a graphical solution for each of the sets in Exercises 1–26.

1. $\{(x, y) \mid x \geq 2\}$
2. $\{(x, y) \mid x < -1\}$
3. $\{(x, y) \mid y > -1\}$
4. $\{(x, y) \mid y \leq 4\}$
5. $\{(x, y) \mid x > 4\}$
6. $\{(x, y) \mid x \leq -2\}$
7. $\{(x, y) \mid y \geq 4\}$
8. $\{(x, y) \mid y < 3\}$
9. $\{(x, y) \mid 1 \leq x \leq 3\}$
10. $\{(x, y) \mid 2 < y \leq 5\}$
11. $\{(x, y) \mid x < 0\}$
12. $\{(x, y) \mid y \geq 0\}$
13. $\{(x, y) \mid -2 < x \leq 1\}$
14. $\{(x, y) \mid 1 \leq x < 3\}$
15. $\{(x, y) \mid y < 3x + 2\}$
16. $\{(x, y) \mid y > x - 5\}$
17. $\{(x, y) \mid y \leq 2x - 3\}$
18. $\{(x, y) \mid y > x\}$
19. $\{(x, y) \mid x + y \leq 2\}$
20. $\{(x, y) \mid y \geq x + 2\}$
21. $\{(x, y) \mid y \leq x\}$
22. $\{(x, y) \mid x + 2y < 2\}$
23. $\{(x, y) \mid 4 \geq 2y - x\}$
24. $\{(x, y) \mid 3x \leq y + 2\}$
25. $\{(x, y) \mid x - y < 2\}$
26. $\{(x, y) \mid y \leq x + 2\}$

REVIEW EXERCISES

1. Define the following terms.
a. Coordinate axes
b. Ordinate
c. Abscissa
d. Origin
e. Quadrants
f. Slope of a line

2. Which of the following points lie on the graph of $x + 2y - 5 = 0$?
a. (1, 4)
b. (7, −1)
c. (0, 0)
d. (−4, −5)
e. (5, 0)

3. Graph each of the following and find the slope and *y*-intercept from the graph.
a. $3x + 2y = 12$
b. $\frac{x}{2} + \frac{y}{5} = 1$
c. $\frac{1}{2}(x - 4) = \frac{1}{4}(y + 2)$
d. $x - 3y - 2 = 0$

4. Check the answers for Exercise 3 by changing each equation into an equivalent equation of the form $y = mx + b$.

5. Find an equation of the line through the given points with slope *m*.
a. $(0, 3)$, $m = \frac{1}{2}$
b. $(1, 5)$, $m = -3$
c. $(-3, -1)$, $m = 0$
d. $(-3, 1)$, $m = -\frac{1}{3}$
e. $(2, -1)$, $m = \frac{1}{4}$
f. $(5, 2)$, slope undefined

6. Find an equation of the line through the given points.

a. $(-3, 0)$ and $(6, 2)$ c. $(-2, -3)$ and $(-4, -5)$

b. $(-3, 6)$ and $(3, -8)$ d. $(7, 5)$ and $(-1, 5)$

7. Which of the following lines are parallel to $2x - 5y = 10$?

a. $5x - 2y = 10$ c. $4x - 10y = 5$

b. $5y = 2x - 1$ d. $5y = 1 - 2x$

8. Find an equation of the line that is parallel to the line whose equation is $2x - 3y = 5$ and that passes through the point $(-1, 4)$.

9. For each of the following determine an equation of the line satisfying the stated conditions:

a. Passing through $(3, -2)$ and $(4, 1)$

b. Parallel to the x-axis with y-intercept 2

c. Passing through the origin with slope $-\frac{3}{5}$

d. Passing through $(5, -7)$ with slope undefined

10. Match column B with column A.

Column A	*Column B*
a. $x + y = 50$ $y + 5x = 90$	1. Equations with no solution
b. $7x - 5y = 0$ $8x + 3y = 0$	2. Equations whose graphs are coincident lines
c. $2x + 6y = 5$ $3x + 9y = 1$	3. A system of equations that can be used to find the number of nickels and cents in a collection of 50 coins worth 90 cents
d. $y = 2 - x$ $x = 2 - y$	4. A system equivalent to $x = 15$, $y = 75$
e. $x + y = 90$ $y = 5x$	5. Equations whose linear graphs intersect at the origin

11. State the coordinates of the point of intersection of the graphs of the equations $y = 3x - 9$ and $x + 3y + 2 = 0$.

12. Solve by the substitution method and check by the graphical method.

a. $2x - 3y = 1$, $x - 2y = 2$ b. $3x + y = 9$, $2x - 3y = 6$

13. Solve by the addition method and check by the graphical method.

a. $3x + 5y = 3$, $2x - y = -11$ b. $2x - y = 10$, $4x + 3y = 5$

14. One week a plumber worked 20 hours and his helper worked 12 hours on a job. They sent the contractor of the job a bill of \$228 for their combined wages. The next week the plumber worked 15 hours and his helper worked 10 hours. This time the bill for their combined wages was \$175. Find the hourly wage of each.

15. Cruising at half-speed against a wind, a traffic helicopter flies 36 miles in 40 minutes. Flying with the same wind at full speed, the helicopter flies 93 miles in 30 minutes. Find the speed of the wind.

16. A rush order was received in an office. On the first day the regular typist worked 10 hours, an extra typist 5 hours, and together they completed two-thirds of the order. The next day both typists worked 4 hours, and they finished the order. How long would it have taken the regular typist to do the work alone?

17. The admission prices at a movie theater were such that one person paid \$24.50 for 4 adults and 6 children, while another person paid \$17.50 for 3 adults and 4 children. What was the admission price for an adult and what was the admission price for a child?

18. A man received a total income of \$480 from \$5000 invested in bonds and \$4000 invested in stocks. The same year his brother received a total income of \$260 from \$3000 invested in the same bonds and \$2000 invested in the same stocks. Find the interest rate they received from each investment.

19. In competitive business, y, the price for each unit of a commodity, depends on x, the number of units demanded by consumers. The equation relating the price and the number of units demanded is called the *demand law.* A certain demand law is represented by $5x + 8y = 60$.

a. Graph this equation for $x \geq 0$ and $y \geq 0$.

b. Find the highest price that will be paid for this commodity—that is, the value of the y-intercept (where $x = 0$).

c. Find the greatest amount that will be demanded—that is, the value of the x-intercept (where $y = 0$).

20. Referring to Exercise 19, y, the price for each unit of a commodity, also depends on x, the number of units that can be supplied. The equation that relates price and number of units that can be supplied is called the *supply law.* A supply law corresponding to the demand law in Exercise 19 is $8y = 6x + 16$.

a. Graph this equation on the same set of axes you used for Exercise 19. Again use $x \geq 0$ and $y \geq 0$.

b. Find the lowest price at which the supplier will sell the commodity—that is, the value of the y-intercept.

c. Find the point of intersection of the demand curve and the supply curve. (This point corresponds to *market equilibrium;* the values of x and y are called *equilibrium quantity* and *equilibrium price,* respectively. In this case the quantity demanded equals the quantity supplied.)

21. Graph each of the following.

a. $\{(x, y| \; x \leq 5\}$

b. $\{(x, y) \mid y > 5\}$

c. $\{(x, y) \mid -2 < x \leq 1\}$

d. $\{(x, y) \mid -2 \leq y < 1\}$

e. $\{(x, y) \mid x + y \geq 2\}$

6

QUADRATIC EQUATIONS

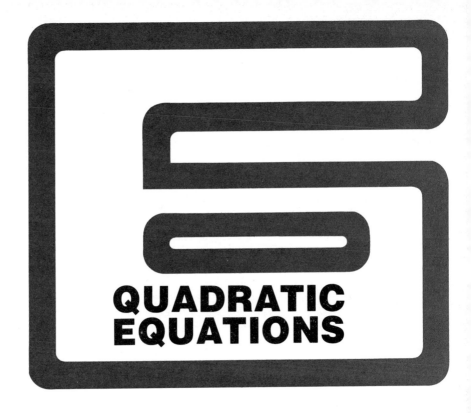

Any algebraic equation that can be written in the form $ax^2 + bx + c = 0$ where $a \neq 0$ is called a **quadratic equation in one variable.** A quadratic equation in one variable is an equation that contains a square of the variable.

The following are examples of quadratic equations: $x^2 = 9$, $4x^2 - 25 = 0$, $x^2 + 2x - 24 = 0$, $3x^2 + 6x = 0$, $5x^2 - x - 6 = 0$

In Chapter 3 we saw that a polynomial equation can readily be solved if the linear factors of the polynomial can be found easily. However, not all polynomials with integral coefficients can be factored over the set of integers; $x^2 - 2$ and $x^2 + x - 1$ are examples. Finding the factors in these cases is more difficult. It is desirable, then, to develop other techniques for solving equations.

Earlier we noted that if $x^2 = 2$ and if x is positive, then $x = \sqrt{2}$. Similarly if $x^2 = 5$ and if x is positive, then $x = \sqrt{5}$.

Since a quadratic polynomial involves terms of the form ax^2, it is reasonable to conclude that the solutions of some quadratic equations will involve radicals such as $\sqrt{2}$ and $\sqrt{5}$. Indeed, this is the case. Therefore, to develop methods for solving quadratic equations, it is first necessary to study radicals.

6.1 SQUARE ROOTS

SYMBOLIC REPRESENTATION OF SQUARE ROOTS

DEFINITION

The number a is a **square root** of b if and only if $a^2 = b$.

This definition implies that the operations of squaring and extracting square roots are inverses of each other, just as addition and subtraction are inverse operations and multiplication and division are inverse operations. For example,

3 is a square root of 9 since $3^2 = 9$
-3 is a square root of 9 since $(-3)^2 = 9$

$\frac{5}{8}$ is a square root of $\frac{25}{64}$ since $\left(\frac{5}{8}\right)^2 = \frac{25}{64}$

$\frac{-5}{8}$ is a square root of $\frac{25}{64}$ since $\left(\frac{-5}{8}\right)^2 = \frac{25}{64}$

0 is a square root of 0 since $0^2 = 0$

Examination of these examples and similar ones reveals the following properties:

1. If x is a real number, then $x^2 \geq 0$. (In other words, the square of a real number is never negative.)
2. Every positive real number has two square roots, a positive real number and its negative. Thus if a is a positive real number ($a > 0$), then the square roots of a^2 are a and $-a$.

Now it is useful to denote a square root by the symbol $\sqrt{x}$. However, the symbolic expression $\sqrt{x}$ must represent exactly one number. Suppose, for example, that $\sqrt{9} = 3$ and $\sqrt{9} = -3$. Then it would follow that $3 = -3$, and this is impossible. Therefore, $\sqrt{9}$ and, in general, $\sqrt{x}$ must represent exactly one number in order to avoid contradictions. Mathematicians agree that $\sqrt{9}$ shall be used to designate $+3$, the positive square root of 9. The negative square root, -3, is indicated by $-\sqrt{9}$.

In general, the following definition is made.

6.1 SQUARE ROOTS

DEFINITION OF $\sqrt{x}$

If $x > 0$, then $\sqrt{x}$ is the unique **positive** real number such $(\sqrt{x})^2 = x$.

Note: If $x < 0$, then $\sqrt{x}$ is not a real number.

The following useful theorem aids in the solution of problems that involve square roots.

THEOREM

$\sqrt{x^2} = x$ if and only if $x \geq 0$

The positive real number $\sqrt{x}$ is called the **principal square root** of x.

IRRATIONAL SQUARE ROOTS

Although every positive real number x has two real square roots, namely, $\sqrt{x}$ and $-\sqrt{x}$, it does not follow that every positive rational number has two rational roots.

Rational numbers such as 49, 81, and $\frac{9}{16}$ are called perfect squares because their square roots are also rational. The number 2, on the other hand, is not a perfect square; its square roots, $\sqrt{2}$ and $-\sqrt{2}$, are not rational but irrational.

Q, the set of rational numbers, was defined as the set of quotients of integers $\frac{p}{q}$ where $q \neq 0$. It can be shown that $\sqrt{2}$ cannot be expressed as the quotient of two integers, and thus $\sqrt{2}$ is irrational.

The terminating decimals and the nonterminating repeating decimals represent the rational numbers. Therefore, it is convenient to think of the irrational numbers as the set of nonterminating, nonrepeating decimals and of the real numbers as the union of these two sets—that is, the set of all decimals.

The table of squares and square roots inside the front book cover is useful in providing a first approximation to the square root of a number.

The square root values in the table are not exact but are approximations to the nearest thousandth.

EXAMPLE 1 Simplify:

a. $(\sqrt{9})^2$ b. $(\sqrt{5})^2$ c. $\sqrt{(-5)^2}$

Solution a. $(\sqrt{9})^2 = 9$ by definition

b. $(\sqrt{5})^2 = 5$ by definition

c. $\sqrt{(-5)^2} = \sqrt{25} = 5$

EXAMPLE 2 Simplify $\sqrt{64} - \sqrt{(-4)^2}$.

Solution $\sqrt{64} - \sqrt{(-4)^2} = \sqrt{64} - \sqrt{16}$
$= 8 - 4 = 4$

EXAMPLE 3 Approximate $\sqrt{12} - \sqrt{20}$ to the nearest hundredth by using the table inside the book cover, or by using a pocket calculator.

Solution From the table,

$$\sqrt{12} = 3.464$$
$$\sqrt{20} = 4.472$$
$$\sqrt{12} - \sqrt{20} = 3.464 - 4.472$$
$$= -1.008$$
$= -1.01$ to the nearest hundredth

THE THEOREM OF PYTHAGORAS

The theorem of Pythagoras is a theorem that has many practical applications. We introduce it here to develop familiarity with it and to provide practice working with square roots. Later in the chapter we shall meet other problems that require its use.

THE THEOREM OF PYTHAGORAS

The square of the length of the hypotenuse of a right triangle is equal to the sum of the squares of the lengths of its legs.

The **hypotenuse** of a right triangle, which is opposite the right angle, is the longest side. The **legs** of a right triangle are the other two sides—that is, the sides that form the right angle.

FIG. 6.1

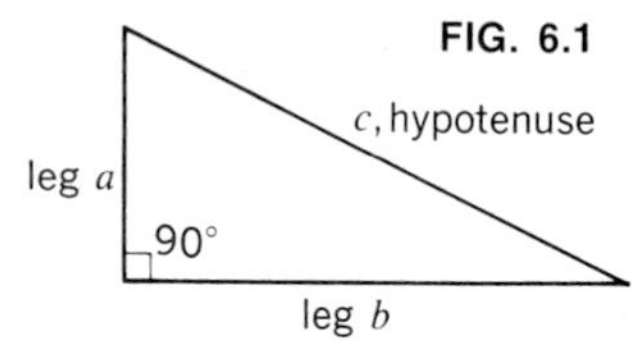

Thus if c represents the length of the hypotenuse in Fig. 6.1 and if a and b represent the lengths of the legs, then

$$c^2 = a^2 + b^2$$

Therefore, a length of $\sqrt{2}$ can be represented by the diagonal of a square (see Fig. 6.2).

Since

$$c^2 = 1^2 + 1^2$$
$$c^2 = 2$$

Thus

$$c = \sqrt{2}$$

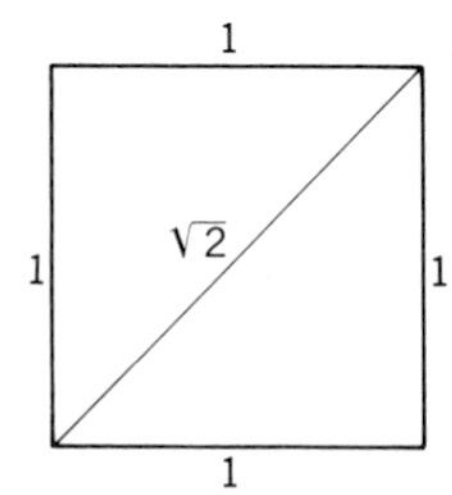

FIG. 6.2

EXAMPLE 4 Find the hypotenuse c of a right triangle if the lengths of its legs a and b are such that $a = 12$ and $b = 35$.

Solution Using the theorem of Pythagoras,

$$c^2 = a^2 + b^2$$
$$c^2 = (12)^2 + (35)^2$$
$$c^2 = 144 + 1225 = 1369$$
$c = \sqrt{1369} = 37$ (See the table.)

EXAMPLE 5 If a, b, and c are the sides of a right triangle whose hypotenuse is c, find b if $a = 16$ and $c = 18$.

Solution Using

$$a^2 + b^2 = c^2$$
$$(16)^2 + b^2 = (18)^2$$
$$b^2 = (18)^2 - (16)^2 = (18 + 16)(18 - 16)$$
$$b^2 = 68$$
$$b = 8.25 \text{ to the nearest hundredth}$$

PYTHAGORAS

Although there are many stories about the life of Pythagoras (ca. 580–501 B.C.), little is known for certain. He was probably born on the island of Samos and he probably traveled to Egypt, and Babylonia. He is known to have settled in Crotona on the Italian coast, where he founded a brotherhood composed of some 300 wealthy young aristocrats. This group, known as the Pythagoreans, became the prototype of all the secret societies of Europe and America. Their motto, "Number rules the universe," expressed the combination of mathematics and mysticism in which they believed. Shakespeare refers to the Pythagorean belief in immortality and transmigration of the soul in *The Merchant of Venice:*

> Thou almost mak'st me waver in my faith,
> To hold opinion with Pythagoras,
> That souls of animals infuse themselves,
> Into the trunks of men.

The name of Pythagoras is most famous in connection with the relationship of the squares of the sides of a right triangle. While Pythagoras did not discover this property (it was already known to the Babylonians), he may have offered the first proof of this statement.

EXERCISES

Simplify in Exercises 1–26. If necessary, use the tables of squares and square roots inside the front cover.

1. $\sqrt{16}$
2. $\sqrt{169}$
3. $\sqrt{(-3)^2}$
4. $\sqrt{(-1)^2}$
5. $-\sqrt{4}$
6. $-\sqrt{(-2)^2}$
7. $\sqrt{400}$
8. $\sqrt{144}$
9. $(\sqrt{3})^2$
10. $(\sqrt{16})^2$
11. $(-\sqrt{4})^2$
12. $(-\sqrt{5})^2$
13. $-(\sqrt{4})^2$
14. $-(\sqrt{5})^2$

15. $\sqrt{5^2} - \sqrt{4^2}$

16. $\sqrt{(25)^2} - \sqrt{7^2}$

17. $\sqrt{(-5)^2} + \sqrt{(12)^2}$

18. $\sqrt{(-8)^2} + \sqrt{(-15)^2}$

19. $\sqrt{(-5)^2 + (12)^2}$

20. $\sqrt{(-8)^2 + (-15)^2}$

21. $\sqrt{\frac{25}{64}}$

22. $\sqrt{\frac{9}{16}}$

23. $\sqrt{0.01}$

24. $\sqrt{0.0001}$

25. $\dfrac{\sqrt{64+36}}{\sqrt{64}+\sqrt{36}}$

26. $\dfrac{4\sqrt{225-144}}{4(\sqrt{225}-\sqrt{144})}$

In Exercises 27–40, use the table of squares and square roots inside the front cover or a pocket calculator. Approximate to the nearest hundredth.

27. $\sqrt{45}$

28. $\sqrt{10}$

29. $\sqrt{86}$

30. $\sqrt{3}$

31. $2\sqrt{5}$

32. $3\sqrt{7}$

33. $5 - \sqrt{3}$

34. $3 - \sqrt{5}$

35. $5\sqrt{8}$

36. $\sqrt{2}\sqrt{6}$

37. $2 + \sqrt{2}$

38. $\sqrt{2} + \sqrt{6}$

39. $\sqrt{5} - \sqrt{3}$

40. $\sqrt{7} + \sqrt{11}$

If a and b represent the lengths of the legs of a right triangle and c represents the length of the hypotenuse of that triangle, determine the length of the missing side or sides in Exercises 41–56.

41. $a = 12, b = 5$

42. $b = 5, c = 13$

43. $b = 5, c = 15$

44. $a = 12, b = 35$

45. $a = 1, b = 1$

46. $a = 2, c = 5$

47. $a = 15, c = 17$

48. $a = 2, c = \sqrt{30}$

49. $a = \sqrt{5}, b = \sqrt{3}$

50. $b = \sqrt{10}, c = \sqrt{30}$

51. $a = b, c = 10$

52. $a = b, c = \sqrt{10}$

53. $c = 2a, b = \sqrt{3}$

54. $c = 2b, a = 6$

55. $a = 2b, c = 10$

56. $b = 2a, c = \sqrt{10}$

6.2 RADICALS: SIMPLIFICATION AND PRODUCTS

In order to solve quadratic equations, you need to know how to add, subtract, multiply, and divide expressions that contain radicals. In this section we will learn how to multiply square root radicals and how to simplify a square root radical.

THEOREM

The product of two square root radicals is the square root of the product of their radicands. In symbols, $\sqrt{r}\sqrt{s} = \sqrt{rs}$ for $r \geq 0$ and $s \geq 0$.

EXAMPLE 1 Simplify $\sqrt{3}\sqrt{12}$.

Solution $\sqrt{3}\sqrt{12} = \sqrt{3 \cdot 12} = \sqrt{36} = 6$

EXAMPLE 2 Simplify $\sqrt{2}\sqrt{5}$.

Solution $\sqrt{2}\sqrt{5} = \sqrt{10}$

A **radical** of the form $\sqrt{M}$, where M is a monomial with an integer for its coefficient, is said to be **simplified** if no perfect squares are factors of the **radicand** M.

The following theorem is useful for simplifying square root radicals.

THEOREM

If x and y are any nonnegative real numbers,

$$\sqrt{x^2y} = \sqrt{x^2}\sqrt{y} = x\sqrt{y}$$

EXAMPLE 3 Simplify $\sqrt{75}$.

Solution The basic idea is to factor the radicand to find the perfect square factors:

$$75 = 3 \cdot 5^2$$

$$\sqrt{75} = \sqrt{5^2 \cdot 3} = \sqrt{5^2}\sqrt{3} = 5\sqrt{3}$$

EXAMPLE 4 Simplify $\sqrt{6}\sqrt{30}$.

Solution

$$\begin{aligned}\sqrt{6}\sqrt{30} = \sqrt{6(30)} &= \sqrt{(2 \cdot 3)(2 \cdot 3 \cdot 5)} \\ &= \sqrt{6^2(5)} \\ &= \sqrt{6^2}\sqrt{5} \\ &= 6\sqrt{5}\end{aligned}$$

EXERCISES

Simplify the radicals in Exercises 1–40.

1. $\sqrt{2}\sqrt{50}$
2. $\sqrt{18}\sqrt{2}$
3. $\sqrt{5}\sqrt{20}$
4. $\sqrt{48}\sqrt{3}$
5. $\sqrt{15}\sqrt{5}$
6. $\sqrt{100}\sqrt{20}$
7. $\sqrt{5}\sqrt{25}$
8. $\sqrt{3}\sqrt{12}$
9. $\sqrt{125}$
10. $\sqrt{27}$
11. $\sqrt{32}$
12. $\sqrt{24}$
13. $\sqrt{8}$
14. $\sqrt{12}$
15. $\sqrt{40}$
16. $\sqrt{54}$
17. $\sqrt{162}$
18. $\sqrt{28}$
19. $\sqrt{98}$
20. $\sqrt{45}\sqrt{5}$

21. $\sqrt{150}$ **22.** $\sqrt{405}$
23. $\sqrt{35}\sqrt{14}$ **24.** $\sqrt{3}\sqrt{60}$
25. $\sqrt{6}\sqrt{30}$ **26.** $\sqrt{8}\sqrt{30}$
27. $\sqrt{108}$ **28.** $\sqrt{363}$
29. $\sqrt{1200}$ **30.** $\sqrt{200}$
31. $\sqrt{300}$ **32.** $\sqrt{500}$
33. $\sqrt{1452}$ **34.** $\sqrt{1849}$
35. $\sqrt{3}\sqrt{5}\sqrt{15}$ **36.** $\sqrt{2}\sqrt{7}\sqrt{14}$
37. $\sqrt{64}\sqrt{12}\sqrt{3}$ **38.** $\sqrt{5}\sqrt{14}\sqrt{28}$
39. $\sqrt{1976}$ **40.** $\sqrt{1776}$

A BABYLONIAN SOLUTION OF A QUADRATIC EQUATION

The following solution of a quadratic equation was found on a Babylonian clay tablet that has been dated around 1700 B.C. It has been freely translated into English, and modern numerical symbols have been used instead of the Babylonian base 60 cuneiform numerals. (The Babylonians did not write their denominators (60, 3600, and so on), just as we do not write the denominators 10, 100, 1000, and so on when we write decimal numerals.) "I have added the area and two-thirds of the side of my square. The result is $\frac{35}{60}$. Find the side of the square. Answer: $\frac{30}{60}$." The method given on the tablet is shown below. Beside it are computations using modern notation.

Babylonian Method	*Our Modern Notation*
	$x^2 + \frac{2}{3}x = \frac{7}{12}$
Two thirds is $\frac{40}{60}$.	
One-half the 'coefficient' $\frac{40}{60}$ is $\frac{20}{60}$.	$\frac{1}{2}\left(\frac{2}{3}\right) = \frac{1}{3}$
Multiply $\frac{20}{60}$ by itself. Result $\frac{6}{60} + \frac{40}{3600}$.	$\left(\frac{1}{3}\right)^2 = \frac{1}{9}$
Add this result to $\frac{35}{60}$. Result $\frac{41}{60} + \frac{40}{3600}$.	$\frac{1}{9} + \frac{7}{12} = \frac{25}{36}$
Take the square root. Result $\frac{50}{60}$.	$\sqrt{\frac{25}{36}} = \frac{5}{6}$
From $\frac{50}{60}$ you subtract $\frac{20}{60}$. Result $\frac{30}{60}$.	$\frac{5}{6} - \frac{1}{3} = \frac{1}{2}$

6.3 OPERATIONS WITH RADICALS

It is often possible to express a sum or difference of two radical terms as a single term. For example, since $\sqrt{5}$ is a real number, so are $3\sqrt{5}$ and $4\sqrt{5}$ and $3\sqrt{5} + 4\sqrt{5}$. Using the distributive axiom,

$$3\sqrt{5} + 4\sqrt{5} = (3 + 4)\sqrt{5} = 7\sqrt{5}$$

Square root radicals that have the same radicand are called **like radicals.** Radicals that are not like are called **unlike.** For example, $3\sqrt{5}$ and $4\sqrt{5}$ are like radicals, whereas $2\sqrt{5}$ and $4\sqrt{3}$ are unlike radicals.

Terms that contain like radicals can be combined by using the distributive axiom, but terms that contain unlike radicals cannot be so combined. Sometimes it is necessary to simplify each radical term in order to identify like radicals.

EXAMPLE 1 Simplify $\sqrt{50} + \sqrt{18}$ if possible.

Solution

$\sqrt{50} + \sqrt{18}$

$= 5\sqrt{2} + 3\sqrt{2}$ (Simplifying each radical)

$= (5 + 3)\sqrt{2}$ (Using the distributive axiom)

$= 8\sqrt{2}$

EXAMPLE 2 Simplify $\sqrt{48} + \sqrt{18} - \sqrt{12}$.

Solution $\sqrt{48} + \sqrt{18} - \sqrt{12}$

$= 4\sqrt{3} + 3\sqrt{2} - 2\sqrt{3}$ (Simplifying)

$= (4\sqrt{3} - 2\sqrt{3}) + 3\sqrt{2}$ (Collecting like radicals)

$= (4 - 2)\sqrt{3} + 3\sqrt{2}$ (Using the distributive axiom)

$= 2\sqrt{3} + 3\sqrt{2}$ (Simplified form)

Since a solution of a quadratic equation ($ax^2 + bx + c = 0$) may have the form $4 + 3\sqrt{6}$ or $\frac{6 - \sqrt{5}}{2}$, one needs to know how to evaluate quadratic polynomials for such values as these in order to check a possible solution.

EXAMPLE 3 Show that $4 + 3\sqrt{6}$ is a solution of $x^2 - 8x = 38$.

Solution First find the value of x^2 for $x = 4 + 3\sqrt{6}$.

$$x^2 = (4 + 3\sqrt{6})^2 = 4^2 + 2(4)(3\sqrt{6}) + (3\sqrt{6})^2$$
$$= 16 + 24\sqrt{6} + 9(6) = 70 + 24\sqrt{6}$$

Then evaluate $-8x$.

$$-8x = -8(4 + 3\sqrt{6}) = -32 - 24\sqrt{6}$$

Combining these results,

$$x^2 - 8x = 70 + 24\sqrt{6} - 32 - 24\sqrt{6} = 38$$

Thus, $x^2 - 8x = 38$ for $x = 4 + 3\sqrt{6}$ and $4 + 3\sqrt{6}$ is a solution.

EXAMPLE 4 Show that $\frac{6-\sqrt{5}}{2}$ is a solution of $4x^2+31=24x$.

Solution

$$4x^2+31=4\left(\frac{6-\sqrt{5}}{2}\right)^2+31$$
$$=4\left(\frac{36-12\sqrt{5}+5}{4}\right)+31$$
$$=41-12\sqrt{5}+31=72-12\sqrt{5}$$
$$24x=24\left(\frac{6-\sqrt{5}}{2}\right)=72-12\sqrt{5}$$

Since both sides of the equation result in the same value, $\frac{6-\sqrt{5}}{2}$ is a solution.

EXAMPLE 5 Simplify $\frac{8+\sqrt{20}}{6}$

Solution First simplify the radical:

$$\sqrt{20}=\sqrt{4\cdot 5}=2\sqrt{5}$$

Then

$$\frac{8+\sqrt{20}}{6}=\frac{8+2\sqrt{5}}{6}$$

Now factor the numerator and the denominator in order to reduce the fraction.

$$\frac{8+2\sqrt{5}}{6}=\frac{2(4+\sqrt{5})}{2(3)}=\frac{4+\sqrt{5}}{3}$$

EXERCISES

In Exercises 1–24, write each expression in simplest radical form.

1. $6\sqrt{5}+2\sqrt{5}$
2. $7\sqrt{2}-4\sqrt{2}$
3. $5\sqrt{6}+\sqrt{6}$
4. $9\sqrt{10}-8\sqrt{10}$
5. $3\sqrt{5}+5\sqrt{3}$
6. $5\sqrt{3}-4\sqrt{3}+2\sqrt{3}$
7. $7\sqrt{3}-5\sqrt{3}$
8. $5\sqrt{7}+4\sqrt{7}$
9. $8\sqrt{6}-7\sqrt{6}$
10. $2\sqrt{15}+\sqrt{15}$
11. $2\sqrt{30}+5\sqrt{30}-4\sqrt{30}$
12. $7\sqrt{5}-5\sqrt{7}$
13. $6\sqrt{28}-4\sqrt{28}$
14. $\sqrt{40}-\sqrt{10}$
15. $\sqrt{28}-2\sqrt{7}$
16. $3\sqrt{20}+\sqrt{5}$
17. $\sqrt{3}+\sqrt{27}$
18. $5\sqrt{18}-4\sqrt{8}$
19. $3\sqrt{24}+2\sqrt{54}$
20. $\sqrt{32}+\sqrt{98}-3\sqrt{2}$
21. $\sqrt{8}-\sqrt{18}-\sqrt{12}$
22. $\sqrt{20}+\sqrt{12}+\sqrt{45}$
23. $\sqrt{63}-\sqrt{28}+2\sqrt{2}$
24. $\sqrt{54}+\sqrt{32}-\sqrt{24}$

6.3 OPERATION WITH RADICALS

Simplify Exercises 25–36.

25. $(5+\sqrt{6})^2$

26. $(2-\sqrt{7})^2$

27. $(-2+\sqrt{7})^2$

28. $(3-\sqrt{10})^2$

29. $(4+3\sqrt{5})^2$

30. $(2-3\sqrt{2})^2$

31. $\sqrt{3}(\sqrt{12}+\sqrt{3})$

32. $\sqrt{2}(\sqrt{8}-\sqrt{6})$

33. $(\sqrt{5}-\sqrt{3})^2$

34. $(\sqrt{6}+2\sqrt{5})^2$

35. $(2\sqrt{5}+1)^2$

36. $(4\sqrt{3}-5)^2$

Simplify Exercises 37–44.

37. $\dfrac{10+\sqrt{18}}{6}$

38. $\dfrac{6-\sqrt{18}}{6}$

39. $\dfrac{-8+\sqrt{20}}{4}$

40. $\dfrac{12-\sqrt{8}}{6}$

41. $\dfrac{14+\sqrt{80}}{2}$

42. $\dfrac{6-\sqrt{54}}{9}$

43. $\dfrac{28-\sqrt{200}}{14}$

44. $\dfrac{-1-\sqrt{44}}{8}$

For Exercises 45–50, find the value of the polynomial when $x=2+\sqrt{3}$.

45. x^2+3x

46. x^2-4x

47. $2x^2+5x$

48. $3x^2-x$

49. x^2+3x+2

50. $4x^2-3x+1$

For Exercises 51–54, find the value of the polynomial when $x=3-\sqrt{2}$.

51. x^2+2x

52. x^2-3x

53. $3x^2+2x$

54. $2x^2+3x$

For Exercises 55 and 56, find the value of the polynomial when $x=\dfrac{-3+\sqrt{17}}{2}$.

55. x^2+3x-2

56. x^2-3x-2

In Exercises 57–60, show that the given value for x is a solution of the given equation.

57. $x=5-\sqrt{2};\ x^2-10x+23=0$

58. $x=5+\sqrt{2};\ x^2-10x+23=0$

59. $x=\dfrac{-1+\sqrt{5}}{2};\ x^2+x-1=0$

60. $x=\dfrac{-1-\sqrt{5}}{2};\ x^2+x-1=0$

6.4 QUADRATIC EQUATIONS: SOLUTION BY FACTORING

The solution of quadratic equations by factoring, which was introduced earlier, involves four basic steps:

1. Find an equivalent quadratic equation whose right side is zero.
2. Factor the quadratic polynomial.
3. Set each factor equal to zero.
4. Solve for the variable.

This method is based on the zero-product theorem, which was introduced in Chapter 3 and is restated below for convenience.

THE ZERO-PRODUCT THEOREM

Let r and s be any real numbers. If $rs = 0$, then $r = 0$ or $s = 0$.

In solving an equation by the factoring method, it is important to remember that the right side of the equation must be zero before the factors on the left side can be equated to zero.

EXAMPLE 1 Solve for x: $x^2 - x = 6$.
Solution

$$x^2 - x = 6$$

1. $x^2 - x - 6 = 0$ (Equivalent equation whose right side is zero)
2. $(x - 3)(x + 2) = 0$ (Factor the quadratic polynomial)
3. $x - 3 = 0$ or $x + 2 = 0$ (Zero-product theorem: If $rs = 0$, then $r = 0$ or $s = 0$)
4. $x = 3$ or $x = -2$

Check

$x^2 - x = 6$	$x^2 - x = 6$
$(3)^2 - 3 = 6$	$(-2)^2 - (-2) = 6$
$9 - 3 = 6$	$4 + 2 = 6$
$6 = 6$	$6 = 6$

Therefore, the solution set is $\{3, -2\}$.

EXAMPLE 2 Solve $(x-2)(x-5)=40$.

Solution

$$(x-2)(x-5)=40$$
$$x^2-7x+10=40$$
$$x^2-7x-30=0$$
$$(x+3)(x-10)=0$$
$$x+3=0 \quad \text{or} \quad x-10=0$$
$$x=-3 \quad \text{or} \quad x=10$$

The solution set is $\{-3, 10\}$.

Check

For $x=-3$, $(x-2)(x-5)=(-3-2)(-3-5)=(-5)(-8)=40$.

For $x=10$, $(x-2)(x-5)=(10-2)(10-5)=(8)(5)=40$.

The equation $x^2=c$ where c is a positive constant is a very special case of a quadratic equation. Since this equation can also be written as $x^2-c=0$ and since $c=(\sqrt{c})^2$,

$$x^2-c=x^2-(\sqrt{c})^2=(x-\sqrt{c})(x+\sqrt{c})$$

Now, solving $x^2=c$,

$$x^2-c=0$$
$$(x-\sqrt{c})(x+\sqrt{c})=0$$
$$x-\sqrt{c}=0 \quad \text{or} \quad x+\sqrt{c}=0$$
$$x=\sqrt{c} \quad \text{or} \quad x=-\sqrt{c}$$

This result can now be stated as the following very useful theorem.

THEOREM

If $x^2=c$ and $c>0$, then $x=\sqrt{c}$ or $x=-\sqrt{c}$.

EXAMPLE 3 Solve $x^2=49$.

Solution $x=7$ or $x=-7$ (Using the theorem and $\sqrt{49}=7$)

EXAMPLE 4 Solve $x^2=75$.

Solution $x=\sqrt{75}$ or $x=-\sqrt{75}$

Simplifying the radical, $\sqrt{75}=\sqrt{25(3)}=5\sqrt{3}$

$$x=5\sqrt{3} \quad \text{or} \quad x=-5\sqrt{3}$$

EXAMPLE 5 Solve $3x^2-2=0$.

Solution $3x^2=2$. To make the left side a perfect square, multiply each side by 3.

$$3(3x^2)=3(2)$$
$$9x^2=6$$
$$3x=\sqrt{6} \quad \text{or} \quad 3x=-\sqrt{6} \qquad \text{(Finding the square root of each side and using the theorem)}$$
$$x=\frac{\sqrt{6}}{3} \quad \text{or} \quad x=\frac{-\sqrt{6}}{3}$$

Check

$$3\left(\frac{\sqrt{6}}{3}\right)^2-2=3\left(\frac{6}{9}\right)-2=2-2=0$$
$$3\left(\frac{-\sqrt{6}}{3}\right)^2-2=3\left(\frac{6}{9}\right)-2=2-2=0$$

A HINDU SOLUTION OF A QUADRATIC EQUATION

The following problem together with its solution appears in the works of the Hindu Brahmagupta around 628. An analysis and a generalization, comparing his solution with our modern technique, is shown at the right.

Hindu Problem	*Our Notation*
ya v 1 ya 1$\dot{0}$ ru $\dot{9}$	$x^2 - 10x = -9$
Adding -9 to the square of half the coefficient of the middle term, namely, 25, makes 16.	$-9 + (-5)^2 = 16$
The square root of 16 is 4.	$\sqrt{16} = 4$
Subtract half the coefficient of the unknown, yielding 9, the value of the unknown.	$4 - (-5) = 9$

Another special case occurs when $c = 0$. The equation reads

$$ax^2 + bx = 0$$

Now there is a common factor, x, for the left member of the equation.

$$ax^2 + bx = 0$$
$$x(ax + b) = 0$$
$$x = 0 \quad \text{or} \quad ax + b = 0 \qquad \text{(zero-product theorem)}$$
$$ax = -b$$
$$x = -\frac{b}{a}$$

The solution set is $\left(0, -\frac{b}{a}\right)$.

EXAMPLE 6 Solve by factoring $3x^2 + 2x = 0$.

Solution

$$3x^2 + 2x = 0$$
$$x(3x + 2) = 0$$
$$x = 0 \quad \text{or} \quad 3x + 2 = 0$$
$$3x = -2$$
$$x = -\frac{2}{3}$$

Therefore, the solution set is $\left\{0, -\frac{2}{3}\right\}$.

Check

If $x = 0$, $3(0)^2 + 2(0) = 0 + 0 = 0$.

If $x = -\frac{2}{3}$, $3x^2 + 2x = 3\left(-\frac{2}{3}\right)^2 + 2\left(-\frac{2}{3}\right)$

$$= 3\left(\frac{4}{9}\right) - \frac{4}{3} = \frac{4}{3} - \frac{4}{3} = 0$$

EXAMPLE 7 Solve $4x^2 = 12x$.

Solution

$$4x^2 = 12x$$
$$4x^2 - 12x = 0$$
$$4x(x - 3) = 0$$
$$4x = 0 \quad \text{or} \quad x - 3 = 0$$

Since $4 \neq 0$, $x = 0$ or $x = 3$.

Check

For $x = 0$, $4x^2 = 4(0)^2 = 0$ and $12x = 12(0) = 0$.
For $x = 3$, $4(3)^2 = 4(9) = 36$ and $12x = 12(3) = 36$.

Note in the preceding examples that each quadratic equation had *two* solutions. If both sides of the equation $4x^2 = 12x$ had been divided by x, this would have yielded $4x = 12$ and $x = 3$, thus losing the solution $x = 0$. Since the equation $4x^2 = 12x$ is true for $x = 0$, dividing both sides by x is the same as dividing both sides by 0, and this is not permitted. In general, division by an expression containing a variable may lose a solution, and multiplication by an expression containing a variable may introduce an extraneous solution (a number that is not a solution of the original equation).

A quadratic equation may have only one number in its solution set. Such a solution is called a **double root.**

EXAMPLE 8 Solve $x^2 - 6x + 9 = 0$.

Solution

$$x^2 - 6x + 9 = (x - 3)^2$$
$$x^2 - 6x + 9 = 0$$
$$(x - 3)^2 = 0$$
$$(x - 3)(x - 3) = 0$$
$$x - 3 = 0 \quad \text{or} \quad x - 3 = 0$$
$$x = 3 \quad \text{or} \quad x = 3$$

The solution set is $\{3\}$, where 3 is called a double root.

When the solutions of a quadratic equation are restricted to real numbers, there are quadratic equations that have no solution, as the following example shows.

EXAMPLE 9 Solve $x^2 + 4 = 0$.

Solution

$$x^2 + 4 = 0$$
$$x^2 = -4$$

Since there is no real number whose square is negative, there is no real solution to this equation. (A solution for this type of equation is provided by the set of complex numbers, which is beyond the scope of this book.)

EXERCISES

Solve the following equations.

1. $(x-5)(x+2)=0$
2. $(x+3)(x-4)=0$
3. $5x(x-4)=0$
4. $2x(x+3)=0$
5. $x^2-5x+6=0$
6. $x^2+x-6=0$
7. $x^2+2x=35$
8. $x^2-3x=18$
9. $(x+3)(x-2)=14$
10. $(x-4)(x-3)=42$
11. $2x^2+x=10$
12. $3x^2=x+4$
13. $6x^2=7x-1$
14. $5x^2+4=21x$
15. $4x^2-25=0$
16. $9x^2-64=0$
17. $4x^2=27$
18. $9x^2=32$
19. $5x^2=6$
20. $2x^2=7$
21. $5x^2=6x$
22. $2x^2=7x$
23. $4x^2-2x=0$
24. $6x^2=24x$
25. $4x^2-2=2x$
26. $5x^2=20x-15$
27. $x^2-12x+36=0$
28. $x^2+25=10x$
29. $4x^2+9=12x$
30. $9x^2=60x-100$
31. $5x^2=20x$
32. $4x^2+36x=0$
33. $5x^2=20$
34. $4x^2-36=0$
35. $3x^2-24x+48=0$
36. $5x^2+100x+500=0$
37. $(x-2)^2=1$
38. $(x+3)^2=4$
39. $(x+5)^2=16$
40. $(x-7)^2=36$
41. $(2x-1)^2=9$
42. $(3x+2)^2=25$
43. $(5x+3)^2=7$
44. $(4x-5)^2=5$

6.5 QUADRATIC EQUATIONS: COMPLETING THE SQUARE

Not all quadratic polynomials can be factored easily, and the solution of quadratic equations could be very time consuming and cumbersome if the factors had to be determined by the trial-and-error method. In order to find the solution more rapidly, other methods are available. One such method is called **completing the square.** The aim of this method is to make the left side of the equation a perfect square trinomial and the right side a constant—that is, $(x+a)^2=k$.

If $k \geq 0$, the equation $(x+a)^2=k$ can be written as
$(x+a)^2-k=0$

and the left side can be factored by the difference of two squares theorem:

$$(x + a)^2 - (\sqrt{k})^2 = 0$$
$$(x + a - \sqrt{k})(x + a + \sqrt{k}) = 0$$
$$x + a - \sqrt{k} = 0 \quad \text{or} \quad x + a + \sqrt{k} = 0$$
$$x = -a + \sqrt{k} \quad \text{or} \quad x = -a - \sqrt{k}$$

In practice, it is convenient to write the solution in the shorter form:

$$(x + a)^2 = k$$
$$x + a = \pm\sqrt{k}$$
$$x = -a + \sqrt{k} \quad \text{or} \quad x = -a - \sqrt{k}$$

If $k < 0$, then there is no solution in the set of real numbers.

EXAMPLE 1 Solve $x^2 + 6x + 4 = 0$ by completing the square.

Solution

1. Subtract the constant from both sides of the equation: $x^2 + 6x = -4$
2. Add to both sides the number that makes $x^2 + 6x$ a perfect square trinomial: $x^2 + 6x + 9 = -4 + 9$
3. Write the left side as the square of a binomial and simplify the right side: $(x + 3)^2 = 5$
4. Take the square root of both sides: $x + 3 = \pm\sqrt{5}$
5. Solve for x: $x = -3 + \sqrt{5}$ or $x = -3 - \sqrt{5}$

Check

If $x = -3 + \sqrt{5}$,

$$x^2 + 6x + 4 = 0$$
$$(-3 + \sqrt{5})^2 + 6(-3 + \sqrt{5}) + 4 = 0$$
$$9 - 6\sqrt{5} + 5 - 18 + 6\sqrt{5} + 4 = 0$$
$$0 = 0$$

If $x = -3 - \sqrt{5}$,

$$x^2 + 6x + 4 = 0$$
$$(-3 - \sqrt{5})^2 + 6(-3 - \sqrt{5}) + 4 = 0$$
$$9 + 6\sqrt{5} + 5 - 18 - 6\sqrt{5} + 4 = 0$$
$$0 = 0$$

Therefore, the solution set is $\{-3 + \sqrt{5}, -3 - \sqrt{5}\}$.

It is useful to recall that the constant term of a perfect square trinomial of the form $x^2 + bx + c$ is found by taking half of the coefficient of the linear term and squaring this number. (Here the linear term is bx.)

Solving a quadratic equation by completing the square is most useful when the coefficient of x^2 is 1 and the coefficient of x is an even number. When this is not the case, fractions are involved. However, the method can still be used for the general case $ax^2 + bx + c = 0$ even when $a \neq 1$. The technique is to multiply each term by the number that makes the x^2 term a perfect square. To complete the square, we need the following result.

$$(rx + s)^2 = r^2x^2 + 2rsx + s^2$$

To find s, given $r^2x^2 + 2rsx$, it is necessary to divide the coefficient of x by $2r$, where $r = \sqrt{r^2}$.

EXAMPLE 2 Solve $3x^2 - 6x + 1 = 0$ by completing the square.

Solution

1. Multiply each term by 3: $9x^2 - 18x + 3 = 0$
2. Subtract the constant 3 from each side. $9x^2 - 18x = -3$
3. Complete the square: $9x^2 - 18x + (-3)^2 = -3 + 9$

   $\sqrt{9} = 3, \dfrac{-18}{2(3)} = -3$

$$(3x - 3)^2 = 6$$
$$3x - 3 = \pm\sqrt{6}$$
$$3x = 3 \pm \sqrt{6}$$
$$x = \frac{3 \pm \sqrt{6}}{3}$$

Thus $x = \dfrac{3 + \sqrt{6}}{3}$ or $x = \dfrac{3 - \sqrt{6}}{3}$

EXAMPLE 3 Solve $12x^2 - 20x + 7 = 0$

Solution

1. Multiply each term by 3, because $3(12x^2) = 36x^2$, a perfect square. $36x^2 - 60x + 21 = 0$
2. Subtract the constant, 21, from each side. $36x^2 - 60x = -21$
3. Complete the square by adding the square of $\dfrac{-60}{2\sqrt{36}}$ or $(-5)^2$ to each side. $36x^2 - 60x + (-5)^2 = -21 + 25$
4. Form the square on the left side and simplify the right. $(6x - 5)^2 = 4$
5. Take square root of each side: $6x - 5 = \pm 2$

   Thus,

$$6x - 5 = 2 \quad \text{or} \quad 6x - 5 = -2$$
$$6x = 7 \quad \text{or} \quad 6x = 3$$
$$x = \frac{7}{6} \quad \text{or} \quad x = \frac{1}{2}$$

Check

For $x = \dfrac{7}{6}$, $12\left(\dfrac{49}{36}\right) - 20\left(\dfrac{7}{6}\right) + 7 = \dfrac{49}{3} - \dfrac{70}{3} + 7 = \dfrac{-21}{3} + 7 = 0$

For $x = \dfrac{1}{2}$, $12\left(\dfrac{1}{4}\right) - 20\left(\dfrac{1}{2}\right) + 7 = 3 - 10 + 7 = 0$

EXERCISES

Solve the following equations.

1. $(x-5)^2 = 2$
2. $(x+3)^2 = 7$
3. $(x+4)^2 = 45$
4. $(x-2)^2 = 8$
5. $x^2 - 4x + 1 = 0$
6. $x^2 - 2x - 5 = 0$
7. $y^2 - 8y - 4 = 0$
8. $y^2 - 6y + 4 = 0$
9. $x^2 = 2x + 19$
10. $x^2 = 10x - 7$
11. $2 - 10t = t^2$
12. $8t = 12 - t^2$
13. $14z = 23 - z^2$
14. $z^2 + 54 = 18z$
15. $a^2 + 12(a+2) = 6$
16. $a^2 + 16(a+2) = 0$
17. $y^2 = 20(y-3)$
18. $y^2 = 12(y-1)$
19. $2x^2 + 7x = 30$
20. $3x^2 - 5x = 12$
21. $4x^2 - 20x + 17 = 0$
22. $9x^2 + 42x + 25 = 0$
23. $5x^2 - 10x - 2 = 10$
24. $6x^2 + 24x + 1 = 0$
25. $36x^2 + 12x - 3 = 0$
26. $25x^2 - 20x - 9 = 0$
27. $6a^2 - 10a + 3 = 0$
28. $9m^2 - 48m + 10 = 0$
29. $(x+3)^2 = (2x-5)^2$
30. $(4x-1)^2 = (2x+3)^2$

6.6 THE QUADRATIC FORMULA

There is a formula that can be used to solve a quadratic equation by applying the method of completing the square to the general quadratic equation $ax^2 + bx + c = 0$, where $a \neq 0$.

The quadratic formula method of solution is most useful when the quadratic equation is not easily factored and when completing the square involves fractions.

Solving $ax^2 + bx + c = 0$

1. Multiply each term by $4a$: $\quad 4a^2x^2 + 4abx + 4ac = 0$
2. Subtract $4ac$ from each side: $\quad 4a^2x^2 + 4abx = -4ac$
3. Complete the square: $\quad 4a^2x^2 + 4abx + b^2 = -4ac + b^2$
4. Form the square: $\quad (2ax + b)^2 = b^2 - 4ac$
5. If $b^2 - 4ac \geq 0$, take the square root of each side: $\quad 2ax + b = \pm\sqrt{b^2 - 4ac}$
6. Solve for x: $\quad 2ax = -b \pm \sqrt{b^2 - 4ac}$

$$x = \frac{-b \pm \sqrt{b^2 - 4ac}}{2a}$$

Since a, b, and c were chosen completely arbitrarily except $a \neq 0$ and $b^2 - 4ac \geq 0$, the set of equations

$$\left\{x = \frac{-b + \sqrt{b^2 - 4ac}}{2a},\ x = \frac{-b - \sqrt{b^2 - 4ac}}{2a}\right\}$$

can be used as a formula for the solution of a quadratic equation.

THE QUADRATIC FORMULA

The quadratic equation $ax^2 + bx + c = 0$, $a \neq 0$, has the solutions

$$x = \frac{-b + \sqrt{b^2 - 4ac}}{2a},\ x = \frac{-b - \sqrt{b^2 - 4ac}}{2a}$$

where $b^2 - 4ac \geq 0$.

EXAMPLE 1 Solve $2x^2 + 3x + 1 = 0$ by using the quadratic formula.

Solution Comparing with $ax^2 + bx + c = 0$,

$$2x^2 + 3x + 1 = 0$$

it is seen that $a = 2$, $b = 3$, and $c = 1$. Therefore

$$x = \frac{-b \pm \sqrt{b^2 - 4ac}}{2a}$$

yields

$$x = \frac{-3 + \sqrt{9 - 4(2)(1)}}{4} = \frac{-3 + 1}{4} = \frac{-2}{4} = -\frac{1}{2}$$

or

$$x = \frac{-3 - \sqrt{9 - 4(2)(1)}}{4} = \frac{-3 - 1}{4} = \frac{-4}{4} = -1$$

Check

If $x = -\frac{1}{2}$,

$$2x^2 + 3x + 1 = 0$$

$$2\left(-\frac{1}{2}\right)^2 + 3\left(-\frac{1}{2}\right) + 1 = 0$$

$$\frac{1}{2} - \frac{3}{2} + 1 = 0$$

$$0 = 0$$

If $x = -1$,

$$2x^2 + 3x + 1 = 0$$

$$2(-1)^2 + 3(-1) + 1 = 0$$

$$2 - 3 + 1 = 0$$

$$0 = 0$$

Therefore, $\left\{-\frac{1}{2}, -1\right\}$ is the solution set.

Note that this equation $(2x^2 + 3x + 1 = 0)$ could also be solved by factoring.

$$2x^2 + 3x + 1 = 0$$

$$(2x + 1)(x + 1) = 0$$

$$2x + 1 = 0 \quad \text{or} \quad x + 1 = 0$$

$$x = -\frac{1}{2} \quad \text{or} \quad x = -1$$

This result agrees with the answers obtained by using the quadratic formula.

EXAMPLE 2 Solve $2x^2 - 3x = x^2 - 1$ by using the quadratic formula.

Solution First an equivalent equation of the form $ax^2 + bx + c = 0$ must be found:

$$2x^2 - 3x = x^2 - 1$$
$$x^2 - 3x + 1 = 0$$
$$a = 1,\ b = -3,\ c = 1$$
$$x = \frac{-(-3) \pm \sqrt{(-3)^2 - 4(1)(1)}}{2}$$
$$x = \frac{3 + \sqrt{5}}{2} \quad \text{or} \quad x = \frac{3 - \sqrt{5}}{2}$$

The solution set is $\left\{\frac{3 + \sqrt{5}}{2}, \frac{3 - \sqrt{5}}{2}\right\}$.

EXAMPLE 3 Solve $2x^2 - 2x - 3 = 0$.

Solution $a = 2,\ b = -2,\ c = -3$

$$x = \frac{-(-2) \pm \sqrt{(-2)^2 - 4(2)(-3)}}{2(2)}$$
$$= \frac{2 \pm \sqrt{4 + 24}}{4} = \frac{2 \pm \sqrt{28}}{4} = \frac{2 \pm 2\sqrt{7}}{4} = \frac{2(1 \pm \sqrt{7})}{2(2)}$$
$$x = \frac{1 \pm \sqrt{7}}{2}$$

Check $x = \frac{1 + \sqrt{7}}{2}$

$$2\left(\frac{1 + 2\sqrt{7} + 7}{4}\right) - 2\left(\frac{1 + \sqrt{7}}{2}\right) - 3 = \frac{8 + 2\sqrt{7}}{2} - 1 - \sqrt{7} - 3$$
$$= 4 + \sqrt{7} - 1 - \sqrt{7} - 3 = 0$$

The check for the other root is similar.

EXAMPLE 4 Solve $9x^2 + 30x + 25 = 0$.

Solution

$$x = \frac{-30 \pm \sqrt{(30)^2 - 4(9)(25)}}{2(9)}$$
$$= \frac{-30 \pm \sqrt{900 - 900}}{2(9)} = \frac{-30}{6(3)} = \frac{-5}{3}$$

The solution set is $\left\{-\frac{5}{3}\right\}$.

Check For $x = -\frac{5}{3}$,

$$9x^2 + 30x + 25 = 9\left(\frac{-5}{3}\right)^2 + 30\left(\frac{-5}{3}\right) + 25$$
$$= 9\left(\frac{25}{9}\right) + 10(-5) + 25 = 25 - 50 + 25 = 0$$

In this case, $-\frac{5}{3}$ is a double root.

THE DISCRIMINANT

The expression $b^2 - 4ac$ that occurs under the radical sign in the quadratic formula

$$x = \frac{-b \pm \sqrt{b^2 - 4ac}}{2a}$$

plays an important role in determining the kind of solutions the equation has. This expression, $b^2 - 4ac$, is called the **discriminant** of the equation $ax^2 + bx + c = 0$.

If $b^2 - 4ac = 0$, then the roots are equal; that is, the equation has a double root.

If $b^2 - 4ac = n^2$ (n being an integer other than zero), and if a, b, and c are integers, then the roots are unequal and rational, in which case the quadratic polynomial $ax^2 + bx + c$ can be factored over the integers.

If $b^2 - 4ac$ is positive but not a perfect square, then the roots are unequal and irrational. In other words, the roots involve radicals.

The quadratic equation also has solutions when $b^2 - 4ac$ is negative, but these solutions are not real numbers and are beyond the scope of this text.

EXAMPLE 5 Find the value of the discriminant, $b^2 - 4ac$. State if the roots are equal or unequal, rational or irrational. If the roots are rational, factor the polynomial.

a. $5x^2 - 8x + 2 = 0$ b. $5x^2 + 9x - 2 = 0$ c. $25x^2 - 20x + 4 = 0$

Solution

a. For $5x^2 - 8x + 2 = 0$, $a = 5$, $b = -8$, and $c = 2$

$$b^2 - 4ac = (-8)^2 - 4(10) = 64 - 40 = 24$$

Since 24 is not a perfect square, the roots are irrational and unequal.

b. For $5x^2 + 9x - 2 = 0$, $a = 5$, $b = 9$, and $c = -2$

$$b^2 - 4ac = 9^2 - 4(-10) = 81 + 40 = 121$$

Since $121 = (11)^2$, the roots are rational and unequal.

Factoring, $5x^2 + 9x - 2 = (5x - 1)(x + 2)$

c. For $25x^2 - 20x + 4 = 0$, $a = 25$, $b = -20$, $c = 4$

$$b^2 - 4ac = (-20)^2 - 4(100) = 400 - 400 = 0$$

The roots are rational and equal. Moreover, the polynomial is a perfect square.

$$25x^2 - 20x + 4 = (5x - 2)^2$$

EXERCISES

Solve the equations in Exercises 1–20 by using the quadratic formula. Check each solution.

1. $x^2 - 3x + 1 = 0$
2. $x^2 + 3x + 1 = 0$
3. $2x^2 + 5x + 2 = 0$
4. $x^2 - 5x - 4 = 0$
5. $2x^2 + 5x - 2 = 0$
6. $2x^2 - 5x - 2 = 0$
7. $x^2 + x = 1$
8. $x^2 + 3x = 3$
9. $y^2 - 5y + 5 = 0$
10. $y^2 + 5y + 5 = 0$
11. $z^2 - z - 1 = 0$
12. $3x^2 - 12x + 4 = 0$
13. $3t^2 - 7t - 3 = 0$
14. $2y^2 - 7y + 3 = 0$
15. $4x^2 + 8x + 3 = 0$
16. $2p^2 + 7p - 3 = 0$
17. $4x^2 - 8x - 3 = 0$
18. $10w = w^2 - 100$
19. $5x^2 + 3 = 9x$
20. $r^2 = 10r - 15$

In Exercises 21–40, find the value of the discriminant, $b^2 - 4ac$. State if the roots are equal or unequal, rational or irrational. If the roots are rational, factor the polynomial.

21. $x^2 + 3x + 2 = 0$
22. $x^2 - 3x - 2 = 0$
23. $x^2 + x - 2 = 0$
24. $x^2 + x - 4 = 0$
25. $2x^2 + 13x - 5 = 0$
26. $2x^2 - 3x - 2 = 0$
27. $3x^2 - 7x - 3 = 0$
28. $3x^2 - 12x - 4 = 0$
29. $5x^2 - 9x + 2 = 0$
30. $5x^2 - 9x - 2 = 0$
31. $x^2 + 8x + 12 = 0$
32. $x^2 + 7x + 10 = 0$
33. $4x^2 + 4x + 1 = 0$
34. $x^2 - 10x + 25 = 0$
35. $9x^2 - 12x + 4 = 0$
36. $x^2 + 5x - 24 = 0$
37. $8x^2 + 3x - 1 = 0$
38. $3x^2 - 2x - 8 = 0$
39. $9x^2 - 4 = 0$
40. $14x^2 + 5x = 0$

Use the quadratic formula to solve the equations in Exercises 41–50 for the indicated variable. Treat any letter other than the variable you are solving for as a constant.

41. $x^2 + px + q = 0$; x
42. $x^2 + 2px + q = 0$; x
43. $3x^2 + 8xy - 3y^2 = 0$; x
44. $4x^2 - 6xy + y^2 = 0$; x
45. $W^2 = L(L - W)$; W
46. $W^2 = L(L - W)$; L
47. $P = EI + RI^2$; I
48. $s = (k - s)^2$; s
49. $px^2 + qx + r = 0$; x
50. $am^2 + bm + c = 0$; m

[redacted]

There are many practical applications that involve solving a quadratic equation. When you are solving verbal problems that involve the application of quadratic equations, it is especially important to check each root of the equation in the statement of the problem to see if the necessary conditions are met. Often the equation will have two roots, but only one may apply to a given problem. For example, lengths of sides of rectangles, triangles, and the like are always positive numbers; ages of individuals are positive numbers; digits in a numeral cannot be fractions; and the number of people at a gathering cannot be fractional or negative.

EXAMPLE 1 One leg of a right triangle is one foot longer than the other leg and 8 feet shorter than the hypotenuse. Find the lengths of the sides of the right triangle.

Solution If the lengths of the legs of the triangle are designated by a and b, where b is the shorter leg, and the length of the hypotenuse by c, the following relationships are given:

1. $a^2 + b^2 = c^2$ (Theorem of Pythagoras)
2. $a = c - 8$ (Given)
3. $b = a - 1$ (Given, and the assumption that b is the shorter leg)

From (2) we obtain the equivalent equation $c = a + 8$. Substituting $(a + 8)$ for c and $(a - 1)$ for b in equation (1) yields the equivalent equation

$$a^2 + (a - 1)^2 = (a + 8)^2$$
$$a^2 + a^2 - 2a + 1 = a^2 + 16a + 64$$

4. $a^2 - 18a - 63 = 0$

Equation (4) is a quadratic equation that can be solved by factoring:

$$(a - 21)(a + 3) = 0$$
$$a - 21 = 0 \quad \text{or} \quad a + 3 = 0$$
$$a = 21 \quad \text{or} \quad a = -3$$

Since the verbal problem contains the assumption $a > 0$, we disregard the solution $a = -3$ and accept $a = 21$. From (2) we know that $a = c - 8$; therefore, $c = 29$. From (3) we know that $b = a - 1$; therefore, $b = 20$. The sides of the triangle are 20 feet, 21 feet, and 29 feet.

EXAMPLE 2 An 18-foot pole and a 30-foot pole are 15 feet apart. What length of wire is needed to join the tops of the two poles?

Solution First make a sketch such as the one in Fig. 6.3. Find the lengths of the legs of the right triangle. The length of the hypotenuse determines the length of the wire.

$$x^2 = (15)^2 + (12)^2$$
$$x^2 = 225 + 144$$
$$x^2 = 369$$
$x = 19.2$ feet, correct to the nearest tenth

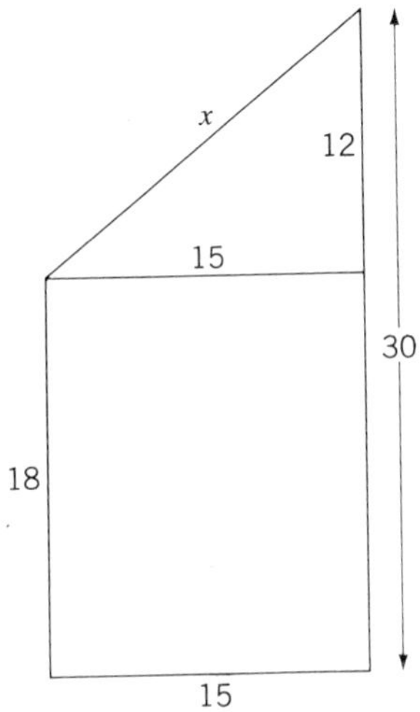

FIG. 6.3

EXAMPLE 3 A square flower bed has a 3-foot walk surrounding it. If the walk were to be replaced and planted with flowers, the new flower bed would have 4 times the area of the original bed. What is the length of one side of the original bed?

Solution

Let x = length of a side of original flower bed

Then x^2 = area of original bed

$x + 6$ = length of a side of new flower bed

and $(x + 6)^2$ = area of new flower bed

$$(x + 6)^2 = 4x^2$$
$$x^2 + 12x + 36 = 4x^2$$
$$3x^2 - 12x - 36 = 0$$
$$3(x^2 - 4x - 12) = 0$$
$$x^2 - 4x - 12 = 0$$
$$(x + 2)(x - 6) = 0$$
$$x + 2 = 0 \quad \text{or} \quad x - 6 = 0$$
$$x = -2 \quad \text{or} \quad x = 6$$

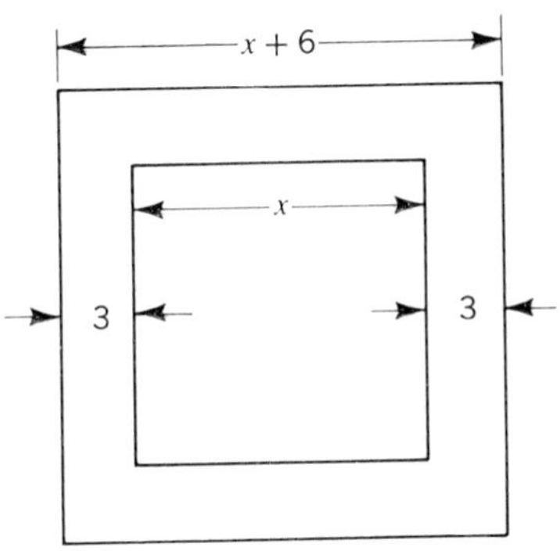

FIG. 6.4

Again we discard the negative answer, and the length of the original side is 6 feet.

Check

Area of original bed $= x^2 = 6^2 = 36$ square feet

Area of new bed $= (x + 6)^2 = (6 + 6)^2 = 12^2$

$= 144$ square feet

Area of new bed = 4 times area of old bed

$$144 = 4 \times 36$$
$$144 = 144$$

EXAMPLE 4 A plane flies 300 miles with a tail wind of 10 mph and returns against a wind of 20 mph. What is the speed of the plane in still air if the total flying time is 4 hours?

Solution Let x represent the speed of the plane in still air.

Then $x + 10 =$ speed with the tail wind

and $x - 20 =$ speed against the wind

Formula	r ·	t =	d
With wind	$x + 10$	$\frac{300}{x + 10}$	300
Against wind	$x - 20$	$\frac{300}{x - 20}$	300

Equation

$$\text{Time going} + \text{time returning} = \text{total time}$$
$$= 4 \text{ hours}$$
$$\frac{300}{x + 10} + \frac{300}{x - 20} = 4$$

Multiplying both sides of this equation by the L.C.M. $(x + 10)(x - 20)$,

$$300(x - 20) + 300(x + 10) = 4(x + 10)(x - 20)$$

Dividing both sides by 4,

$$75(x - 20) + 75(x + 10) = (x + 10)(x - 20)$$
$$150x - 750 = x^2 - 10x - 200$$
$$x^2 - 160x + 550 = 0$$

Solving this equation by completing the square, since the coefficient of x^2 is 1 and since the coefficient of x is even,

$$x^2 - 160x + (-80)^2 = -550 + 6400$$
$$(x - 80)^2 = 5850$$
$$x - 80 = \pm\sqrt{5850}$$
$$= \pm 76.5 \text{ to the nearest tenth}$$

Therefore $x = 80 + 76.5$ or $x = 80 - 76.5$

$x = 156.5$ or $x = 3.5$

Since speed is always a positive number, $x \neq 3.5$, because $x - 20$ would then be a negative number. Therefore, the speed of the plane in still air is 156.5 mph, correct to the nearest tenth.

AL-KHOWARIZMI'S SOLUTION OF A QUADRATIC EQUATION

Around 825 the Arab al-Khowarizmi showed two methods for solving quadratic equations, both based on the geometric methods of the Greeks. To solve $x^2 + 10x = 39$, he drew a square like the one to the right and then gave the solution that follows.

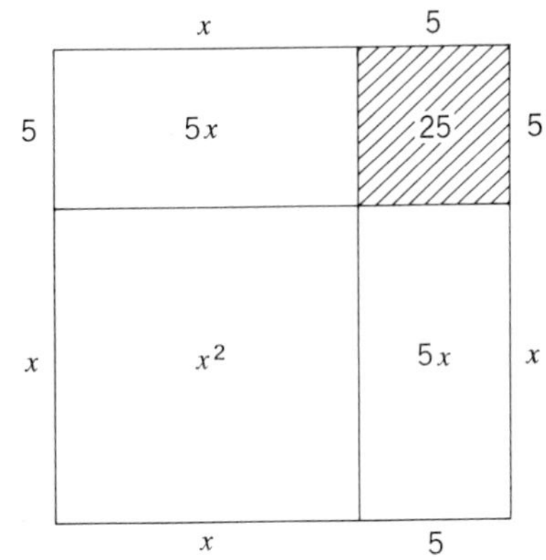

> You halve the number of roots, yielding 5 in this case.
> You multiply this number by itself; the product is 25.
> Add this to 39; the sum is 64.
> Now take the root of this, which is 8.
> From 8 subtract half the number of roots, 5 in this case.
> The remainder is 3.
> Three is the root of the square you wanted; the square itself is 9.

Comparing the solution of $x^2 + 10x = 39$ to the solution of $x^2 + px = q$, that is,

$$\sqrt{\left(\frac{10}{2}\right)^2 + 39} - \frac{10}{3} \quad \text{to} \quad \sqrt{\left(\frac{p}{2}\right)^2 + q} - \frac{p}{2}$$

we note that his method is similar to our "completing the square" method. Note also that the negative solution -13 was ignored.

EXAMPLE 5 Working alone, a carpenter can make a set of cabinets in 3 hours less time than his helper can. Working together, they can make the set of cabinets in 6 hours. Find the time (correct to the nearest minute) that each requires to make the set alone.

Solution Let x = time it takes helper alone
Then $x - 3$ = time it takes carpenter alone

Formulas

$tr = w$, and w of first + w of second = w of both = 1, where t = time, r = rate, and w = amount of work done.

	Working Alone			*Working Together (Whole Job)*		
Formula	t ·	r	= w	t ·	r	= w
Carpenter	$x - 3$	$\frac{1}{x-3}$	1	6	$\frac{1}{x-3}$	$\frac{6}{x-3}$
Helper	x	$\frac{1}{x}$	1	6	$\frac{1}{x}$	$\frac{6}{x}$

Equation

Work of helper + work of carpenter = whole job

$$\frac{6}{x} \quad + \quad \frac{6}{x-3} \quad = \quad 1$$

with restrictions $x > 0$ and $x - 3 > 0$

$$6(x-3) + 6x = x(x-3)$$
$$12x - 18 = x^2 - 3x$$
$$x^2 - 15x + 18 = 0$$

Since $x^2 - 15x + 18$ is not readily factorable, and since $\frac{b}{a} = -15$ is not an even integer, the method using the quadratic formula is recommended for solving the equation.

Solution of equation

$ax^2 + bx + c = 0$ if and only if

$$x = \frac{-b \pm \sqrt{b^2 - 4ac}}{2a}$$

If $x^2 - 15x + 18 = 0$, then $a = 1$, $b = -15$, $c = 18$. Thus

$$x = \frac{-(-15) \pm \sqrt{(-15)^2 - 4(18)}}{2} = \frac{15 \pm \sqrt{225 - 72}}{2}$$

$$x = \frac{15 + \sqrt{153}}{2} \quad \text{or} \quad x = \frac{15 - \sqrt{153}}{2}$$

Approximating (by using the tables), $\sqrt{153} = 12.37$. Thus, approximately to the nearest hundredth,

$$x = \frac{15 + 12.37}{2} \quad \text{or} \quad x = \frac{15 - 12.37}{2}$$

$$x = \frac{27.37}{2} \quad \text{or} \quad x = \frac{2.63}{2}$$

$$x = 13.68 \quad \text{or} \quad x = 1.32$$

and $x - 3 = 10.68$ or $x - 3 = -1.68$. (This solution is rejected, since $x - 3 > 0$.) Thus $x = 13.68$ and $x - 3 = 10.68$ are correct to the nearest hundredth. Since there are 60 minutes in an hour, 0.68 hours = 0.68 (60) minutes = 40.8 minutes. Therefore, correct to the nearest minute,

$x = 13$ hours, 41 minutes, time of helper alone

$x - 3 = 10$ hours, 41 minutes, time of carpenter alone

EXERCISES

Solve the following exercises.

1. The hypotenuse of a right triangle is 3 units and the legs are equal in length. Find the length of a leg of the triangle.

2. The length of a rectangle is 1 inch more than 3 times its width. The area is 52 square inches. Find the dimensions of the rectangle.
3. A certain number exceeds its reciprocal by $\frac{15}{4}$. Find the number.
4. The sum of two numbers is 7 and the difference of their reciprocals is $\frac{1}{12}$. Find the numbers.
5. The roof line of a certain house has a pitch of 3 to 12. This means that for each vertical rise of 3 feet, there is a horizontal run of 12 feet. To find the length of lumber he must cut for the roof, the carpenter has to calculate the length of the hypotenuse of a right triangle whose legs are the height of the roof and the half-span of the roof. Find the length of this hypotenuse, correct to the nearest inch, for this house having a half-span of 13 feet.
6. A concrete walk of uniform width extends around a rectangular lawn having dimensions 20 feet by 80 feet. Find the width of the walk if the area of the walk is 864 square feet.
7. The hypotenuse of a right triangle is 13 inches. If one leg is 7 inches longer than the other, how long are the legs of the triangle?
8. If 4 times a number is added to 3 times its square, the sum is 95. Find the number.
9. Find two consecutive odd integers the sum of whose squares is 514.
10. A 36-inch length of copper tubing is bent to form a right triangle with a 15-inch hypotenuse. Find the lengths of the other two sides of the triangle.
11. A wire is stretched from the top of a 4-foot fence to the top of a 20-foot vertical pole. If the fence and the pole are 30 feet apart, find the length of the wire.
12. One of two outlets can fill a swimming pool in 6 hours. The time for the other outlet to fill the pool is 2 hours longer than the two outlets together. Find the time it takes for the two outlets together to fill the tank, correct to the nearest minute.
13. One inlet pipe takes 12 minutes longer than another inlet pipe to fill a tank. An outlet pipe can empty the tank in 45 minutes. When all three pipes are open, it takes 15 minutes to fill the tank. Find the time it takes to fill the tank if only the larger inlet pipe is open.
14. It takes John 3 hours longer to do a certain job than it does his brother Bob. For 3 hours they worked together; then John left and Bob finished the job in one hour. How many hours would it have taken Bob to do the whole job by himself?
15. A rectangular piece of sheet metal is twice as long as it is wide. From each of its four corners a square piece 2 centimetres on a side is cut out. The flaps are then turned up to form an uncovered metal box. If the volume of this box is 320 cubic centimetres, find the dimensions of the original piece of sheet metal.

16. A fisherman trolled upstream in a motorboat to a spot 6 miles from his campsite and then returned to camp. If the rate of the current was $1\frac{1}{2}$ mph and if the round trip took 3 hours, find the rate of the motorboat in still water.
17. A jet plane flying against a head wind of 20 mph takes 20 minutes longer to fly a distance of 2610 miles than a plane with the same still air speed flying in the opposite direction. Find the still air speed of the plane.
18. A boat that travels 12 mph in still water takes 2 hours less time to go 45 miles downstream than to return the same distance upstream. Find the rate of the current.
19. A baseball diamond has the shape of a square with each side 90 feet long. The pitcher's mound is 60.5 feet from home plate on the line joining home plate to second base. Find the distance from the pitcher's mound to second base.
20. The bending moment M of a beam fixed at one end and simply supported at the other is related to its length L, its uniform load distribution w, and the distance x from the fixed end by the relation

$$M = \frac{-w}{8}(4x^2 - 5Lx + L^2)$$

A certain beam has a length L of 12 feet and a uniform load distribution w of 100 pounds per foot.

a. For what position x on the beam is the bending moment zero?

b. For what position x on the beam is the bending moment 100 foot-pounds?

REVIEW EXERCISES

Approximate the square roots for Exercises 1–8 correct to the nearest hundredth.

1. $\sqrt{27}$
2. $\sqrt{39}$
3. $(\sqrt{14})^2$
4. $\sqrt{14^2}$
5. $\sqrt{87}$
6. $-\sqrt{44}$
7. $-\sqrt{8^2}$
8. $\sqrt{(-8)^2}$

Write the radicals for Exercises 9–20 in simplest form.

9. $\sqrt{5}\sqrt{20}$
10. $\sqrt{20}$
11. $\sqrt{160}$
12. $\sqrt{500}$
13. $\sqrt{20} - \sqrt{45}$
14. $\sqrt{28} + 2\sqrt{63}$

15. $\dfrac{24-10\sqrt{8}}{6}$

16. $\dfrac{14+\sqrt{60}}{4}$

17. $\dfrac{-8-\sqrt{56}}{8}$

18. $(3+2\sqrt{5})^2$

19. $(2-3\sqrt{7})^2$

20. $\sqrt{5}(\sqrt{10}-\sqrt{5}-\sqrt{45})$

Solve the equations in Exercises 21–26 by completing the square.

21. $x^2+2x-1=0$
22. $2x^2+3x-1=0$
23. $x^2-1=4x$
24. $x^2-6=4x$
25. $5x^2+6x=1$
26. $6x^2-10x=3$

Solve the equations in Exercises 27–40 either by factoring or by using the quadratic formula. Use the discriminant to see if the polynomial can be factored.

27. $3x^2+6x+2=0$
28. $3x^2-6x+2=0$
29. $(2x-3)(x+2)=0$
30. $(3x+4)(2x-1)=0$
31. $(x-4)(x+2)=4$
32. $(2x+1)(x-5)=12$
33. $(2y-5)^2=4$
34. $(3y+2)^2=6$
35. $2x^2-5x-6=0$
36. $3x^2=4x+3$
37. $12z^2=48z$
38. $a^2+18a+81=0$
39. $6x^2-10x+2=0$
40. $9x^2=2(3x+1)$

41. John can mow his lawn in 20 minutes less time with his power mower than with his hand mower. One day his power mower broke down 15 minutes after he started mowing, and he had to complete the job with his hand mower. It took him 25 minutes to finish mowing by hand. How long does it take John to do the complete job with the power mower?
42. Find a number whose square is equal to the number itself.
43. The sum of the reciprocals of two consecutive numbers is $\frac{11}{30}$. Find the numbers.
44. The perimeter of a rectangle is 36 feet and its area is 45 square feet. Find the dimensions of the rectangle.
45. A pilot left a Chicago airport and flew 200 miles south to a town T with a tail wind of 20 mph. From T he flew back to Chicago against a head wind of 30 mph. If his total flying time was $2\frac{1}{3}$ hours, what was the average speed of the plane in still air?
46. One leg of a right triangle is 9 inches longer than the other leg. The hypotenuse is 45 inches long. Find the lengths of the legs of the triangle.
47. The height H of a projectile at the end of t seconds is given by
$$H=cvt-\frac{1}{2}gt^2$$
Solve for t.
48. The total surface area T of a right circular cylinder of radius r and height h is given by $T=2\pi r(r+h)$. Solve for r.

A

ANSWERS

EXERCISES FOR SECTION 1.1, PP. 8–9

1. 24
3. 2
5. 15
7. 8
9. 25
11. 64
13. 9
15. 49
17. 729
19. 23
21. 6
23. 200
25. 11
27. 0
29. 20
31. 5
33. 100
35. 5
37. 216
39. 13
41. $x + 8$
43. n^2
45. $y - 4$
47. $n - m$
49. c^2
51. $x + y$
53. $y - x$
55. $(25)(45)$
57. $\sqrt[3]{7 - p}$
59. $t^3\sqrt[3]{s}$
61. $r + s$
63. $\sqrt{m}$
65. $7 - x$
67. ab^2
69. p^2q
71. $(15)(5)$
73. $x - 10$
75. $\sqrt[3]{x}$
77. $x - 8$
79. $\dfrac{8}{x}$

EXERCISES FOR SECTION 1.2, PP. 13–14

1. {18, 20, 22, 24}
3. {57, 59, 61}
5. {30, 33, 36, 39, 42, 45, 48}
7. {10, 20, 30, 40, 50, 60, 70, 80, 90}
9. {1, 2, 4, 7, 14, 28}
11. {1, 2, 3, 5, 6, 10, 15, 30}
13. {1, 2, 5, 10, 25, 50}
15. {2, 3, 5, 7, 11, 13, 17, 19}
17. {53, 59, 61, 67, 71, 73, 79}
19. {20, 21, 22, 24, 25, 26}
21. {2, 7}
23. {2, 3, 5}
25. {2, 5}
27. {2, 4, 6, 12, 18, 36}
29. {1}
31. $\varnothing$
33. {15, 30, 45}

35. $\{36, 72, 108, 144, 180\}$
37. $\{1, 2, 3, 6\}$
39. $3 \cdot 5$
41. $2 \cdot 3^2$
43. $2 \cdot 3 \cdot 11$
45. $2 \cdot 3 \cdot 13$
47. $2 \cdot 7^2$
49. true
51. false; the set of factors of 39 is $\{1, 3, 13, 39\}$
53. true
55. true

EXERCISES FOR SECTION 1.3, PP. 18–19

1. 15
3. 15
5. 12
7. 60
9. 30
11. 12
13. 3
15. 2
17. 20
19. 6
21. 52
23. 50
25. 2
27. 7
29. 9
31. 22
33. 4
35. 73
37. 16
39. 2
41. 200
43. 50
45. 120
47. 1
49. 8
51. $x + 2y$
53. $2xy$
55. $y - (x + 3)$
57. $(y + 2)^2 - 7$
59. $3x + y$
61. $\frac{a + 7}{7a}$
63. $\sqrt{x^2 - 5^2}$
65. $(4^2 - 3^2) - 2^2 - 1$

EXERCISES FOR SECTION 1.4, PP. 22–25

1. 74
3. 180
5. 0
7. 12
9. 180
11. 45
13. 120
15. 64
17. 34
19. 25
21. 196
23. 2
25. 213
27. 19
29. 19
31. 125
33. 4
35. 19
37. 122
39. 240
41. 49
43. 14
45. 60
47. 4
49. 45
51. 180 sq. ft.
53. 63 sq. in.
55. 120
57. 100 degrees
59. $740
61. 44.1 metres
63. $\frac{4}{81}$ or 0.05
65. 75

EXERCISES FOR SECTION 1.5, PP. 30–33

1. positive
3. signed
5. signed
7. positive
9. signed
11. signed
13. positive
15. signed
17. positive
19. signed
21. 35° south latitude
23. 20° below 0°*F*
25. force of 20 lb. away
27. loss of 150 BTU
29. clockwise rotation of 40°
31. 80° west longitude
33. 70 ft. below sea level
35. 15 mph north wind
37. 6 steps downward
39. 35 pounds underweight
41. 3
43. -4
45. 4
47. 1
49. -5
51. 5

53. −4

55. $-2\frac{1}{2}$

57. −2

59. 2

61

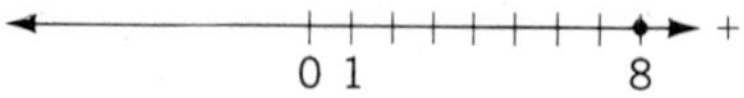

63

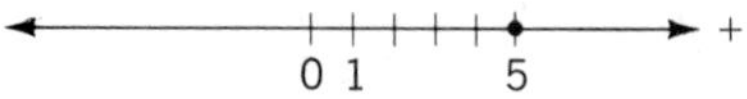

65

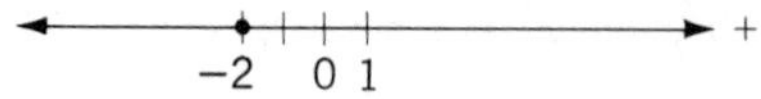

67

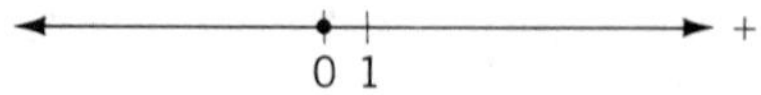

69

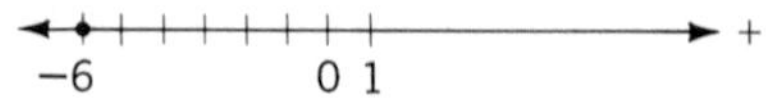

71

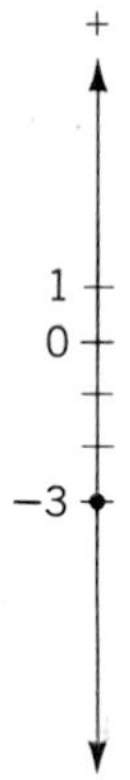

73

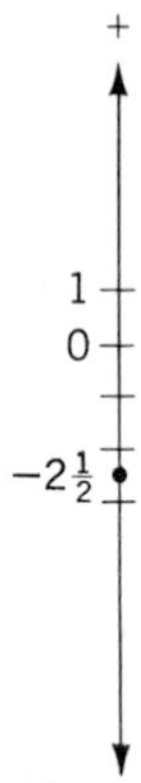

75

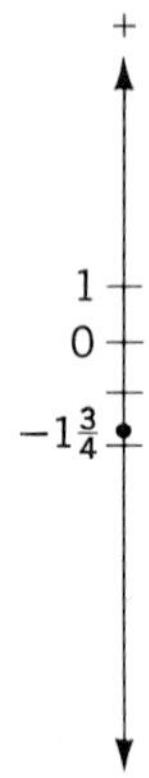

77

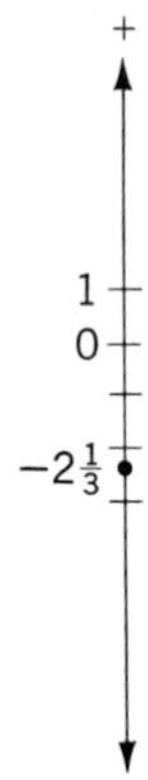

79

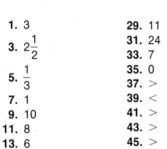

EXERCISES FOR SECTION 1.6, PP. 37–38

1. 3

3. $2\frac{1}{2}$

5. $\frac{1}{3}$

7. 1

9. 10

11. 8

13. 6

15. 0

17. −5

19. 12

21. 2

23. 0

25. $1\frac{3}{4}$

27. 12

29. 11

31. 24

33. 7

35. 0

37. $>$

39. $<$

41. $>$

43. $>$

45. $>$

47. $<$

49. $<$

51. $=$

53. $<$

55. $>$

57. $>$

59. $>$

61. $<$

63

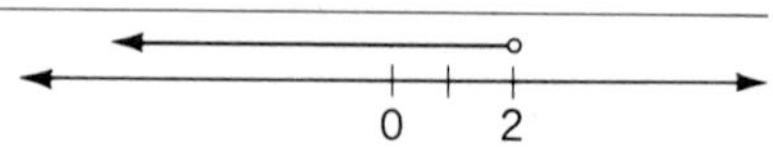

65

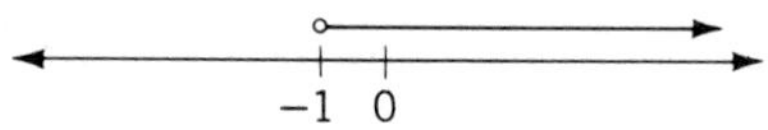

67

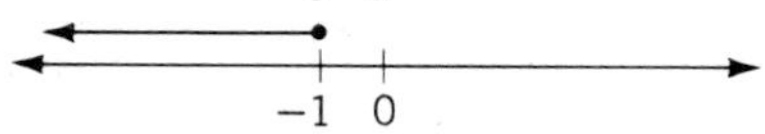

69

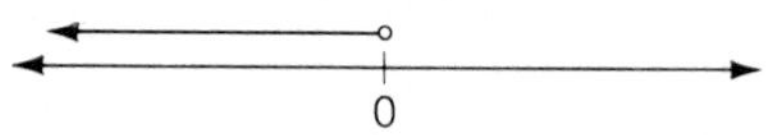

71

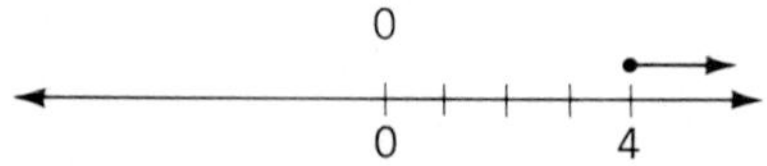

73

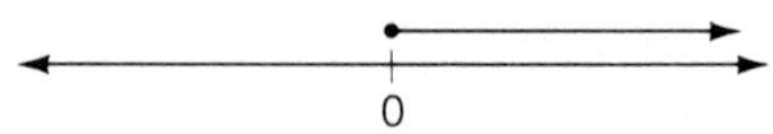

75

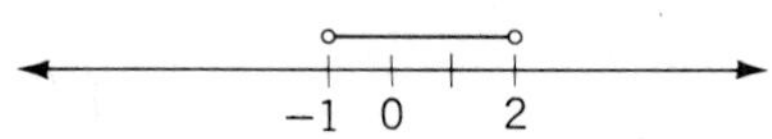

77

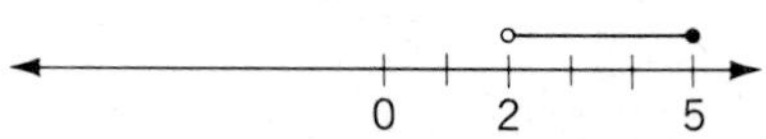

79

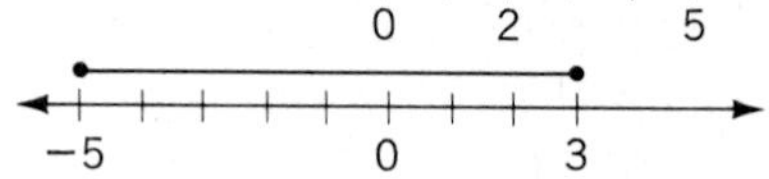

EXERCISES FOR SECTION 1.7, PP. 40–42

1. 11
3. 5
5. −5
7. −30
9. 5
11. 15
13. −1
15. 0
17. −15
19. −100
21. −20
23. 70
25. −9
27. 0
29. −4
31. −10
33. −40
35. −7
37. −12
39. −15
41. −20
43. −4
45. −27
47. −1
49. 0
51. $404
53. 66 kg
55. 50 mph
57. −5, (5 cm below 0)
59. −1
61. 1
63. a. $c = 4$ b. $N = -3$
c. $Al = 3$

EXERCISES FOR SECTION 1.8, PP. 44–46

1. 6
3. 14
5. 6
7. −7
9. −6
11. 1
13. 35
15. 0
17. 14
19. 3
21. 4
23. 10
25. −10
27. 0
29. −14
31. −28
33. 10
35. −2
37. 7
39. −23
41. −9
43. −10
45. 59
47. 46
49. 50
51. 15
53. −9
55. 35
57. −5
59. −9
61. 6 degrees
63. 9 degrees
65. 5 degrees
67. 51 degrees
69. 6 degrees
71. 19,757 ft.
73. 154 ft.
75. 30,320 ft.
77. 250 years
79. 925 − 1 = 924 years

EXERCISES FOR SECTION 1.9, PP. 50–51

1. 35
3. 35
5. 16
7. −1000
9. −1000
11. 1000
13. −88
15. 1225
17. −250
19. 0
21. 0
23. 90
25. −700
27. 100
29. −36
31. −48
33. −54
35. −125
37. −32
39. −686
41. −15
43. 0
45. −36
47. 24
49. 32
51. −40
53. 35
55. 16
57. 1000
59. −6
61. 3000
63. −560
65. 7500
67. −3
69. 1
71. $\frac{-88}{10{,}000{,}000} = \frac{-11}{1{,}250{,}000}$
73. $\frac{-12}{1{,}000{,}000{,}000} = \frac{-3}{250{,}000{,}000}$
75. $\frac{-99}{100{,}000{,}000}$

EXERCISES FOR SECTION 1.10, PP. 53–55

1. 7
3. −7
5. −8
7. −20
9. undefined
11. −8
13. −3
15. 3
17. 0
19. −7
21. 5
23. −7
25. −11
27. 25
29. 5
31. 0
33. −1
35. −60
37. −10
39. −1
41. 6
43. −2
45. −1
47. −5
49. 5
51. −5
53. −3
55. undefined
57. −4
59. −27
61. −20
63. −1
65. −2
67. −2
69. 75
71. $\frac{5}{16}$
73. −9
75. 14
77. −4
79. 1

EXERCISES FOR SECTION 1.11, PP. 57–59

1. 0
3. −4
5. 4
7. 6
9. 10
11. 2
13. −6
15. 30
17. 0
19. −4
21. −40
23. 46
25. 0
27. −7
29. 9
31. 7
33. 35
35. −4
37. 4
39. −2
41. $\frac{45}{2}$
43. −22
45. 28
47. −20 degrees
49. 25
51. 60 centimetres
53. (a) 6 (b) −50 (c) 575 (d) −20 (e) 340
55. (a) $-843\frac{3}{4}$ (b) 300
57. −2.5

REVIEW EXERCISES FOR CHAPTER 1, PP. 60–61

1. 12
2. 6
3. −24
4. −4
5. −7
6. −25
7. 0
8. undefined
9. −1
10. −4
11. $x + y$
12. xy
13. $5x - 4$
14. $\frac{2ab}{a + b}$
15. $\sqrt{x} + x^2$
16. $6x > 12$
17. $\frac{r}{7} \le 4$
18. $2(x + 7) < 7x$

19. $9 + 6x \geq 8$
21. a. 14 b. -6 c. 24
23. a. 6 b. 4 c. -1
25. a. 5 b. -2 c. -3
27. a. -56 b. 0 c. 20
29. a. 9 b. 1
31. a. 700 b. -24
33. true
35. true
37. true
39. false
41. true

43
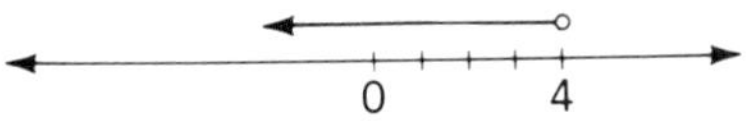

45
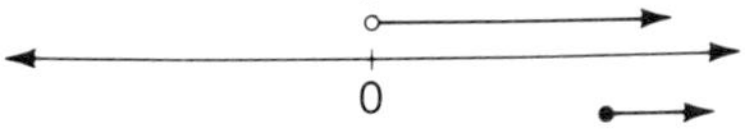

47
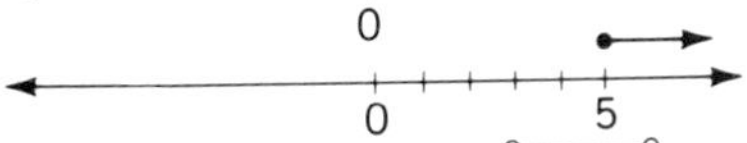

49
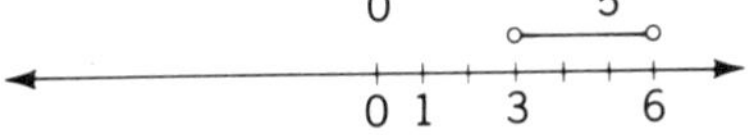

51
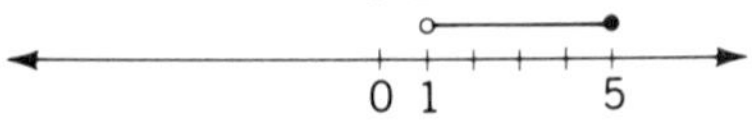

53. $-\frac{1}{2}$
55. 80

20. $\sqrt{x + y} < y^2$
22. a. -16 b. 0 c. -1
24. a. 9 b. -7 c. -15
26. a. 12 b. -4 c. 36
28. a. 13 b. -29
30. a. -25 b. -10
32. a. -4 b. $\frac{-4}{3}$
34. false
36. true
38. false
40. true
42. true

44
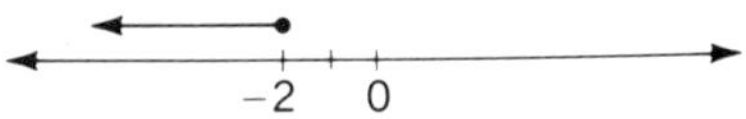

46
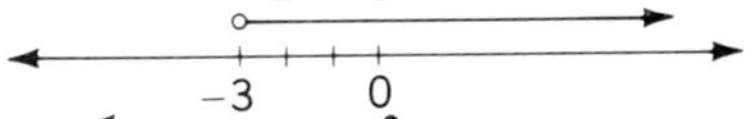

48
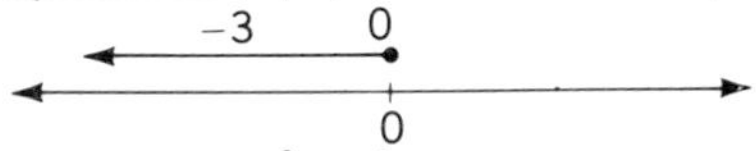

50
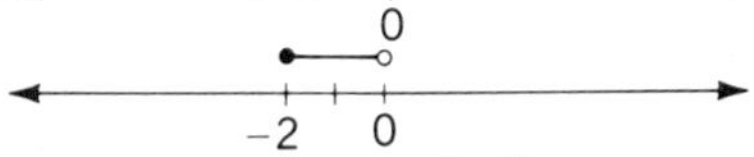

52
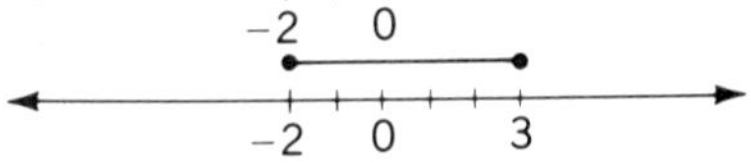

54. -550
56. $\frac{1}{2}$

EXERCISES FOR SECTION 2.1, PP. 67–68

1. $x + y + 4$
3. $-x$
5. $36x^2y^2$
7. $2ab - 4$
9. $m + n - 7$
11. $-15x^2$
13. $x + y - 9$
15. 3
17. $24abc$
19. $-abcn^3$
21. $2x + 10$
23. $5n - 35$
25. $-x + 5$
27. $y - 6$
29. $-x + 3y$
31. $6ay - 3by$
33. $x - y - 5$
35. $a - 2b + 2c - 6$
37. $3a - 6b + 4x + 8y$
39. $4x^3 - 4x^2 - x + 1$
41. $5x$
43. x
45. $-2xy$
47. $2x + 5$
49. $-7t + 6$
51. $3z^2 + 5z + 4$
53. $6x^2 + 7xy - 10y^2$
55. $3z^2 + 2z$
57. $x^2 - x + 5$
59. $-x + 6$
61. $5s + t$
63. $3x^2 - xy - 10y^2$
65. $9x^2 - 16y^2$
67. $3x + 1$
69. $3x^2 - 3x + 3$
71. $8x + 8y$
73. $a - b$
75. $2xy - 12x + 15y$
77. $k - 4$
79. $4x + 5$
81. $4y^2 - 8y + 9$
83. $3x + 3y$
85. $4y$
87. $-24y$
89. $-x - 6$
91. $11k - 4$
93. $-3m + 12n$
95. $5x - 8$

EXERCISES FOR SECTION 2.2, PP. 76–77

1. 2
3. −2
5. −7
7. 7
9. −7
11. −1
13. −26
15. 3
17. −2
19. 2
21. −2
23. 3
25. −2
27. −2
29. −7
31. 4
33. ∅
35. 1
37. −8
39. 8
41. 2
43. 20
45. 5
47. R (identity)
49. 11
51. −8
53. R (identity)
55. 1
57. −3
59. ∅

EXERCISES FOR SECTION 2.3, P. 80

1. −5
3. 1
5. −3
7. 10
9. 4
11. ∅
13. −1
15. 1
17. 9
19. R
21. 4
23. −5
25. −8
27. −2
29. 2
31. 2
33. 5
35. R
37. 2
39. 24
41. ∅
43. 7
45. −2
47. 2
49. R
51. 3
53. ∅
55. −6
57. 7
59. 2

EXERCISES FOR SECTION 2.4, PP. 82–83

1. $x > 2$

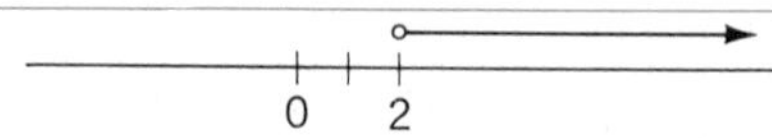

3. $x > 3$

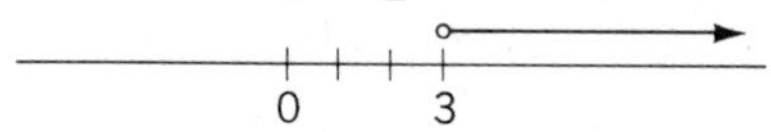

5. $x < -6$

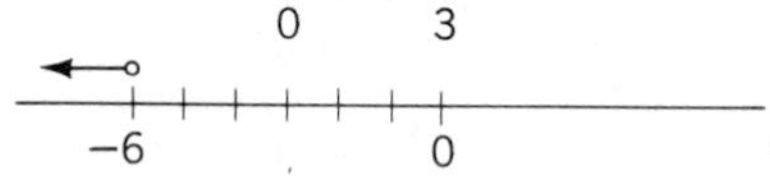

7. $x \geq 2$

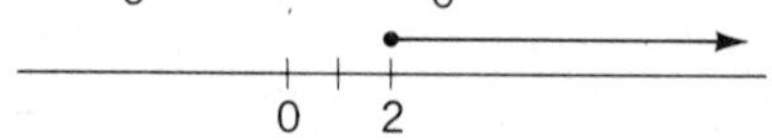

9. $x \leq 5$

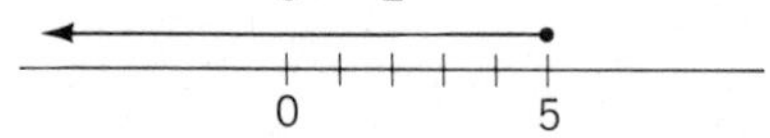

11. $x > -1$

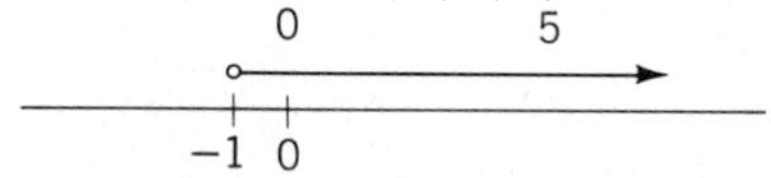

13. $x < -3$

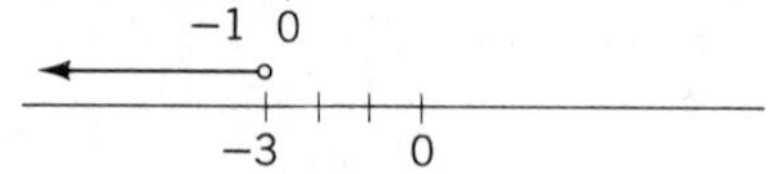

15. R, the set of all real numbers

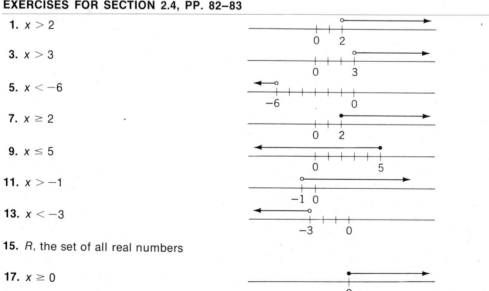

17. $x \geq 0$

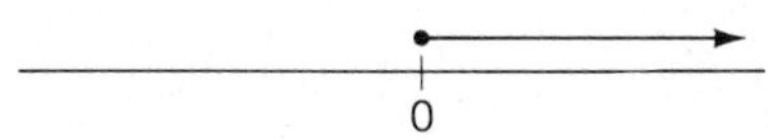

19. $x \leq -1$

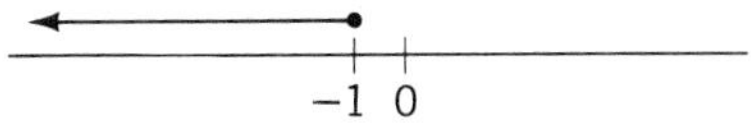

21. $x \geq 3$

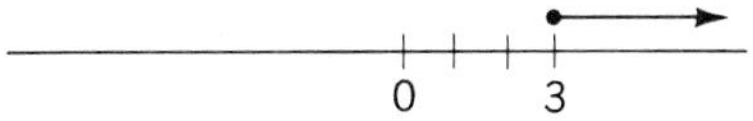

23. $x \leq 12$

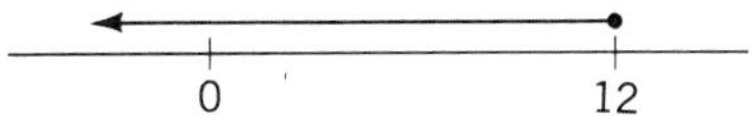

25. $x \geq -3$

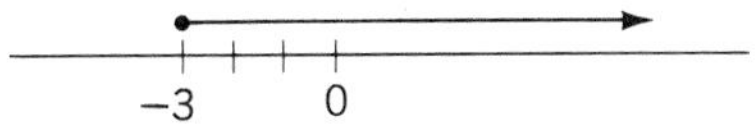

27. $x > 8$

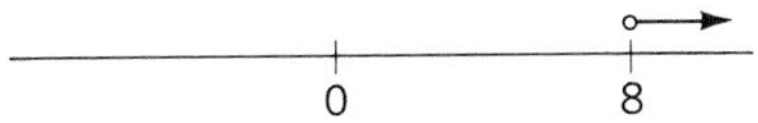

29. $x > 46$

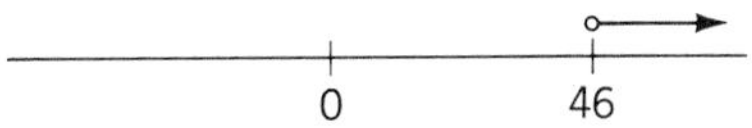

31. $x < 0$

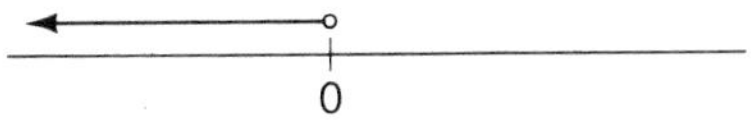

33. $\varnothing$

35. $x < 2$

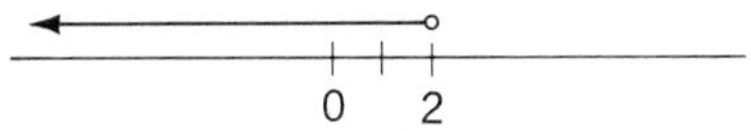

37. $x < 2$

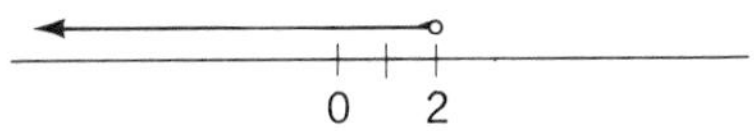

39. R, the set of all real numbers

EXERCISES FOR SECTION 2.5, PP. 85–87

1. $L = \dfrac{A}{W}$

3. $h = \dfrac{V}{\pi r^2}$

5. $t = \dfrac{D}{r}$

7. $h = \dfrac{2A}{b}$

9. $r = \dfrac{A - P}{Pt}$

11. $r = \dfrac{C}{2\pi}$

13. $s = \dfrac{A - a^2}{2a}$

15. $C = \dfrac{5}{9}(F - 32)$

17. $B = 180 - A - C$

19. $n = \dfrac{D}{A} + 1$

21. $C = \dfrac{100M}{Q}$

23. $n = \dfrac{C - S}{R}$

25. $d = \dfrac{SD}{s}$

27. $t = \dfrac{pvT}{PV}$

29. $p = \dfrac{PVt}{vT}$

31. $W = \dfrac{CL}{100}$

33. $a = \dfrac{r}{c} - x$

35. $A = \dfrac{C(y + 12)}{y}$

37. $f = \dfrac{s - ps}{p}$

39. $G = E - \dfrac{rE}{R}$

41. $y = 8 - x$

43. $y = 3x - 6$

45. $x = 9 + 2y$

47. $x = 2y + 4$

49. $x = \dfrac{7y + 8}{2}$

51. $y = 10 + 5x$

53. $x = 12 - 4y$

55. $x = -y - 1$

57. $y = \dfrac{6 - 3x}{2}$

59. $y = \dfrac{-ax - c}{b}$

EXERCISES FOR SECTION 2.6, PP. 91–92

1. $2(x+5) = 13 + x;\ x = 3$

3. $4x - 24 = 5x - 18;\ x = -6$

5. $5x - 2x = x + 16;\ x = 8$

7. $(x+6) + (3+2x) + \frac{x}{2} = 100$
$x = 26$
$x + 6 = 32$ singles
$3 + 2x = 55$ doubles
$\frac{x}{2} = 13$ twins

9. $x + (2x-6) + (x+9) + (x-3) = 460$
$x = 92$ French
$2x - 6 = 178$ Spanish
$x + 9 = 101$ Swahili
$x - 3 = 89$ Japanese

11. $2(x+4) = 3x - 14$
26 to 22

13. $x - 1,\ x + 1$

15. $x + (x+1) + (x+2) = 42$
13, 14, 15

17. $2(x+4) + 3x = 73$
13, 15, 17

19. $x + 6 = 2x - 5$
11, 13, 15, 17

21. $\frac{x + (x+2) + (x+4) + (x+6)}{4} = -1$
$-4, -2, 0, 2$

23. $\frac{x + (x+2) + (x+4) + (x+6) + (x+8) + (x+10)}{6} = -9$
$-14, -12, -10, -8, -6, -4$

25. $2x - 5 = 3(x-5)$
barn: 20 years
farmhouse: 10 years

27. John's age now $= x$ years
Sister's age now $= x - 3$
Father's age now $= x + 28$
$(x + 28 - 5) = 2[(x-5) + (x-3-5)] + 1$
John: 16 years
Sister: 13 years
Father: 44 years

29. age of building now $= x$ years
$x + 12 = 2x$
$x = 12;\ 3(12) = 36$
$12 + y = 36$
$y = 24$
in 24 years

EXERCISES FOR SECTION 2.7, PP. 95–97

1. $2x + 2(x-8) = 96$
28 cm by 20 cm

3. $16x = 64$
4 ft.

5. $2x + 2(2x-2) = 29$
9 ft. by $5\frac{1}{2}$ ft.

7. $2(12+2x) + 2(18+2x) = 84$
3 in.

9. $10x + 10(x + 1) + 10(x + 2) = 180$
   50 degrees, 60 degrees, 70 degrees
11. $60(70) + 60x + 70x = 5240$
   $x = 8$, $x^2 = 64$ (answer)
13. $x + 2(2x - 5) = 180$
   38 degrees, 71 degrees, 71 degrees
15. $x(x + 1) = x(x - 1) + 6$
   3 ft., 2 ft.
17. $5(9 - 2x) = 40$
   $\frac{1}{2}$ in.
19. $(w + 20)(w - 10) = w(w + 5)$
   125 ft.

EXERCISES FOR SECTION 2.8, PP. 100–102

1. $40x + 35(300) = 37(x + 300)$
   200 litres
3. $100d + 10(50d) + 25(10d + 60) = 10{,}000$
   10 dollars, 500 dimes, 160 quarters
5. $280(45) + 360x = 300(45 + x)$
   15 pounds of rare coffee
7. $12x + 7(36 - x) = 322$
   14 donuts at 12 cents
   22 donuts at 7 cents
9. $4a + 3(a + 4) + 2(a + 3) = 45$
   3 units of A, 7 units of B, 6 units of C
   $\text{GPA} = \frac{45}{16} \approx 2.81$
11. $0.0825(5000 - x) = 0.06x + 156$
   \$1800 at 6 percent
   \$3200 at $8\frac{1}{4}$ percent
13. $0.10x + 0.07(7500 - x) = 0.08(7500)$
   \$2500 in stocks
15. $x + 0.40x + 0.65(0.40x) = 3071$
   state pays \$1850
   county pays \$740
   city pays \$481
17. $6 + 2x = 1.5(6 + x)$
   6 grams of double strength
19. $0.75(100 - x) = 0.30(100)$
   60 litres

EXERCISES FOR SECTION 2.9, PP. 103–105

1. $55x + 50x = 210$
   2 hr.
3. $3x + 3(x + 15) = 465$
   70 mph
5. $4x = 5(x - 100)$
   500 kph
7. rate of faster car $= \frac{585}{6.5} = 90$ kph
   rate of slower car $= 75$ kph
   $75x = 630$
   $x = 8.4$ hr. $= 8$ hr. 24 min.
9. $3x + 3(x + 80) = 2190$
   325 mph, 405 mph
11. $60x = 0.5 + 40x$
   $1\frac{1}{2}$ minutes
13. $5x + 5(x + 20) = 520$
   42 mph, 62 mph
15. $30x = 20(6 - x)$
   72 miles
17. $4x = 3(x + 15)$
   45 mph
19. $95x = 35(x + 6)$
   332.5 miles

REVIEW EXERCISES FOR CHAPTER 2, PP. 105–107

1. 5
2. 5
3. -7
4. $\varnothing$
5. -2
6. 2
7. 4
8. 4
9. -5
10. 6
11. -12
12. 1
13. -5
14. $\frac{3}{2}$
15. 8
16. 6
17. -7
18. 4
19. 1
20. $\varnothing$
21. R
22. 4
23. $\frac{1}{2}$
24. -2
25. -5
26. 5
27. -3
28. 7
29. $\varnothing$
30. 3
31. 0
32. -9
33. 2
34. -3
35. R
36. -5
37. 3
38. -5
39. 2
40. 4
41. $y = 3x - 5$
42. $x = \frac{5 + y}{3}$
43. $y = -2x - 5$
44. $x = \frac{-y - 5}{2}$
45. $x = \frac{10 + 2y}{5}$
46. $y = \frac{5x - 10}{2}$
47. $x = \frac{y - 2}{3}$
48. $y = \frac{x - 2}{3}$
49. $y = \frac{c - ax}{b}$
50. $x = \frac{c - by}{a}$
51. $d = \frac{C}{\pi}$
52. $t = \frac{A - P}{Pr}$
53. $y = P - x - z$
54. $b = \frac{S - 2a}{2}$
55. $t = \frac{RT - g}{R}$
56. $d = \frac{M - n^2}{2n}$
57. $A = 30 - 2B$
58. $H = \frac{W + 190}{5}$
59. $B = \frac{20 - A + 3C}{2}$
60. $C = \frac{A + 2B - 20}{3}$

61. $6 + 2x = 5(x - 3)$; 7

62. $3(2x - 15) - 3x = 135$; bus, 60 kph; train, 105 kph

63. $x + 0.4(18) = 0.5(x + 18)$; 3.6 grams

64. $2x + 2(2x - 2) = 50$; $x = 9$; $\frac{3(9)(16)}{400} = 1.08$ gallons

65. $29x + 25(2x) + 10(2x - 1) = 221$;
$2\frac{1}{3}$ pounds peaches, $4\frac{2}{3}$ pounds plums, $3\frac{2}{3}$ pounds bananas

66. $\frac{1}{2}x(x + 11) - 2310 = \frac{1}{2}x(x - 10)$; $x = 220$ ft.

67. $x + (x + 3) + \frac{x}{2} + 17 = 70$; 20 years

68. $1.5(2x + 5 - 40) = 28.5$; 27 kg, 32 kg

69. $65x + 50(x + 1) = 280$; $x = 2$ hours, 2 hours after 11 a.m. = 1 p.m.

70. $x > -4$

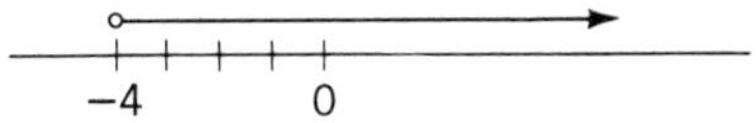

71. $x \geq 5$

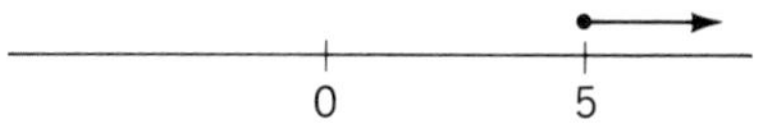

72. $x \geq 3$

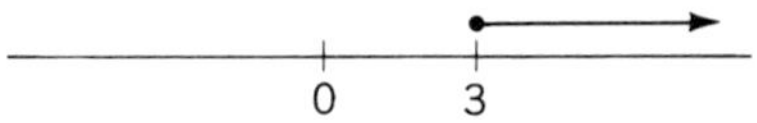

73. true for all real numbers

74. $\varnothing$

75. $x \geq -\frac{1}{2}$

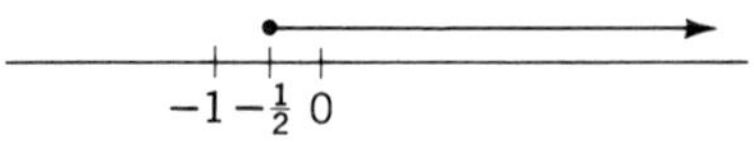

EXERCISES FOR SECTION 3.1, PP. 111–112

1. z^7
3. $12x^6$
5. x^5
7. $6y^6$
9. $-6x^6$
11. $2y^8$
13. $-24x^5$
15. $-a^6$
17. $-15x^7$
19. $24a^2b^2$
21. $-z^6$
23. $15x^3yz$
25. x^8
27. x^6
29. $5z^6$
31. y^{12}
33. xy^{11}
35. $-x^6$
37. ab^{21}
39. $-y^4$
41. $2^5 = 32$
43. $2^6 = 64$
45. $3^6 = 729$
47. $(-2)^6 = 64$
49. $4^3 = 64$
51. $3^3 = 27$
53. $4^2 = (2^2)^2 = 2^4$; $2^7 = 128$
55. x^{3+a}
57. x^{ab}
59. x^{m+2}
61. x^{3n}
63. $x^{n+1}y^{m+2n}$
65. $x^{b+1}y^2$
67. t^{2n-1}
69. y^{2pq}
71. $r^{k+1}t^{2k}$
73. $x^{2n}y^{2n}$

EXERCISES FOR SECTION 3.2, PP. 115–116

1. $7x^2 + 5x + 1$
3. $x^3 + x^2 + 5x + 1$
5. $2x^2 + 3x + z$
7. $5a$
9. $-6a + 13$
11. $a - 2b - 2c$
13. -1
15. $14a - 7b$
17. $25x^4 - 19x^2 - 6x$
19. $-3x^2 + 3y^2$
21. $4x^2 + 1$; $107 + (-2) + 40 = 145$
23. $2t - 9$; $(-45) - (-46) = 10 - 9 = 1$
25. $x^3 - 2x^2 - 2x - 1$; $(-7) + 2 = -5$
27. $-a^2 - 3ab + 4b^2$
29. $a + 5b - c$; $(-6) - (-18) = 12$
31. $-5x^2 - 2x + 10$; $(-1) - (-4) = 3$
33. $6x^4 + x^3 - x^2 + 21x - 6$
35. $-3x^4 + 11x^3 - 11x^2 + x - 1$
37. $-2a^3 + 3b^3 + a^2b - 4ab^2$
39. $3x^3 - 10x^2y - 2xy^2 + y^3 + 4$

EXERCISES FOR SECTION 3.3, PP. 117–118

1. $x^2 - 4x$
3. $3x^3 - x^2$
5. $3a^3 + a^2 + 2a$
7. $2x^3y^3 - 4x^2y^3 + 2xy^4$
9. $-3y^4 + xy^3 - 2x^2y^2$
11. $-6z^5 + 12z^4 - 3z^3 + 9z^2$
13. $3x^5y - 2x^4y^2 + x^3y^3 - x^2y^4$
15. $x^2 + 8x + 15$
17. $x^2 - 2x - 15$
19. $10x^2 + 9x + 2$
21. $10x^2 - x - 2$
23. $20x^2 - 17x + 3$
25. $2x^2 + 7x - 15$
27. $2x^2 - 7x - 15$
29. $x^4 - 2x^2 - 15$
31. $6x^4 - 13x^2 + 6$
33. $x^3 + 3x^2 + 2x$
35. $6x^3 + x^2 - x$
37. $2x^3 + 9x^2 + 10x + 3$
39. $6x^3 - 5x^2 + 3x - 1$
41. $x^2 + 4x + 4$
43. $x^2 - 9$
45. $25x^2 - 49$
47. $x^4 - 4$
49. $x^3 + 6x^2 + 9x$
51. $2x^5 - 98x$
53. $-100x^3y + 9xy^3$
55. $y^3 - 15y^2 + 75y - 125$
57. $x^3 - 216$
59. $x^4 - y^4$
61. $a^3b^3 + 3a^2b^2 + 3ab + 1$
63. $a^2 - 2ab + b^2 - 16$
65. $x^2 + 2xy + y^2 - z^2 - 6z - 9$
67. $a^2 + b^2 + c^2 - 2ab + 2ac - 2bc$
69. $y^{3n} + y^{2n} - y^n - 1$
71. $x^{2a+1} + x^{a+1} + x$
73. $x^{3n} - 4x^n - 3$
75. $x^{2a} + 6x^a + 9$

EXERCISES FOR SECTION 3.4, PP. 120–121

1. $x^2 + 4x + 4$
3. $x^2 - 4x + 4$
5. $x^2 + 8x + 16$
7. $9x^2 + 6x + 1$
9. $4x^2 - 12x + 9$
11. $16x^2 + 40x + 25$
13. $9 - 6x + x^2$
15. $4 + 28x + 49x^2$
17. $16 + 24a + 9a^2$
19. $x^2 + 2xy + y^2$
21. $4x^2 + 20xy + 25y^2$
23. $4x^2 - 20xy + 25y^2$
25. $x^3 + 9x^2 + 27x + 27$
27. $x^3 - 9x^2 + 27x - 27$
29. $8a^3 + 60a^2 + 150a + 125$
31. $729 + 486y + 108y^2 + 8y^3$
33. $y^2 - 1$
35. $9x^2 - 4$
37. $16a^2 - 25b^2$
39. $4x^4 - 9$
41. $x^4 + 2x^2 + 1$
43. $x^6 + 3x^4 + 3x^2 + 1$
45. $x^3 + 6x^2y + 12xy^2 + 8y^3$
47. $x^4 - y^4$
49. $x^6 + 3x^4y^2 + 3x^2y^4 + y^6$

EXERCISES FOR SECTION 3.5, P. 124

1. $4(x + 3)$
3. $3(2x - 1)$
5. $3(x^2 + 2x + 3)$
7. $4(2ab - 3a + 1)$
9. $4y^2(y - 25)$
11. $a(y - 1)$
13. $x^3(x - 1)$
15. $x^4(1 - x)$
17. $x^2(24x - 30 + y)$
19. $cn^2(c + n)$
21. $a(x + y - z)$
23. $ax(a - x)$

25. $6(4x^2 + 2x + 1)$
27. $c(c^3 - c^2 + c - 2)$
29. $-5x(5x^2 + 3)$
31. $-xy(y^2 + y + 1)$
33. $rs(r - s - 4)$
35. $9(3a^2b^2 + 2ab - 7)$
37. $-x^2(x^2 - 2x + 6)$
39. $3p^2q(1 + 3q - 4q^2)$
41. $x^{50}(x + 1)$
43. $x(3y + x - 3)$
45. $c(c - x + y)$
47. $(x + y)(a + 3)$
49. $(x + 5)(x^2 - 2y^2)$
51. $(t^2 + 4)(5a^2 - 1)$
53. $(t^3 + 1)(t - 1)$
55. $(a + b)(4x^2 + 2x + 1)$
57. $x^n(x^n - 1)$
59. $y^n(y^{3n} - z)$

EXERCISES FOR SECTION 3.6, PP. 128–129

1. $x + 2$
3. $x - 13$
5. $x + 4$
7. $x + 1$
9. $x + y$
11. $(x - 2)(x - 4)$
13. $(x + 2)(x - 3)$
15. $(y + 1)(y + 8)$
17. not factorable
19. $(x - 4)(x - 5)$
21. $(r - 4)(r + 8)$
23. $(x + 2)(x + 3)$
25. $(y - 3)(y - 4)$
27. not factorable
29. $(x + y)^2$
31. $(r - s)(r + 2s)$
33. $(a + 2b)(a + 5b)$
35. $(x - 2a)(x + 5a)$
37. $(x + 2)(x - 5)$
39. $(x - 4y)(x + 5y)$
41. $(x + t)(x - 20t)$
43. $(p + 5q)^2$
45. $(x + y)(x + 10y)$
47. $(x^2 + 2)(x^2 + 1)$
49. $(y^2 - 3)(y^2 + 2)$
51. $3(x - 1)(x - 2)$
53. $150x^2(x - 2)(x - 5)$
55. $20(y^2 + 7y - 6)$
57. $4(x + 3)(x + 5)$
59. $100x(x + 2)(x - 4)$
61. $15(y^2 + 2y + 3)$
63. $-cd(d - 4)(d + 5)$
65. $2x(x - 6y)(x + 10y)$
67. $-nk^2(k - 4)(k + 7)$
69. $u^2(u - v)(u + 3v)$

EXERCISES FOR SECTION 3.7, PP. 133–134

1. $2x + 11$
3. $3x - 2$
5. $3y - 5$
7. $5x - 1$
9. $5x + 1$
11. $3x - 4$
13. $y - 4$
15. $5p - 2$
17. $x - 6$
19. $x + 6$
21. $(x - 1)(3x + 1)$
23. $(x - 6)(3x + 1)$
25. $(x - 6)(6x + 25)$
27. $3(y - 2)(2y + 25)$
29. $(a - 3)(8a - 11)$
31. $(2a - 11)(4a - 3)$
33. $(2x + 3)^2$
35. $(2p - 3)(4p + 7)$
37. $(x - 1)(2x - 1)$
39. $(4x - 1)(3x - 5)$
41. $(2x - 1)(6x - 5)$
43. $(3a + 7)(a - 1)$
45. $(3a + 1)(a - 7)$
47. not factorable
49. $(3y + 4)^2$
51. $(2x + 7)(5x - 1)$
53. $(2x + 1)(x + 1)$
55. $(2x + 5)(2x + 3)$
57. $(4x + 1)(x + 1)$
59. $(4x - 3)(x - 2)$
61. $2(3a + 1)(a + 1)$
63. $(8y - 5)(2y + 1)$
65. $a(3x + 1)(3x - 8)$
67. $(3a - b)(a - 2b)$
69. $(2m - n)(m + 3n)$
71. $(3x - y)(5x + y)$
73. $3x(2a^2 + 4a - 7)$
75. $x^3(3x - 1)(x + 7)$
77. $2x^2y^2(x + 5)(x - 2)$
79. $6(5x + 2)(x - 3)$
81. 4, −4, 5, −5
83. 21, −21, 36, −36, 69, −69

EXERCISES FOR SECTION 3.8, PP. 136–137

1. 9
3. 49
5. 1
7. 36
9. 81
11. $9y^2$
13. $25z^2$
15. $18y$
17. $12a$
19. $8xy$
21. $4xy$
23. $9x^2$
25. $4(x+2)^2-16$
27. $10(a-1)^2-10$
29. $8(y+1)^2-8$
31. yes, $(x+4)^2$
33. not a square
35. yes, $(x-7y)^2$
37. not a square
39. not a square
41. $(x+2)^2$
43. $(x+9)^2$
45. $(y+8)^2$
47. $(4p-1)^2$
49. $(8y-3)^2$
51. $(2x-3)^2$
53. $(11n-1)^2$
55. $(4x-3)^2$
57. $9(x+2)^2$
59. $(3x-4)^2$
61. $(2x-7)^2$
63. $(a+6)^2$
65. not factorable
67. $(11u+1)^2$
69. not factorable

EXERCISES FOR SECTION 3.9, PP. 139–140

1. $(x-9)(x+9)$
3. $(2x-7)(2x+7)$
5. $(6x-5y)(6x+5y)$
7. $(4-3a)(4+3a)$
9. not factorable
11. $(x+1)(x^2-x+1)$
13. $(x-a)(x^2+ax+a^2)$
15. $(x+a)(x^2-ax+a^2)$
17. $(2p+3)(4p^2-6p+9)$
19. $(x^2-3)(x^2+3)$
21. $y^2(y+2)(y-2)$
23. $(4x+5y^2)(16x^2-20xy^2+25y^4)$
25. $x(8x-3)(8x+3)$
27. not factorable
29. $8y^2(y^2-2)$
31. $x(x+6)(x^2-6x+36)$
33. $2yz(y-3z)(y^2+3yz+9z^2)$
35. $(a+b-c)(a+b+c)$
37. $[3(x+y)+4][3(x+y)-4]=(3x+3y+4)(3x+3y-4)$
39. $[6-(n+2)][6+(n+2)]=(4-n)(8+n)$
41. $[(a+b)-(a-b)]\cdot[(a+b)+(a-b)]=(2b)(2a)=4ab$
43. $(a+b+c)[(a+b)^2-c(a+b)+c^2]$
45. $[3x-(y+z)][9x^2+3x(y+z)+(y+z)^2]$
47. $(x^n-y^n)(x^n+y^n)$
49. $(x^n+y^n)(x^{2n}-x^ny^n+y^{2n})$
51. $(x-1)(x^4+x^3+x+1)$

EXERCISES FOR SECTION 3.10, PP. 142–143

1. 1, 2; $3(y^2-4)=3(y+2)(y-2)$
3. 1, 2; $2(9-4x^2)=2(3+2x)(3-2x)$
5. 1, 6; $9(x^2-x-2)=9(x-2)(x+1)$
7. 1, 7; $2(2x^2-3x-5)=2(2x-5)(x+1)$
9. 1, 7; $2x(6x^2+7x-5)=2x(3x+5)(2x-1)$
11. 1, 5; $9(4a^2-4a+1)=9(2a-1)^2$
13. 1, 6; $5(x^2-3x-10)=5(x+2)(x-5)$
15. 2, 2; $(x^2-4)(x^2+4)=(x-2)(x+2)(x^2+4)$
17. 2, 2; $(9a^2-16)(9a^2+16)=(3a-4)(3a+4)(9a^2+16)$
19. 1; $x^2(x^2+4)$
21. 6, 2; $(x^2-9)(x^2-4)=(x+3)(x-3)(x+2)(x-2)$
23. 1, 3; $5(x^3-125)=5(x-5)(x^2+5x+25)$
25. 1, 3; $a^4(a^3-1)=a^4(a-1)(a^2+a+1)$
27. 4; $(x^2+y^2)(x^4-x^2y^2+y^4)$
29. 1, 4; $n^3(n^3+64)=n^3(n+4)(n^2-4n+16)$
31. 1, 2; $x(64x^2-1)=x(8x+1)(8x-1)$
33. 1, 6; $-x^2(x^2-4x-5)=-x^2(x-5)(x+1)$
35. 1, 6; $3x(x^2+x-42)=3x(x+7)(x-6)$
37. 1, 5; $4x^2(x^2-12x+36)=4x^2(x-6)^2$
39. 1, 6, 2; $5a(a^4+12a^2-64)=5a(a^2-4)(a^2+16)=5a(a-2)(a+2)(a^2+16)$
41. 1, 5; $2c^2(25c^2-10c+1)=2c^2(5c-1)^2$
43. 6, 2; $(t^2-49)(t^2+1)=(t+7)(t-7)(t^2+1)$
45. 1, 4; $3x(x^3+27)=3x(x+3)(x^2-3x+9)$
47. 2, 2, 2; $(x^4+y^4)(x^4-y^4)=(x^4+y^4)(x^2+y^2)(x^2-y^2)=(x+y)(x-y)(x^2+y^2)(x^4+y^4)$
49. 1, 2, 2; $2(x^4y^4-16)=2(x^2y^2-4)(x^2y^2+4)=2(xy-2)(xy+2)(x^2y^2+4)$
51. 2; $(a+b+2a)(a+b-2a)=(3a+b)(b-a)$
53. 1, 2; $a^2[(b+c)^2-d^2]=a^2(b+c+d)(b+c-d)$
55. 1; $(x+2y)(1-a)$
57. 1, 2; $5(x^{2n}-1)=5(x^n-1)(x^n+1)$
59. 1, 6; $y^n(y^2+2y-15)=y^n(y+5)(y-3)$

EXERCISES FOR SECTION 3.11, PP. 146–148

1. $\{-2, 3\}$
3. $\left\{\frac{3}{2}, -2\right\}$
5. $\{-5, -2\}$
7. $\left\{\frac{1}{4}, -\frac{3}{2}\right\}$
9. $\left\{-2, -\frac{3}{2}\right\}$
11. $\{1, 2\}$
13. $\{0, 5\}$
15. $\{0, -2\}$
17. $\{3, -9\}$
19. $\{-3, 11\}$
21. $\{3\}$
23. $\{3, -1\}$
25. $\{3, -2\}$
27. $\{-2, -5\}$
29. $\{15, -3\}$
31. $\{-3, -4\}$
33. $\{9, -1\}$
35. $\{0, 3, -2\}$
37. $\{-3, 3\}$
39. $\{-10, 10\}$
41. $\{-4, 4\}$
43. $\{-6, 6\}$
45. $\{0\}$
47. $\{0, -1\}$
49. $\{-2, 2\}$
51. $x^2=6x+91$; 13 or -7
53. $x(x+2)=255$; 15, 17 or $-17, -15$
55. $10x-18=\frac{x^2}{2}$; 2 or 18

57. a. $M = \frac{W(4x - L)(x - L)}{8}$
b. -200
59. a. $s^2 = 4h(2r - h)$
b. $s^2 = 80(80)$, $s = 80$
61. 1591
63. 396
65. 1156
67. 1209
69. 81
71. 1596
73. 1575
75. 7221
77. 1764
79. 2024

REVIEW EXERCISES FOR CHAPTER 3, PP. 148–149

1. x^5
2. r^{13}
3. x^4
4. p^9
5. $-12x^4$
6. $-2a^8$
7. $-10n^3x^4$
8. $3a^6$
9. $12x^3$
10. x^{2n}
11. $x^3 + 3x^2 + 2x$
12. $x^4 + 2x^2 - x$
13. $6x^3 - 8x^2 - 2x$
14. $4ax^3 - 4bx^2 + 4cx$
15. $x^2 - 5x + 6$
16. $y^2 - 3y - 4$
17. $6a^2 + 7a - 3$
18. $a^2 + 10a + 25$
19. $25x^2 - 1$
20. $4y^2 - 12y + 9$
21. $2x^3 - 3x^2 - 14x$
22. $2x^5 + x^4 - 2x^3$
23. $-3x^7 - 2x^5 + 4x^4$
24. $6x^2 - 29xy - 16y^2$
25. $2x^3 + 3x^2 - 20x$
26. $18x^3 + 24x^2 + 8x$
27. $x^3 + 8x^2 + 21x + 18$
28. $x^3 - x^2 - 10x - 8$
29. $6x^3 - x^2 + 8x + 3$
30. $x^4 + 2x^3 - 8x^2 - 13x + 6$
31. $3x(x - 2 + 8y)$
32. $(t + 3)(t + 8)$
33. $(x + 5)^2$
34. $(7y^2 - 1)(7y^2 + 1)$
35. $(x - 1)(x^2 + x + 1)$
36. $(a + 1)(a^2 - a + 1)$
37. $-3x(x^2 - 9) = -3x(x - 3)(x + 3)$
38. $(3a + 1)(2a - 3)$
39. $3x(12 + x^2 - x^4) = -3x(x^4 - x^2 - 12)$
$= -3x(x^2 - 4)(x^2 + 3)$
$= -3x(x - 2)(x + 2)(x^2 + 3)$
40. $25(4p^2 - q^2) = 25(2p - q)(2p + q)$
41. $4y(16y^2 - 9) = 4y(4y - 3)(4y + 3)$
42. $(x^3 - y^3)(x^3 + y^3) = (x - y)(x + y)(x^2 + xy + y^2)(x^2 - xy + y^2)$
43. $2y(6x^2 - 11x - 10) = 2y(2x - 5)(3x + 2)$
44. $(a + b)(8a - 3b)$
45. $2y(y - 3)(y + 3)(y^2 + 9)$
46. $3ax^4(5x^2 + 14x - 3) = 3ax^4(x + 3)(5x - 1)$
47. $(5r + 1)^2$
48. $(6x - 1)^2$
49. $(2p - 5q)^2$
50. $(x + 3)(y + 2)$
51. $(p + 5)(x - 3)$
52. $-x^3 - 4x^2 + 3x = -x(x^2 + 4x - 3)$
53. $yz(y[a - 1] + 1) = yz(ay - y + 1)$

54. $(a + 2)[x(a + 2) + y] = (a + 2)(ax + 2x + y)$
55. $(x + y)(3 - 2[x + y]) = (x + y)(3 - 2x - 2y)$
56. 9
57. 64
58. 16
59. $12ab$
60. $14yz$
61. $\left\{-2, \frac{7}{2}\right\}$
62. $\{0, -7\}$
63. $\{5, -12\}$
64. $\{0, 3\}$
65. $\{2, 9\}$
66. $\{-1\}$
67. $\{-1\}$
68. $\{1, 6\}$
69. $\{0, 3\}$
70. $\{8, -8\}$
71. $x(x + 2) = 15(x + 2) + 18$; 16, 18
72. $5x^2 + 10x = 315$; 7 or -9
73. a. $b^2 = (c - a)(c + a)$
    b. 1: $b^2 = (85 - 84)(85 + 84) = 169$; $b = 13$
    2: $b^2 = (37 - 35)(37 + 35) = 144$; $b = 12$
74. a. $A = 2\pi r(h + r)$
    b. $A = 2\left(\frac{22}{7}\right)(15)(35) = 3300$
75. a. $D = ckw(L^2 - 4cL + 4c^2) = ckw(L - 2c)^2$
    b. $D = \frac{1}{4}\left(\frac{1}{500}\right)(200)\left(12 - \frac{1}{2}\right)^2 = \frac{529}{40} = 13.225$
76. a. $1200x - x^2 = 0$
    $x = 0$ or $x = 1200$
    b. $320{,}000 = 1200x - x^2$
    $x = 400$ or $x = 800$
77. $x = 2$ or $x = \frac{2}{3}$; since the number of moles that react must be less than 1, the only answer is $x = \frac{2}{3}$.

EXERCISES FOR SECTION 4.1, PP. 154–156

1. $\frac{1}{3}$
3. $\frac{-3}{5}$
5. $\frac{-3}{4}$
7. 1
9. $\frac{1}{3x^2}$
11. $\frac{-1}{m^2n}$
13. $4x^2y$
15. -1
17. $\frac{1}{3xy}$
19. $\frac{1}{ac}$
21. $\frac{x + 3}{x}$
23. $\frac{x - 4}{x - 2}$
25. $\frac{y - 8}{y}$
27. $\frac{x - y}{x + y}$
29. $\frac{y}{5}$
31. $\frac{c}{2d}$
33. $\frac{r}{4}$
35. $\frac{a + b}{a - b}$
37. $\frac{m^2 + 1}{m + 1}$
39. $2y - 3$
41. $\frac{y}{3}$
43. $\frac{c - d}{6}$
45. $\frac{y}{3}$
47. $\frac{x - y}{x + y}$

49. $\frac{a^2+1}{a+1}$
51. $x+2$
53. -1
55. $\frac{x+1}{x+4}$
57. $\frac{2(t+2)}{3(t-3)}$
59. $\frac{m-n+1}{m+n-1}$
61. $\frac{x+1}{x+7}$
63. $\frac{a-4}{2(a+4)}$
65. $-(3x+2y)$
67. $\frac{x-5}{x^2-5x+25}$
69. $\frac{2}{y-4}$
71. $\frac{a+b}{a-b}$
73. $\frac{4a}{a+b}$
75. $\frac{2(n+1)}{n-2}$
77. $\frac{-1}{x+7}$
79. $\frac{n-8}{n-1}$
81. $\frac{y(2y-1)}{3}$
83. $\frac{1}{x-3}$

EXERCISES FOR SECTION 4.2, PP. 159–160

1. $\frac{20}{36}$
3. $\frac{12}{21}$
5. $\frac{-28}{42}$
7. $\frac{16}{36}$
9. $\frac{-18}{42}$
11. $\frac{3x}{45}$
13. $\frac{6xy}{15xy}$
15. $\frac{6x^3}{45x^2}$
17. $\frac{-28x^3yz}{42x^2z^2}$
19. $\frac{-15x^3}{40x^2}$
21. $\frac{-18x^2y^2}{42xyz}$
23. $\frac{10}{2x+2}$
25. $\frac{5x-15}{5x+20}$
27. $\frac{2x^2}{2x^2-10x}$
29. $\frac{3y^2-9y}{y^2-9}$
31. $\frac{x^2+3x+2}{x+1}$
33. $\frac{x}{x-7}$
35. $\frac{-y^2-4y}{y^2-16}$
37. $\frac{a^2+2a+1}{a^2-2a-3}$
39. $\frac{t^2+5t-14}{14+9t+t^2}$
41. $\frac{4x^2+2x}{4x^2-1}$
43. $\frac{r^2-3r}{r^2-r-12}$
45. $\frac{6x^2-17x+10}{x-2}$
47. $\frac{t}{t-1}$
49. $\frac{2r+7}{4r^2-49}$
51. $\frac{y^2-7y+6}{12-8y+y^2}$
53. $\frac{5x^2+10x}{5x+10}$
55. $\frac{x^3-25x^2}{3x^2-75x}$
57. $\frac{12a^3+18a^2}{10a^2+13a-3}$
59. $\frac{-2a^3+5a^2}{4a^2-10a}$
61. $\frac{15n^3+30n^2+15n}{3n^3-3n}$

EXERCISES FOR SECTION 4.3, PP. 165–167

1. $\frac{5}{7}$
3. $\frac{7-2a}{b}$
5. $\frac{x-y}{5}$
7. $\frac{19}{24}$
9. $\frac{19}{14a}$
11. $\frac{x}{8y^2}$
13. $\frac{131}{180}$
15. $\frac{57}{60}$
17. $\frac{1}{3x}$
19. $\frac{3x^2+8x-1}{6x^3}$
21. $\frac{1}{b(b-1)}$
23. $\frac{y+5}{(y+1)(y+2)}$
25. $\frac{18y^2+4y-3}{30y^3}$
27. $\frac{-x}{y(y+1)}$
29. $\frac{-x^2+3x-4}{(x-1)(x-2)}$
31. $\frac{a^2+b^2}{ab}$
33. $\frac{10y^2+39y-72}{(2y-3)^2(2y+3)}$
35. $\frac{x^2+2x}{x+1}$
37. $\frac{x^2+6x+12}{(x+1)(x+3)(x+4)}$
39. $\frac{4y^2-y+9}{(y-2)(y-3)(2y+1)}$
41. $\frac{5a-13}{6(a+1)}$
43. $\frac{13x}{2(x-4)(x+6)}$
45. $\frac{1}{y(y-5)}$
47. $\frac{x+1}{x}$
49. $\frac{x-y}{x+y}$
51. -1
53. $\frac{y+15}{(4y+3)(5y-1)}$
55. $\frac{2}{(a-1)(a+1)^2}$
57. $\frac{3}{t+1}$
59. -2

EXERCISES FOR SECTION 4.4, PP. 171–172

1. $\frac{8}{9}$
3. $\frac{1}{4}$
5. $\frac{1}{2}$
7. 3
9. $\frac{25}{54}$
11. $\frac{6xy}{(x-3)(y-2)}$
13. $\frac{3}{11b}$
15. $\frac{4x}{9acy}$
17. $\frac{x^2-y^2}{16}$
19. $\frac{5y}{x^3}$
21. $\frac{-b}{az}$
23. $\frac{2a(a-5)}{a-1}$
25. $\frac{x+3}{3x}$
27. $\frac{(a-b)^2}{a}$
29. $\frac{2(n-2)}{n(n+3)}$
31. 1
33. $\frac{8}{5}$
35. $\frac{7x(x+7)}{(x-7)^3}$
37. $\frac{12y}{y+4}$
39. $\frac{3x(5x-1)}{x+1}$
41. $\frac{2x}{x-3}$
43. $\frac{x(x-1)}{x-9}$
45. 1
47. $\frac{y(x-3)}{1-3xy}$
49. $\frac{y}{(y+1)^2}$
51. $\frac{(x-1)(x-3)}{(x+1)(x+3)}$
53. $\frac{(x-2)(x^2-3x+9)}{x^2}$
55. -1
57. $(y-1)(y^3+1)$
59. $x-y$

EXERCISES FOR SECTION 4.5, PP. 174–175

1. $\frac{22}{31}$
3. $\frac{6}{5}$
5. $\frac{11}{20}$
7. $\frac{y}{y-1}$
9. $\frac{3-x}{3}$
11. $\frac{1}{t}$
13. $\frac{10x+2y^2}{xy^2}$
15. $\frac{a}{a^2-3}$
17. $\frac{x-2}{x-5}$
19. $\frac{y+3}{y-4}$
21. $\frac{xy}{x+y}$
23. $\frac{x-1}{x+1}$
25. $\frac{a+1}{a(a+3)}$
27. $\frac{13}{8}$
29. $1-x$

EXERCISES FOR SECTION 4.6, PP. 179–180

1. $x^2+3x-2+\frac{4}{x}$
3. $3y-2+\frac{3}{2y}$
5. $3x-2+\frac{5}{2x}$
7. $x^5-5x^2+3+\frac{2}{x^2}$
9. $3x^2y+2x-\frac{2}{3}$
11. $2x^2-3x+9-\frac{29}{x+4}$
13. $2x^2-3x-2$
15. $2x^2-2x-1-\frac{7}{2x+7}$
17. $5x^2+\frac{2x-1}{x^2-6}$
19. $2x^2-x-1+\frac{4}{x-1}$
21. $a^2+9a+81$
23. $4x^3+4x^2+x+8+\frac{7}{x-1}$
25. $y^3-3y^2-3y+11+\frac{6y-31}{y^2+3}$
27. $2x^2-10-\frac{19}{3x^2-1}$
29. $2x^2+3+\frac{1}{x-5}$
31. x^3+x^2+x+1
33. $2x^3+4+\frac{7}{x^2-3}$
35. $5a^2-2ab+b^2-\frac{b^3}{5a+2b}$
37. $x+y+3$
39. $a-2b+5$

EXERCISES FOR SECTION 4.7, PP. 184–185

1. $\{-4\}\ x \neq 0$
3. $\{-11\}\ a \neq 0, -5$
5. $\{3\}\ x \neq -2, \frac{7}{3}$
7. $\left\{-\frac{3}{2}\right\}\ y \neq 0, 1, -1$
9. $\left\{\frac{1}{4}\right\}\ x \neq 0$

11. $\{6\}\ y \neq -\frac{1}{2}$
13. $\varnothing,\ x \neq 0$
15. $\varnothing,\ x \neq -1, -6$
17. $\{12\}\ y \neq 4, -4$
19. $\{-5\}\ x \neq 0$
21. $\{-2\}\ x \neq 3, -\frac{1}{2}$
23. $\left\{\frac{1}{6}\right\}\ t \neq 0$
25. $\{1\}\ t \neq 5, -4$
27. $\{13\}\ x \neq -1$
29. $\left\{\frac{5}{2}\right\}\ x \neq -\frac{3}{5}, \frac{1}{2}$
31. $\{-2\}\ x \neq 0, 1$
33. $\{3, -2\}\ x \neq -3, -1$
35. $x = 2a - 3b,\ x \neq b$
37. $x = \frac{a}{5};\ x \neq 0, a, -a$
39. $N = \frac{Pn}{p - P},\ N \neq 0,$
$N \neq -n,\ p \neq P$

EXERCISES FOR SECTION 4.8, PP. 187–188

1. 35 cm by 56 cm
3. 20 cups; $1\frac{1}{3}$ cups
5. 13
7. 175 pounds sodium
115 pounds chlorine
9. 12 cans for 69 cents
is the better buy.
11. \$12,000, \$14,400
13. 78 cents
15. 24 and 32
17. 3 and 12 or −3 and −12
19. 56.25 mph
21. \$36.00
23. 12 cu. ft. cement
36 cu. ft. sand
60 cu. ft. rock
25. \$7000

EXERCISES FOR SECTION 4.9, 190–192

1. $\frac{x + 4}{(x + 12) - 3} = \frac{3}{4};\ x = 11;$
original fraction $= \frac{11}{23}$
3. $\frac{x}{8} + \frac{x}{12} = 1;\ 4\frac{4}{5}$ days
5. $\frac{x}{12} + \frac{x}{15} + \frac{x}{20} = 1;$
$x = 5$ minutes
$1000x = 5000$ minutes
$= 83\frac{1}{3}$ hours
7. $\frac{6}{15} + \frac{6}{x} = 1;$ 10 days
9. $\frac{15}{80} + \frac{3(15)}{80} + \frac{15}{x} = 1;$ 60 minutes
11. $\frac{x}{9} + \frac{x}{12} - \frac{x}{18} = 1;$
$7\frac{1}{5}$ hrs. = 7 hrs. 12 min.
13. $\frac{1}{x} + \frac{1}{4x} = \frac{3}{4};$
$\frac{5}{3}, \frac{20}{3}$
15. $\frac{1}{5} = \frac{1}{4b} + \frac{1}{b}$
where $a = 4b$;
25 in.

REVIEW EXERCISES FOR CHAPTER 4, PP. 192–194

1. $\frac{2x^2z}{3y^2}$

2. $\frac{5a^3y}{2b}$

3. -1

4. $\frac{9(x+2y)}{x-2y}$

5. $\frac{2x-15}{2x-3}$

6. $\frac{-4x^3(x-1)}{3(x+1)}$

7. 1

8. $\frac{x-1}{3}$

9. $\frac{(a-4)(a^2-3a+9)}{a^2}$

10. $\frac{x+1}{x+3}$

11. $\frac{5-x}{x+3}$

12. $\frac{6x^2-3x}{x^2-9}$

13. $\frac{4x-15}{(x-5)(x-1)}$

14. $\frac{4}{x(x+1)(x-1)}$

15. $\frac{x^2+14x+4}{2x(x+2)}$

16. $\frac{1}{(x+3)(x+4)}$

17. $\frac{16}{(x-2)^2(x+2)^2}$

18. $\frac{xy+3}{xy-3}$

19. $\frac{-1}{3(x+3)}$

20. $\frac{5(5x+2)}{12(3x+1)}$

21. $x^2-x-\frac{1}{x-3}$

22. $x^2-2+\frac{4}{x^2+3}$

23. $3x^2-2x+4-\frac{1}{5x+10}$

24. a^2+a+1

25. $5x^2-2x-3-\frac{7}{2x+1}$

26. $\left\{-\frac{1}{2}\right\}$, $x \neq 6, -6$

27. $\{0\}$, $x \neq -2$

28. $\{9\}$, $x \neq 3, -3$

29. $\left\{-\frac{1}{4}\right\}$, $x \neq 1, -3$

30. $\left\{\frac{1}{7}\right\}$, $x \neq 0, -\frac{1}{3}$

31. $\varnothing$, $x \neq 4, -4$

32. all real numbers except $x = 1$

33. $\{-5\}$, $x \neq 0, 3$

34. $x = \frac{a-b}{2}$; $x \neq a, -b$; $a \neq -b$

35. $x = \frac{p-1}{c+1}$; $c \neq -1$, $x \neq 0$

36. $\frac{(x-3)-2}{x+1} = \frac{1}{4}$; $\frac{4}{7}$

37. original fraction: $\frac{3x}{5x}$;
$\frac{3x-20}{5x+10} = \frac{1}{2}$
$\frac{3x}{5x} = \frac{150}{250}$

38. $\frac{x}{10} + \frac{x}{15} = 1$; 6 hrs.

39. $\frac{2}{\frac{7}{2}} + \frac{2}{x} = 1$;
$4\frac{2}{3}$ hrs. = 4 hrs. 40 min.

40. 3

41. $\frac{720}{16} = \frac{450}{x}$; 10 gallons

42. $\frac{20}{9} = \frac{120}{x}$; 54 kilograms

43. $\frac{1}{3.8} = \frac{5}{x}$; 19 litres

44. $\frac{30.5}{1} = \frac{x}{6}$; 183 cm

45. a. -3
b. 3
c. 2

ANSWERS

EXERCISES FOR SECTION 5.1, PP. 200–201

1. (−3, −1)
3. (2, 4)
5. (3, −5)
7. (−4, 3)
9. (3, 0)

11.
13.
15.
17.
19.
21.

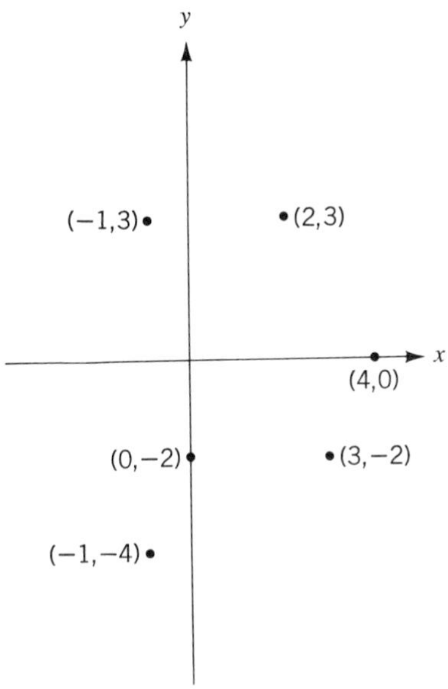

23. (1, 0)

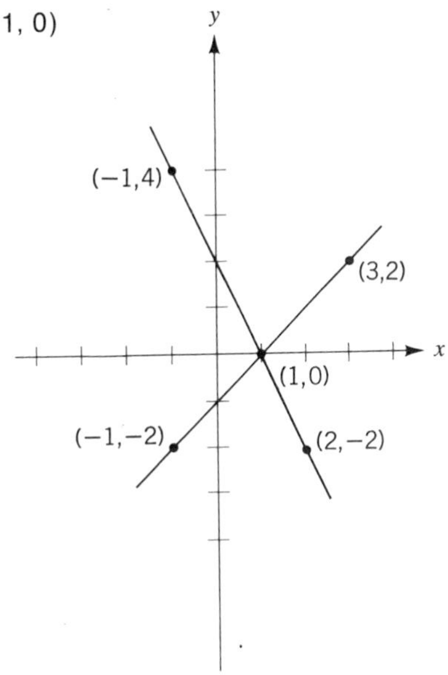

25. yes
27. no
29. yes
31. yes
33. no
35. yes
37. no
39. yes
41. no
43. (0, 5), (3, 0)
45. (3, 5), (5, −3)
47. (3, 5), (0, 5)
49. (−2, 6)
51. (2, 6), (6, −2)
53. (−2, 6), (−2, 0)

55.

x	y
0	−6
2	0
1	−3
−2	−12
1	−3

straight line

57.

x	y
0	−8
8	0
−2	−10
4	−4
3	−5

straight line

EXERCISES FOR SECTION 5.2, PP. 206–208

1. x-intercept $= 3$,
y-intercept $= -6$

3. x-intercept $= 4$,
y-intercept $= 4$

5. x-intercept $= 2$,
y-intercept $= -3$

7.

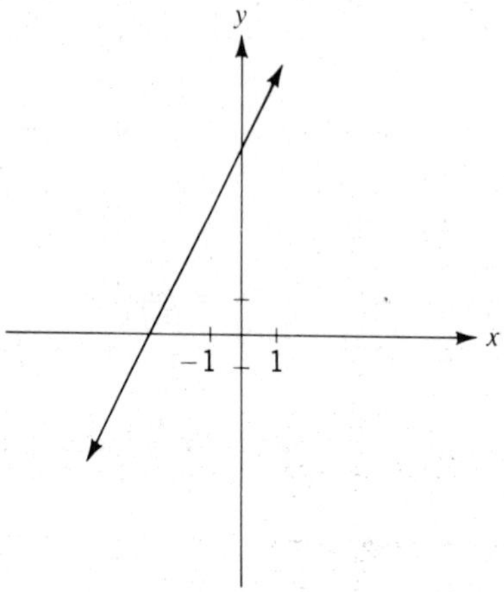

9.

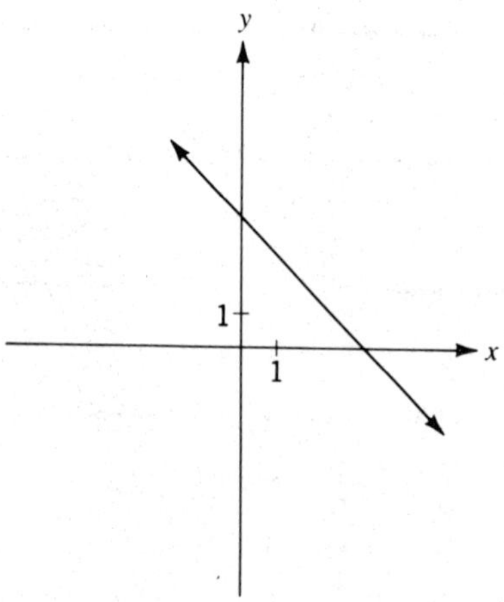

11.

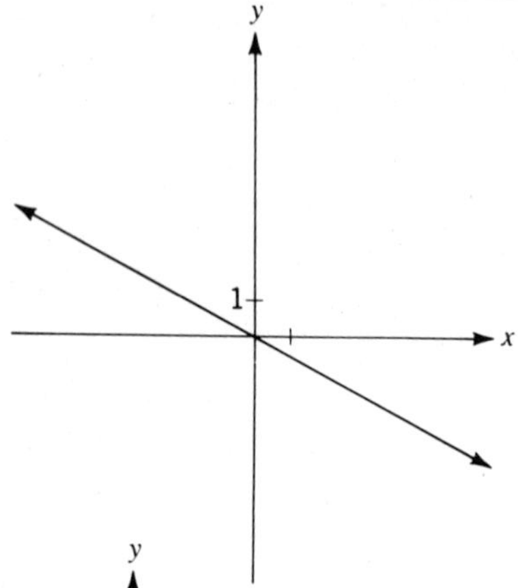

13.

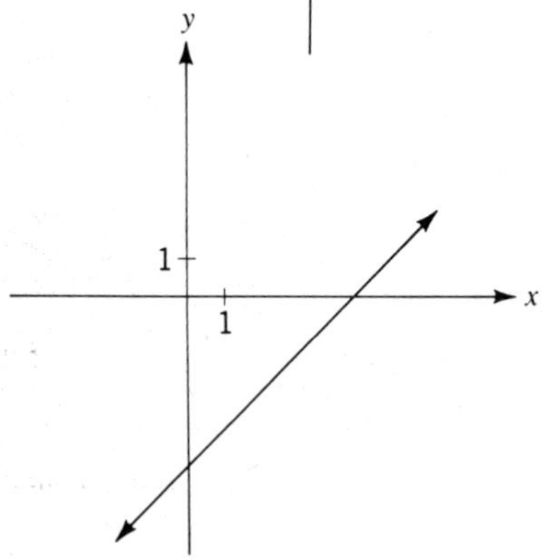

15.

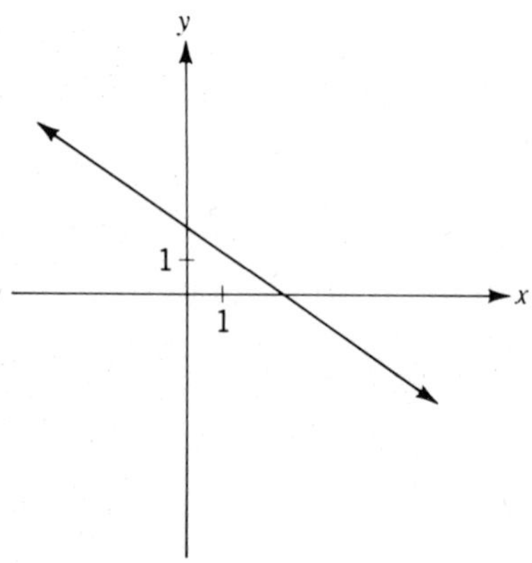

ANSWERS

17.

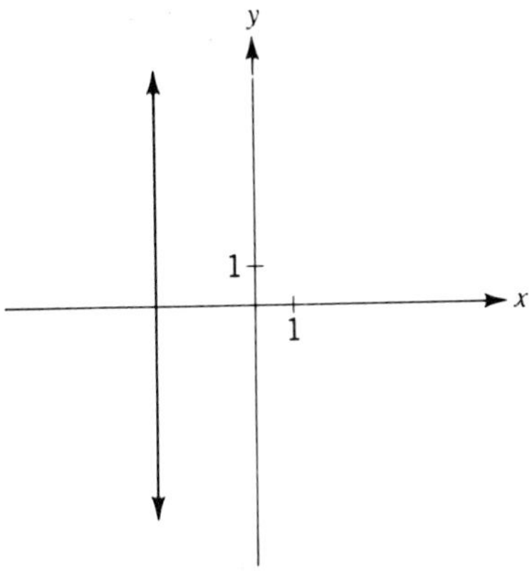

19.

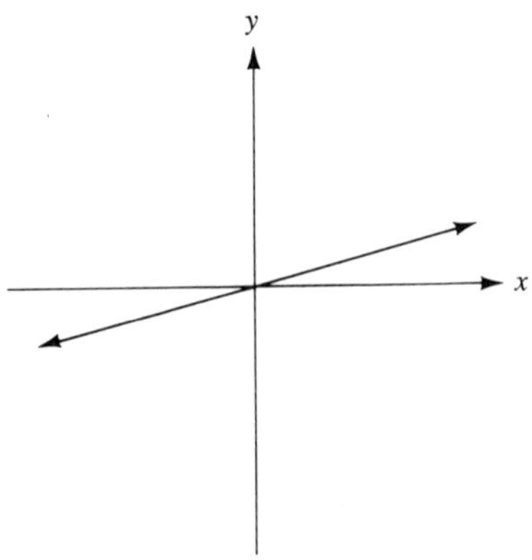

21.

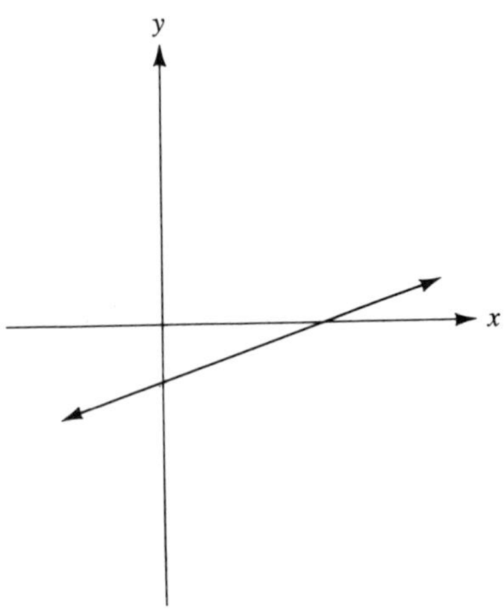

23.

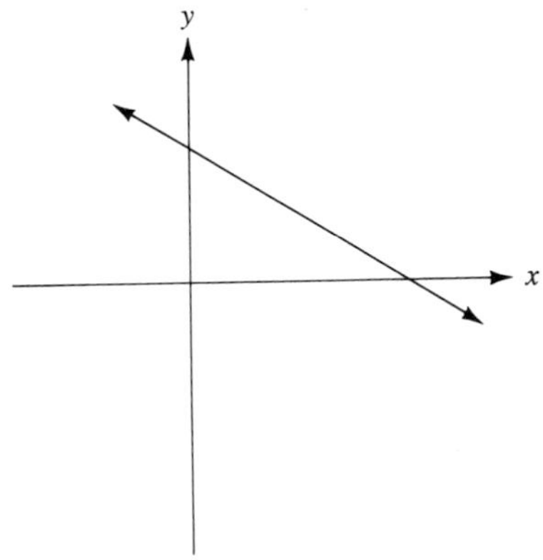

25. They graph as parallel lines, but they intersect the axes at different points.

27. a. $k = 5$ b. $k = 9$

29. a. b.

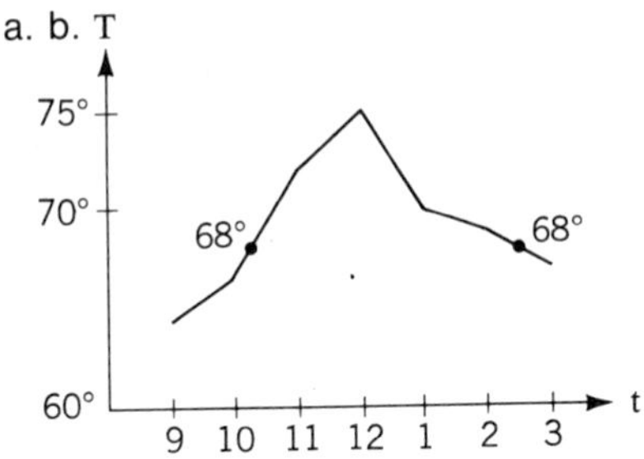

c. about 4 hours

31. a.

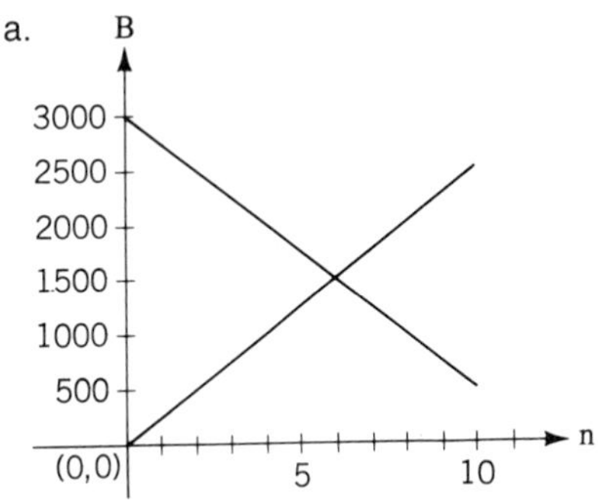

b. \$1625 c. $4\frac{1}{2}$ years

d. 6 years

EXERCISES FOR SECTION 5.3, PP. 215–216

1. $\frac{1}{2}$

3. $-\frac{4}{3}$

5. 1

7. -1

9. $\frac{1}{2}$

11. $m=-2$, $b=5$

13. $m=2$, $b=-8$

15. $m=\frac{5}{2}$, $b=-5$

17. $m=1$, $b=\frac{3}{5}$

19. $m=0$, $b=5$

21. $m=2$, $b=-4$

23. $m=-\frac{3}{2}$, $b=2$

25. $m=\frac{3}{2}$, $b=\frac{3}{2}$

27. slope undefined; no y-intercept

29. $m=1$, $b=0$

31. parallel; $m=-1$

33. not parallel

35. not parallel

37. parallel; $m=1$

39. parallel; slope undefined

41. parallel; $m=\frac{1}{3}$

43. $k=6$

45. $k=0$

47. $k=\frac{3}{2}$

49. a. 132 ft.
b. 85.8 ft.

EXERCISES FOR SECTION 5.4, PP. 218–220

1. $2x+y-8=0$

3. $6x-y+9=0$

5. $x-2y-8=0$

7. $3x+4y+25=0$

9. $y=7$

11. $m=\frac{1}{2}$; $x-2y=0$

13. $m=\frac{1}{3}$; $x-3y-7=0$

15. $m=\frac{1}{4}$; $x-4y+3=0$

17. $m=0$; $y=3$

19. slope undefined; $x=-2$

21. $3x+2y-7=0$

23. $x+2y-3=0$

25. $y-2=0$

27. $2x-y+3=0$

29. $4x+3y+8=0$

31. no, slope of line $AB \neq$ slope of line BC

33. $K=\frac{8}{3}$

35. a. and b.

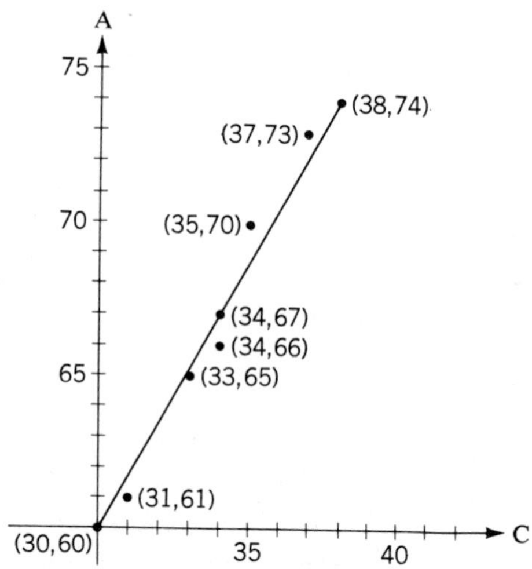

c. $7C-4A+30=0$

d. $63\frac{1}{2}$ in., $70\frac{1}{2}$ in., $75\frac{3}{4}$ in.

ANSWERS

EXERCISES FOR SECTION 5.5, PP. 226–227

1. a. $m_1 = -1$, $m_2 = 1$

   b. $b_1 = \frac{4}{3}$, $b_2 = -\frac{4}{3}$

   c. intersect

   d. one solution

3. a. $m_1 = -1$, $m_2 = -1$

   b. $b_1 = \frac{4}{3}$, $b_2 = \frac{4}{3}$

   c. coincide

   d. line of solutions

5. a. m_1 undefined, $m_2 = -3$

   b. no y-intercept, $b_2 = 0$

   c. intersect

   d. one solution

7. a. $m_1 = \frac{3}{2}$, $m_2 = -\frac{5}{2}$

   b. $b_1 = -\frac{3}{2}$, $b_2 = \frac{5}{2}$

   c. intersect

   d. one solution

9. a. m_1 undefined, $m_2 = 0$

   b. no y-intercept, $b_2 = -\frac{4}{3}$

   c. intersect

   d. one solution

11. a. $m_1 = \frac{1}{2}$, $m_2 = \frac{1}{2}$

    b. $b_1 = -\frac{5}{2}$, $b_2 = \frac{5}{2}$

    c. parallel

    d. no solution

13. (4, 3)

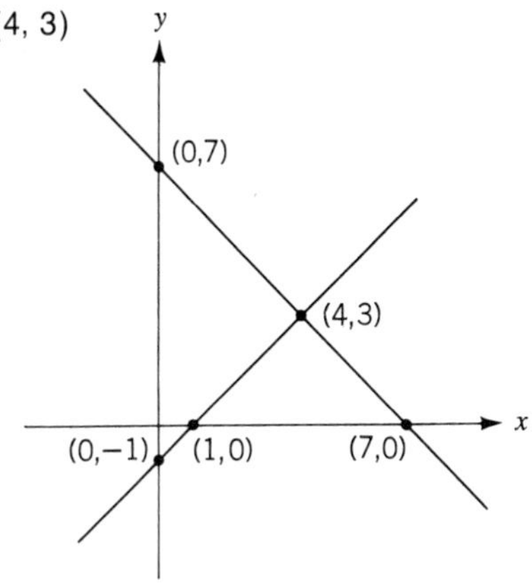

15. (2, −1)

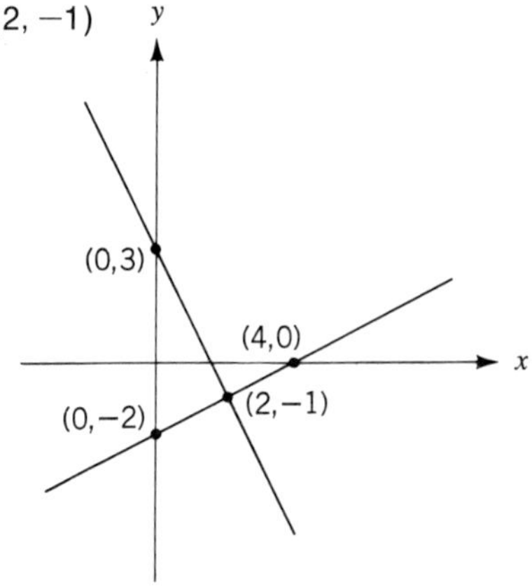

17. (8, 1)

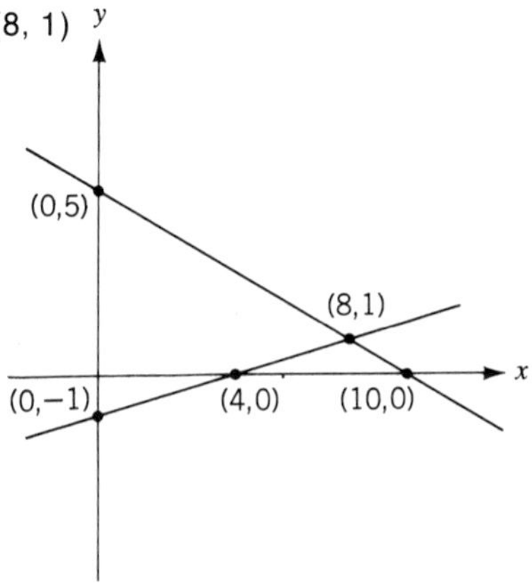

19. (2, 2)

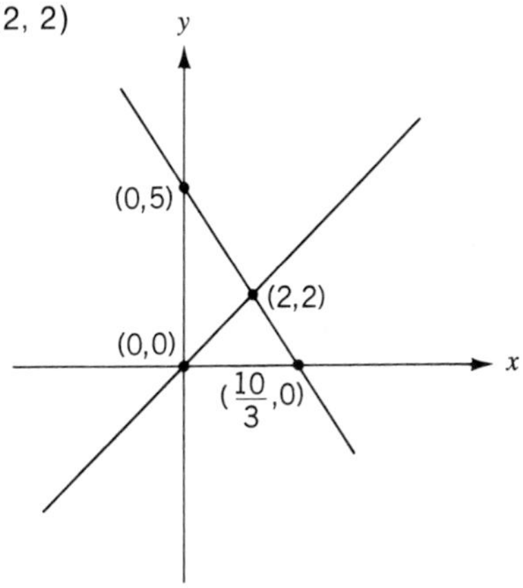

21. $(-2, -6)$

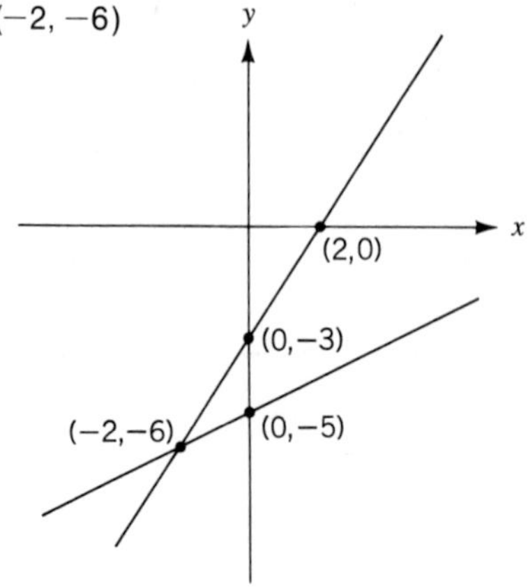

23. 30 units Food A
20 units Food B

EXERCISES FOR SECTION 5.6, P. 230

1. $(2, 4)$
3. $(14, 25)$
5. $(-2, -11)$
7. $(-3, -3)$
9. $(2, 3)$
11. $(-1, 2)$
13. $(-3, -3)$
15. $\left(4, -\frac{1}{2}\right)$
17. $\left(-\frac{1}{2}, \frac{7}{2}\right)$
19. $\varnothing$
21. $(-7, -2)$
23. $\left(-2, \frac{7}{2}\right)$
25. The solution set contains all (x, y) which are solutions of $3y = x - 1$
27. $(0, 0)$
29. $\left(\frac{11}{5}, -\frac{4}{5}\right)$

EXERCISES FOR SECTION 5.7, P. 233

1. $(5, -2)$
3. $(-3, -1)$
5. $(0, -5)$
7. $(2, 1)$
9. $(-5, -1)$
11. $(7, -4)$
13. $\varnothing$
15. $\left(\frac{-2}{5}, \frac{-1}{5}\right)$
17. $(-5, -19)$
19. $\left(\frac{7}{3}, -\frac{2}{3}\right)$
21. $\left(\frac{19}{11}, -\frac{17}{11}\right)$
23. $\left(-\frac{2}{5}, -\frac{1}{5}\right)$
25. $\left(\frac{4}{5}, \frac{4}{5}\right)$
27. $(0, 0)$
29. all (x, y) which are solutions of $4x + 10y - 3 = 0$

EXERCISES FOR SECTION 5.8, PP. 235–236

1. 14 and -5
3. 69 and 46
5. bread, 72 cents per loaf;
butter, 85 cents per pound
7. milk, 46 cents a quart;
eggs, 77 cents a dozen
9. 12 miles
11. rate of current 1.5 mph
rate of crew in still water 6 mph
13. 25 mph
15. A: 65 percent silver
B: 45 percent silver
17. 10 items of product A
9 items of product B

ANSWERS

EXERCISES FOR SECTION 5.9, P. 240

1.

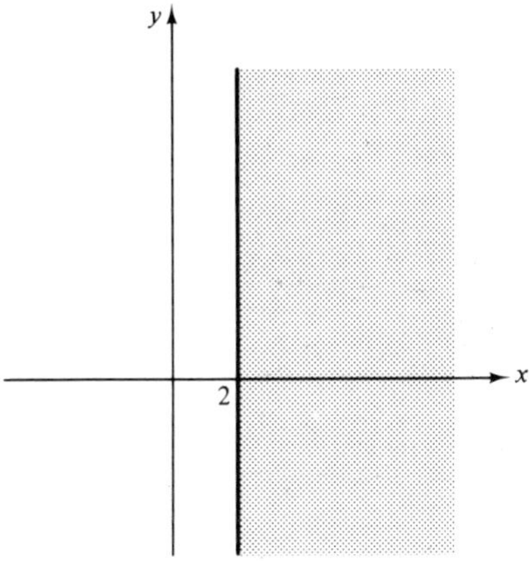

3.

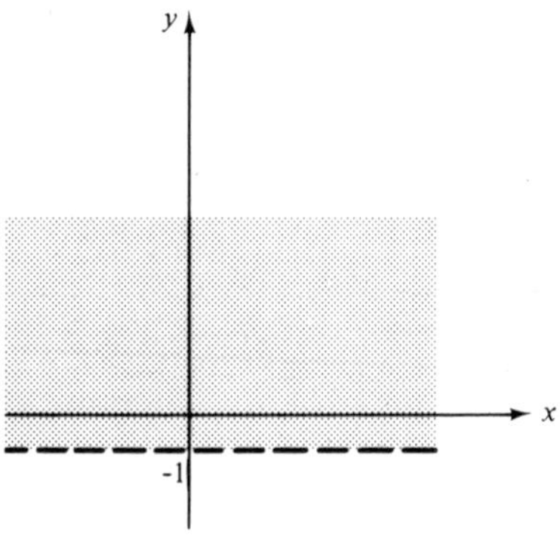

5.

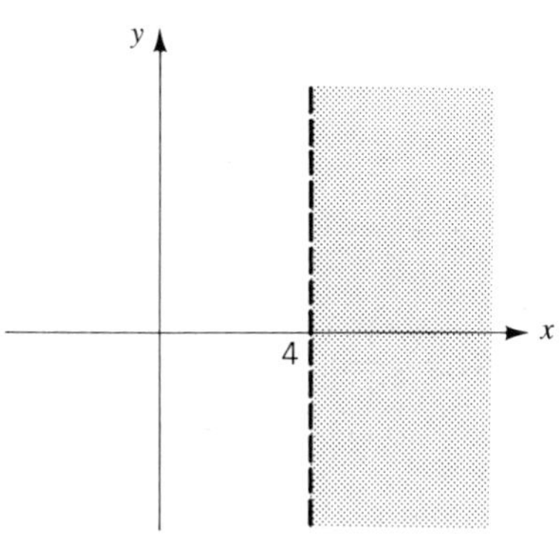

7.

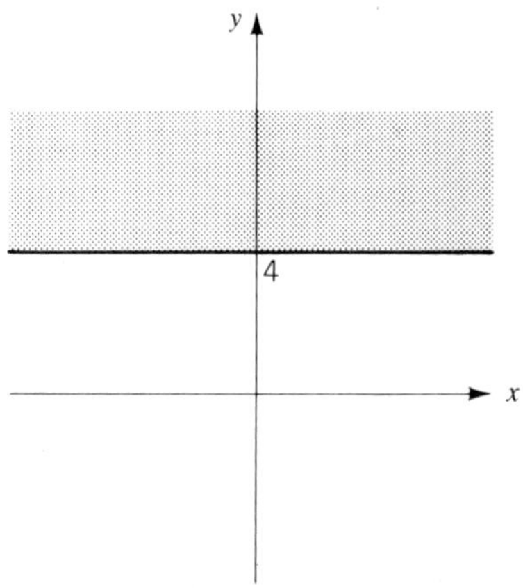

9.

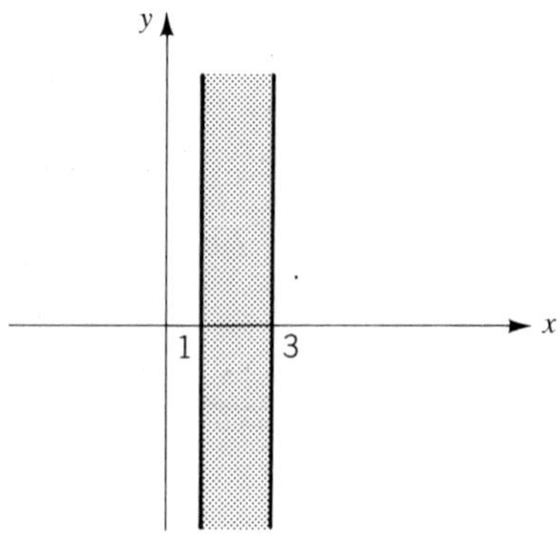

11.

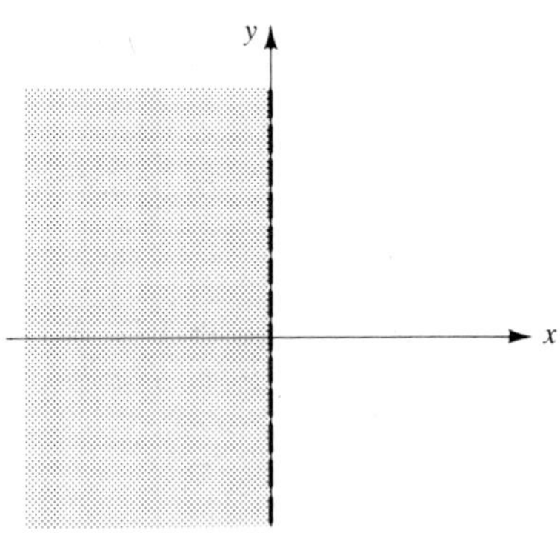

13.

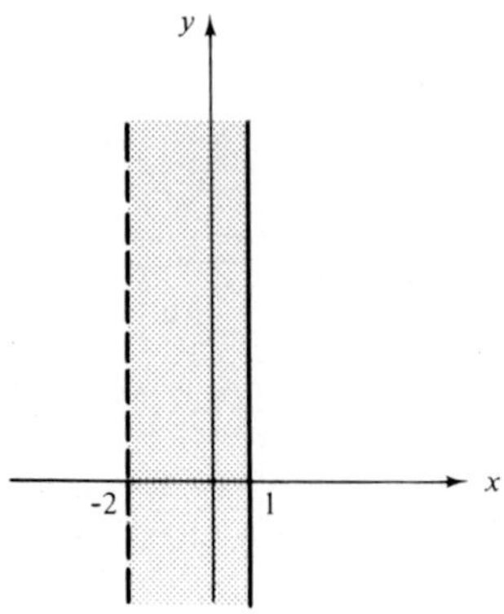

19.

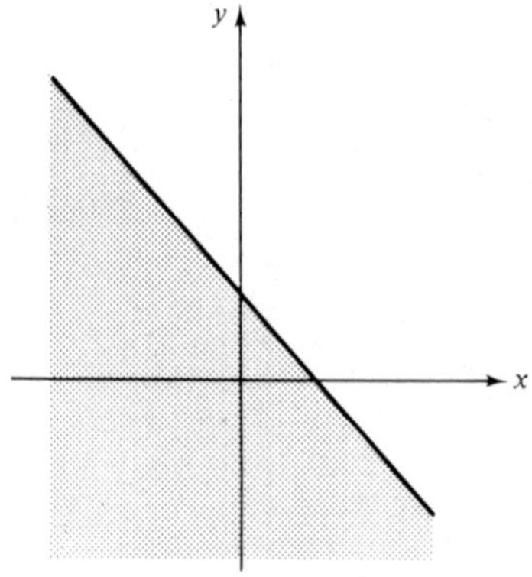

15.

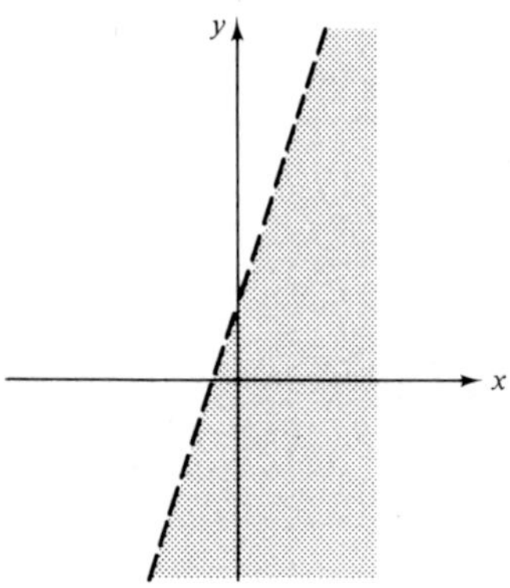

21.

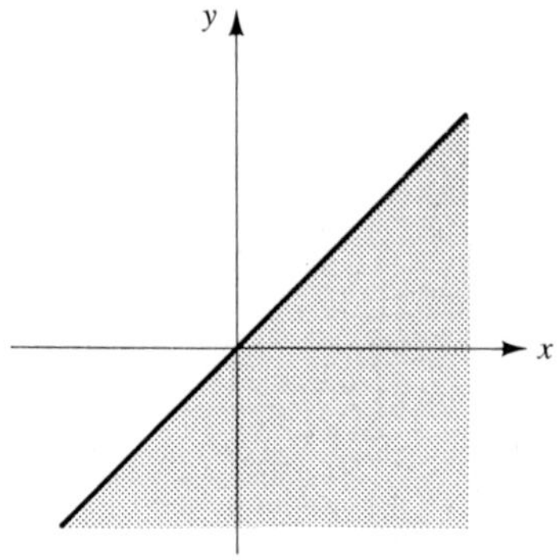

17.

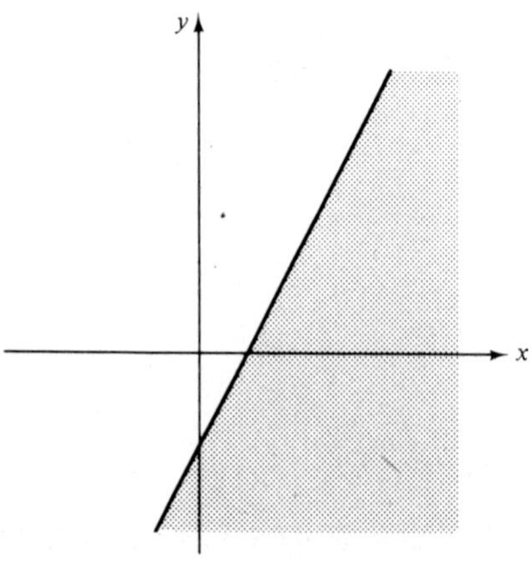

23.

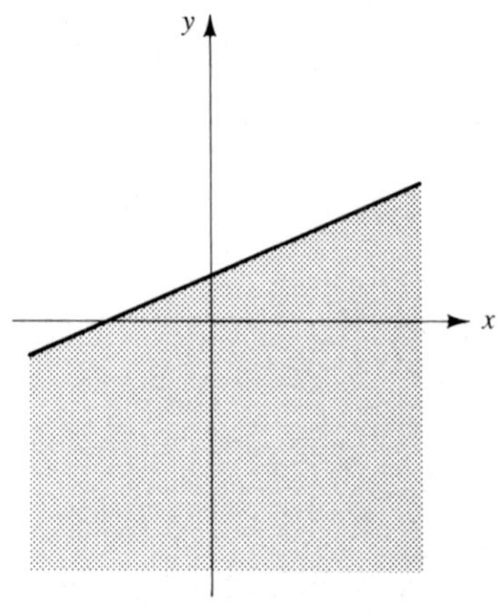

25.

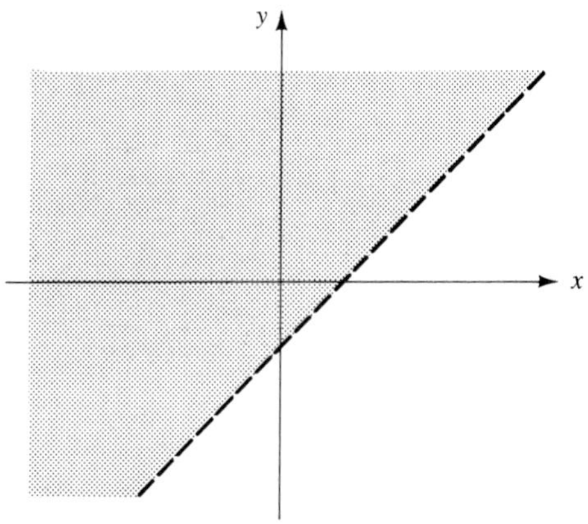

REVIEW EXERCISES FOR CHAPTER 5, PP. 240–242

1. Refer to text.

2. b. and e.

3. a. $m = -\frac{3}{2}, b = 6$
b. $m = \frac{-5}{2}, b = 5$
c. $m = 2, b = -10$
d. $m = \frac{1}{3}, b = \frac{-2}{3}$

4. a. $y = \frac{-3}{2}x + 6$
b. $y = \frac{-5}{2}x + 5$
c. $y = 2x - 10$
d. $y = \frac{1}{3}x - \frac{2}{3}$

5. a. $x - 2y + 6 = 0$
b. $3x + y - 8 = 0$
c. $y = -1$
d. $x + 3y = 0$
e. $x - 4y - 6 = 0$
f. $x = 5$

6. a. $2x - 9y + 6 = 0$
b. $7x + 3y + 3 = 0$
c. $x - y - 1 = 0$
d. $y = 5$

7. b. and c.

8. $2x - 3y + 14 = 0$

9. a. $3x - y - 11 = 0$
b. $y = 2$
c. $3x + 5y = 0$
d. $x = 5$

10. a. 3, b. 5, c. 1, d. 2, e. 4

11. (2.5, −1.5)

12. a. (−4, −3) b. (3, 0)

13. a. (−4, 3) b. (3.5, −3)

14. $9.00, $4.00

15. 26 mph

16. 20 hours

17. $3.50 adult and $1.75 child

18. bonds, 4 percent; stocks, 7 percent

19. a.

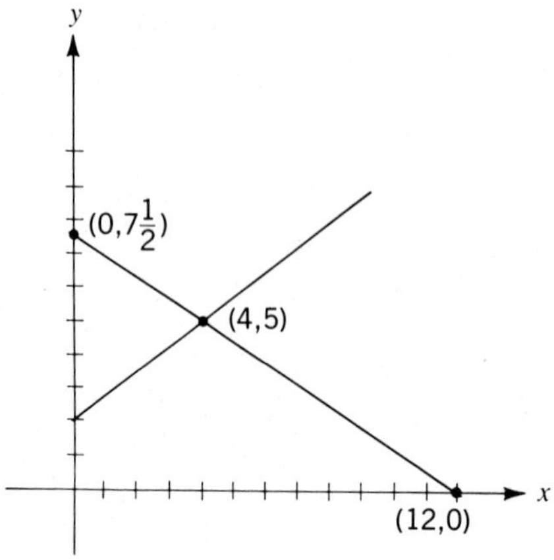

b. $\frac{15}{2}$ or $7.50   c. 12 units

20. a. See figure for Exercise 19 to the left.   b. 2   c. (4, 5)

21. a.

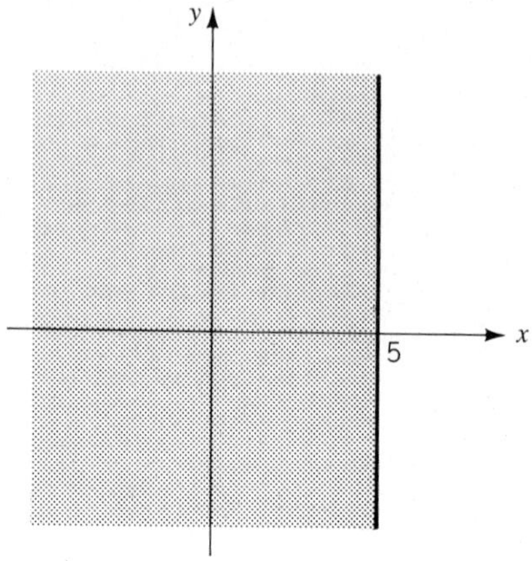

21. b.

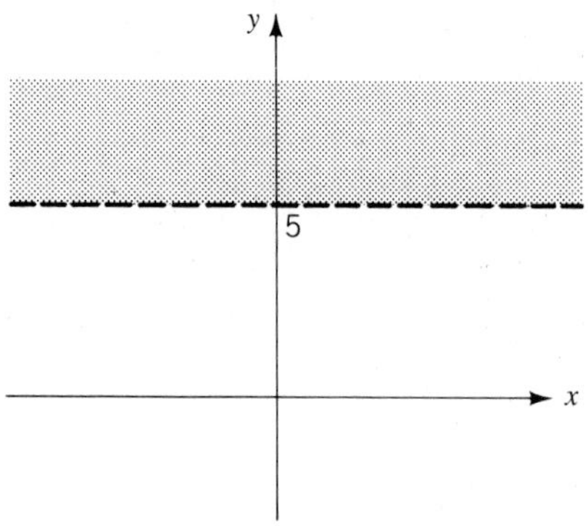

21. c.

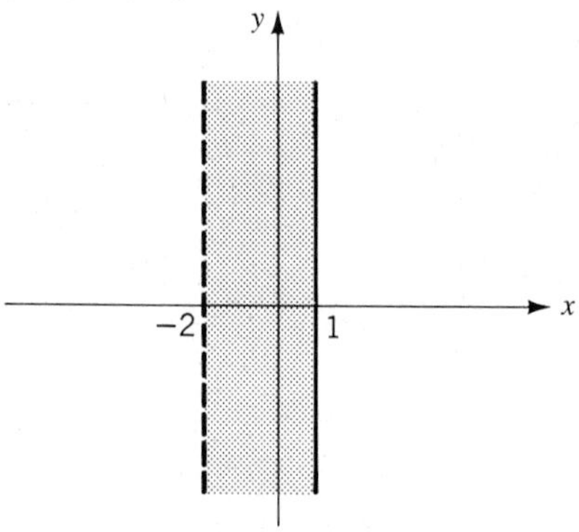

21. d.

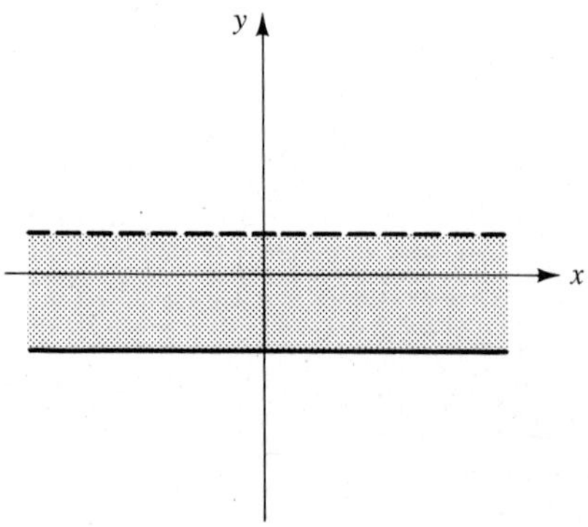

21. e.

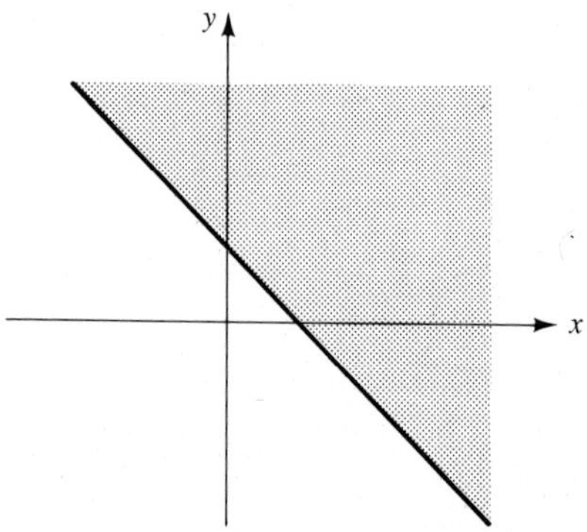

EXERCISES FOR SECTION 6.1, PP. 247–248

1. 4
3. 3
5. −2
7. 20
9. 3
11. 4
13. −4
55. $b = \sqrt{20} = 4.47$, $a = 8.94$
15. 1
17. 17
19. 13
21. $\frac{5}{8}$
23. 0.1
25. $\frac{5}{7}$
27. 6.71
29. 9.27
31. 4.48
33. 3.27
35. 14.14
37. 3.41
39. 0.51
41. 13
43. $\sqrt{200} = 14.14$
45. $\sqrt{2} = 1.41$
47. $\sqrt{64} = 8$
49. $\sqrt{8} = 2.83$
51. $\sqrt{50} = 7.07$
53. $a = 1$, $c = 2$

EXERCISES FOR SECTION 6.2, PP. 249–250

1. 10
3. 10
5. $5\sqrt{3}$
7. $5\sqrt{5}$
9. $5\sqrt{5}$
11. $4\sqrt{2}$
13. $2\sqrt{2}$
15. $2\sqrt{10}$
17. $9\sqrt{2}$
19. $7\sqrt{2}$
21. $5\sqrt{6}$
23. $7\sqrt{10}$
25. $6\sqrt{5}$
27. $6\sqrt{3}$
29. $20\sqrt{3}$
31. $10\sqrt{3}$
33. $22\sqrt{3}$
35. 15
37. 48
39. $2\sqrt{494}$

EXERCISES FOR SECTION 6.3, PP. 252–253

1. $8\sqrt{5}$
3. $6\sqrt{6}$
5. $3\sqrt{5} + 5\sqrt{3}$
7. $2\sqrt{3}$
9. $\sqrt{6}$
11. $3\sqrt{30}$
13. $2\sqrt{28} = 4\sqrt{7}$
15. 0
17. $4\sqrt{3}$
19. $12\sqrt{6}$
21. $-\sqrt{2} - 2\sqrt{3}$
23. $\sqrt{7} + 2\sqrt{2}$
25. $31 + 10\sqrt{6}$
27. $11 - 4\sqrt{7}$
29. $61 + 24\sqrt{5}$
31. 9
33. $8 - 2\sqrt{15}$
35. $21 + 4\sqrt{5}$
37. $\frac{10 + 3\sqrt{2}}{6}$
39. $\frac{-4 + \sqrt{5}}{2}$
41. $7 + 2\sqrt{5}$
43. $\frac{14 - 5\sqrt{2}}{7}$
45. $13 + 7\sqrt{3}$
47. $24 + 13\sqrt{3}$
49. $15 + 7\sqrt{3}$
51. $17 - 8\sqrt{2}$
53. $39 - 20\sqrt{2}$
55. 0
57. $(5 - \sqrt{2})^2 - 10(5 - \sqrt{2}) + 23 = 27 - 10\sqrt{2} - 50 + 10\sqrt{2} + 23 = 0$
59. $\left(\frac{-1 + \sqrt{5}}{2}\right)^2 + \left(\frac{-1 + \sqrt{5}}{2}\right) - 1 = \frac{6 - 2\sqrt{5}}{4} + \frac{-1 + \sqrt{5}}{2} = 0$

EXERCISES FOR SECTION 6.4, P. 258

1. $\{5, -2\}$
3. $\{0, 4\}$
5. $\{2, 3\}$
7. $\{-7, 5\}$
9. $\{-5, 4)$
11. $\left\{-\frac{5}{2}, 2\right\}$
13. $\left\{1, \frac{1}{6}\right\}$
15. $\left\{-\frac{5}{2}, \frac{5}{2}\right\}$
17. $\left\{-\frac{3\sqrt{3}}{2}, \frac{3\sqrt{3}}{2}\right\}$
19. $\left\{\frac{-\sqrt{30}}{5}, \frac{\sqrt{30}}{5}\right\}$
21. $\left\{0, \frac{6}{5}\right\}$
23. $\left\{0, \frac{1}{2}\right\}$
25. $\left\{1, -\frac{1}{2}\right\}$
27. $\{6\}$ double root
29. $\left\{\frac{3}{2}\right\}$ double root
31. $\{0, 4\}$
33. $\{-2, 2)$
35. $\{4\}$ double root
37. $\{1, 3\}$
39. $\{-9, -1\}$
41. $\{-1, 2\}$
43. $\left\{\frac{-3 - \sqrt{7}}{5}, \frac{-3 + \sqrt{7}}{5}\right\}$

EXERCISES FOR SECTION 6.5, P. 261

1. $5 \pm \sqrt{2}$
3. $-4 \pm 3\sqrt{5}$
5. $2 \pm \sqrt{3}$
7. $4 \pm 2\sqrt{5}$
9. $1 \pm 2\sqrt{5}$
11. $-5 \pm 3\sqrt{3}$
13. $-7 \pm 6\sqrt{2}$
15. $-6 \pm 3\sqrt{2}$
17. $10 \pm 2\sqrt{10}$
19. $-6, \frac{5}{2}$
21. $\frac{5 \pm 2\sqrt{2}}{2}$
23. $\frac{5 \pm \sqrt{85}}{5}$
25. $-\frac{1}{2}, \frac{1}{6}$
27. $\frac{5 \pm \sqrt{7}}{6}$
29. $8, \frac{2}{3}$

EXERCISES FOR SECTION 6.6, P. 265

1. $\frac{3 \pm \sqrt{5}}{2}$
3. $-\frac{1}{2}, -2$
5. $\frac{-5 \pm \sqrt{41}}{4}$
7. $\frac{-1 \pm \sqrt{5}}{2}$
9. $\frac{5 \pm \sqrt{5}}{2}$
11. $\frac{1 \pm \sqrt{5}}{2}$
13. $\frac{7 \pm \sqrt{85}}{6}$
15. $-\frac{1}{2}, -\frac{3}{2}$
17. $\frac{2 \pm \sqrt{7}}{2}$
19. $\frac{9 \pm \sqrt{21}}{10}$
21. 1; rational and unequal, $(x+2)(x+1)$
23. 9; rational and unequal $(x+2)(x-1)$
25. 209; irrational and unequal
27. 85; irrational and unequal
29. 41; irrational and unequal
31. 16; rational and unequal $(x+2)(x+6)$
33. 0; rational and equal $(2x+1)^2$
35. 0; rational and equal $(3x-2)^2$
37. 41; irrational and unequal
39. 144; rational and unequal $(3x-2)(3x+2)$
41. $x = \frac{-p \pm \sqrt{p^2 - 4q}}{2}$
43. $x = \frac{-8 \pm \sqrt{64y^2 + 36y^2}}{6} = \frac{y}{3}$ or $-3y$
45. $W = \frac{-L \pm \sqrt{L^2 + 4L^2}}{2} = \frac{-L \pm L\sqrt{5}}{2}$
47. $I = \frac{-E \pm \sqrt{E^2 + 4RP}}{2R}$
49. $x = \frac{-q \pm \sqrt{q^2 - 4\,pr}}{2p}$

EXERCISES FOR SECTION 6.7, PP. 270–272

1. $\frac{3\sqrt{2}}{2} = 2.12$
3. 4 or $-\frac{1}{4}$
5. 13 ft. 5 in.
7. 5 in., 12 in.
9. (−17 and −15) or (15 and 17)
11. 34 ft.
13. 18 minutes
15. 12 cm by 24 cm
17. 560 mph
19. 66.8 ft. (approx.)

REVIEW EXERCISES FOR CHAPTER 6, PP. 272–273

1. 5.20
2. 6.24
3. 14
4. 14
5. 9.33
6. −6.63
7. −8
8. 8
9. 10
10. $2\sqrt{5}$
11. $4\sqrt{10}$
12. $10\sqrt{5}$
13. $-\sqrt{5}$
14. $8\sqrt{7}$
15. $\frac{12 - 10\sqrt{2}}{3}$
16. $\frac{7 + \sqrt{15}}{2}$
17. $\frac{-4 - \sqrt{14}}{4}$
18. $29 + 12\sqrt{5}$
19. $67 - 12\sqrt{7}$
20. $-20 + 5\sqrt{2}$
21. $-1 \pm \sqrt{2}$
22. $\frac{-3 \pm \sqrt{17}}{4}$
23. $2 \pm \sqrt{5}$
24. $2 \pm \sqrt{10}$
25. $\frac{-3 \pm \sqrt{14}}{5}$
26. $\frac{5 \pm \sqrt{43}}{6}$
27. $\frac{-3 \pm \sqrt{3}}{3}$
28. $\frac{3 \pm \sqrt{3}}{3}$
29. $\frac{3}{2}, -2$
30. $-\frac{4}{3}, \frac{1}{2}$
31. $1 \pm \sqrt{13}$
32. $\frac{9 \pm \sqrt{217}}{4}$
33. $\frac{3}{2}, \frac{7}{2}$
34. $\frac{-2 \pm \sqrt{6}}{3}$
35. $\frac{5 \pm \sqrt{73}}{4}$
36. $\frac{2 \pm \sqrt{13}}{3}$
37. 0, 4
38. −9 (double root)
39. $\frac{5 \pm \sqrt{13}}{6}$
40. $\frac{1 \pm \sqrt{3}}{3}$
41. 30 minutes
42. 0 or 1
43. 5 and 6
44. 3 ft. by 15 ft.
45. 180 mph
46. 27 in., 36 in.
47. $\frac{cv \pm \sqrt{c^2v^2 - 2gH}}{g}$
48. $\frac{-\pi h \pm \sqrt{\pi^2h^2 + 2\pi T}}{2\pi}$

INDEX

Alejandra Lutch

SOME APPROXIMATE METRIC CONVERSIONS

1 in = 25.4 mm	1 mm = 3.9×10^{-2} in
1 in = 2.54 cm	1 mm = 3.3×10^{-3} ft
1 in = 2.54×10^{-2} m	1 mm = 1.1×10^{-3} yd
1 ft = 30.48 cm	1 cm = 3.3×10^{-2} ft
1 yd = 91.44 cm	1 cm = 1.1×10^{-2} yd
1 yd = 9.144×10^{-1} m	1 m = 1.1 yd
	1 m = 39 in
1 mi = 1.69 km	1 km = 0.62 mi
1 oz = 28.35 g	1 g = 3.53×10^{-2} oz
1 lb = 4.536×10^{-1} kg	1 kg = 2.20 lb
1 pt = 4.73×10^{2} ml	1 ml = 2.12×10^{-3} pt
1 qt = 9.46×10^{-1} l	1 l = 1.06 qt
1 gal = 3.78 l	1 l = 2.65×10^{-1} gal